UD 9 7 50

Fundamentals

of Physical Chemistry

SECOND EDITION

Fundamentals

of Physical Chemistry

H. D. Crockford & Samuel B. Knight

Professors of Chemistry, University of North Carolina

John Wiley & Sons, Inc., NEW YORK · LONDON · SYDNEY

SECOND PRINTING, SEPTEMBER, 1966

Library of Congress Catalog Card Number: 64-23833
Printed in the United States of America

Preface

In the first edition of *Fundamentals of Physical Chemistry*, published in 1959, we stated that our experience in teaching short courses in physical chemistry to premedical and biological students indicated the need for a text especially suited to their mathematical and chemical backgrounds. At the same time the purpose of such courses had to be kept clearly in mind, namely good coverage of the fundamentals of physical chemistry. Such a book should present the subject matter in a challenging and stimulating manner so that the importance of physical chemistry for an understanding of biological phenomena becomes apparent.

We now find that a text adapted to the needs of biological students also finds extensive use in courses in theoretical chemistry for high school science teachers. Therefore the needs of these teachers have been kept in mind and we have modified this book to make it essentially a brief course in physical chemistry rather than a text slanted to the premedical and biological points of view. We hope this book will appeal to anyone who wishes to pursue a short course in theoretical chemistry for the sole purpose of acquiring a more fundamental understanding of chemistry.

The book is written for students with the usual background in general chemistry, and with some experience in qualitative and quantitative analysis. A previous course in organic chemistry is not essential but would be helpful. The student needs to be able to handle simple algebra and logarithms in following most of the mathematical procedures. While calculus has been introduced in a limited number of places the presentation can be followed by the average student.

No major fundamental changes have been made in the subject matter of this edition over that of the first edition. We have moved the chapters on thermodynamics to positions nearer the front of the book. This helps the instructor to use the principles of thermodynamics if he so wishes in several of the treatments that follow, especially in the chapter on electromotive force. This increasing emphasis on mathematical procedures is in line with the increasing ability of students to grasp mathematical concepts.

As in the first edition each chapter is headed by a brief statement concerning the contents and objectives of the chapter. We have also kept the procedure of the first edition in numbering subheads, examples, diagrams, and equations. This makes cross reference easy. The quantitative treatment has been developed by simple derivations of most of the fundamental formulas and by the extensive use of examples. A set of review questions and two extensive sets of problems accompany each chapter. Answers are given for the first set of problems.

We have not hesitated in a few cases to give mathematical relationships without any attempt at proof or justification except the need for them in the development of the subject matter. We have not found it possible always to go into a complete discussion of the topic in question. However, a student who has achieved a proficiency in the subject matter as presented should have little trouble reading and understanding more advanced textbooks in physical chemistry. References are kept to a minimum. Rather than cite the best sources of information we have deemed it wise to list only a limited number of textbooks and laboratory manuals. In this way a teacher will find it easy to keep a complete set of reference books available to the student. Such a set should stimulate the student to do additional reading on the various topics. The two laboratory manuals listed not only add to the text material but also enable the student to study experimental procedures associated with the various topics.

H. D. CROCKFORD
S. B. KNIGHT

Chapel Hill, North Carolina
August 1964

Contents

Table of Symbols and Abbreviations

$^{\circ}A$	Temperature in degrees Absolute	G	Free energy
a	Activity	ΔG	Change in free energy
a	Pressure correction constant in the van der Waals equation	γ	Activity coefficient
α	Degree of ionization	γ	Surface tension
		H	Enthalpy
b	Volume correction term in the van der Waals equation	ΔH	Change in enthalpy
		ΔH	Heat of reaction at constant pressure
β	Degree of hydrolysis	h	Height
C	Cell constant	I	Electrical current in amperes
$^{\circ}C$	Temperature in degrees Centigrade	J	Electrical energy in joules
C_p	Molar heat capacity at constant pressure	K	Equilibrium constant
		K	Debye-Hückel constant
C_v	Molar heat capacity at constant volume	K_a	Ionization constant of an acid
		K_b	Ionization constant of a base
c	Concentration—identical with molarity	K_{In}	Apparent ionization constant of an indicator
c	Root-mean-square velocity of a molecule	K_{sp}	Solubility product
		K_w	Ion product of water
cc	Cubic centimeter	κ	Specific conductance
cm	Centimeter	k	Specific reaction rate constant
D	Dielectric constant	k	Henry's law constant
d	Density	kg	Kilogram
d	Differential	L	Conductance in mhos
E	Electromotive force	L	Length
E	Internal energy	Λ	Equivalent conductance
ΔE	Change in internal energy	Λ°	Equivalent conductance at infinite dilution
ΔE	Heat of reaction at constant volume	λ	Radioactive decay constant
ΔE_a	Energy of activation	M	Molarity
E°	Standard electrode or cell potential	MW	Molecular weight
		m	Mass
η	Coefficient of viscosity	m	Molality
F	Faraday	ml	Milliliter
F	Force between charged bodies	mv	Millivolt
g	Acceleration of gravity	$m\mu$	Millimicron
		μ	Ionic strength

μ	Micron	r	Rate
N	Avogadro's number	s	Speed, velocity
N	Normality	S	Entropy
N	Number of molecules	ΔS	Change in entropy
n	Number of moles	STP	Standard conditions (also
P	Pressure (gas)		NTP)
P	Osmotic pressure	T	Temperature in degrees abso-
$p°$	Vapor pressure of a pure sub-		lute
	stance	t	Temperature in degrees centi-
p	Vapor pressure		grade
Q	Quantity of electricity in cou-	t	Time
	lombs	v	Volt
q	Electrostatic charge	V	Volume
R	Resistance in ohms	x	Mole fraction
R	Universal gas constant	Z	Valence of an ion
r	Radius	Σ	Sum
r	Distance		

Values of Some Useful
Physical-Chemical Constants

(*Chemical and Engineering News*, pages 43–44, November 18, 1963)

Liter (1000 ml)	1000.028 cm^3
Atmosphere	1.013250 × 10^6 dynes cm^{-2}
Gram-molecular volume of a gas at STP	22.4136 liters
Absolute zero of temperature	$-273.16°C$
Calorie, defined	4.1840 absolute joules
Gas constant	8.3143 × 10^7 ergs per degree per mole
	1.98717 calories per degree per mole
	0.082054 liter-atmospheres per degree per mole
Faraday	96,487 coulombs per gram-equivalent
Avogadro's number	6.0225 × 10^{23} per mole

Conversion of Logarithms

$$\log_e = \log_{10} \times 2.303$$

Significant Figures

In the solution of problems students are to assume that all data are as accurate as the most accurate figure given in the problem. Suppose that you are asked to calculate the pH of a $1M$ solution of acetic acid from the value of the ionization constant. The molarity should be assumed to be as accurate as the number of significant figures in the ionization constant.

ONE

Introduction

THE SCOPE AND PURPOSE OF PHYSICAL CHEMISTRY

1a. The Scientific Method. Law and Theory. The rapid progress of the various sciences over the past century demonstrates the effectiveness of the scientific method to the expansion of knowledge. Observation and experimentation together form the base of the structure of science. Only through observation and experimentation can facts be established, and no matter how facts conflict with a prevailing notion, they can never be ignored. The respect for demonstrable truth, held in common by different people working on related phenomena, leads to an arrangement of facts in an orderly system from which great generalizations often appear.

The steps in the scientific procedure may be outlined as follows. An interest develops in a certain phenomenon. The phenomenon is then subjected to close study and investigation to see whether any orderly set of conclusions can be formed. Usually the first conclusions are only qualitative statements of behavior. With continued experimentation and refinement of techniques, it often becomes possible to draw quantitative conclusions. When well-defined mathematical relations are discovered, they are termed *laws*. A law, then, is a *mathematical statement of regularity of behavior*. The ideal gas law, for example, is a mathematical expression for the quantity-volume-pressure-temperature relations in a gas. A further accumulation of data may show a given law to be only approximate and may lead to a more exact expression than was at first attained.

The next step after the development of a law or a set of laws is to work out a *hypothesis*, which depicts a mechanism that explains the observed phenomena and the conclusions reached in the laws. If the hypothesis explains a number of laws and if predictions based upon it prove to be correct, it becomes a *theory*. A theory may be looked upon as a well-established hypothesis. The great value of a theory or hypothesis rests not only on the fact that it explains already established laws but that it

1

also enables the investigator to predict other laws and to formulate experiments to test these predicted laws. For example, the kinetic theory of gases is a plausible explanation of how gases behave and from it can be predicted most of the observed gaseous phenomena. The actual, or final, proof of a theory is, in most cases, an impossibility. Scientists are certain that the atomic theory is essentially correct, but its actual proof has never been completely accomplished.

The development from observation and fact to laws, to hypothesis, and then to theory, is known as the *scientific method*. The development of chemistry as a science provides one of the best examples of its application.

1b. The Purpose of Physical Chemistry. General and organic chemistry contain a great amount of descriptive material. In both subjects, however, many laws are set forth and numerous theories are advanced to explain them. Analytical chemistry involves the application of several laws from general chemistry, with special emphasis on the laws and theories of ionic equilibria. It is the major purpose of physical chemistry to organize, expand, and systematize the laws and theories underlying the whole of chemistry. Physical chemistry may be defined as that branch of chemistry concerned with the physical properties and structure of matter and with the laws and theories of physical and chemical changes. Physical chemistry is so named because it makes use of many of the concepts of physics in achieving its purpose. Like the other branches of chemistry, it rests on experimentation and observation.

1c. The Methods of Approach to Physical Chemistry. There are two main methods of approach to physical chemistry, the *kinetic* and the *thermodynamic*. In the kinetic approach an attempt is made to describe a mechanism to explain chemical phenomena. This is done by picturing atoms and molecules doing specific things as a result of their structure and characteristics.

In the thermodynamic approach the emphasis is placed on the energy changes associated with the phenomena rather than on the mechanism of the processes. Hence no postulates as to the fundamental structure of matter are necessary. The thermodynamic treatment is far more rigorous and often more direct and straightforward. It does involve, however, a knowledge and understanding of mathematics, especially calculus, beyond that necessary for the kinetic approach.

In this book the kinetic approach is used primarily but thermodynamics is used in certain cases where feasible. Three chapters are devoted to elementary thermodynamic principles to give those who wish to learn more about this approach a chance to do so. These are Chapters 4, 5, and 10.

FUNDAMENTAL CONCEPTS, MEASURABLE PROPERTIES, AND FUNDAMENTAL UNITS

1d. The Atomic-Molecular Theory of Matter. The nature of matter has been the subject of much speculation and study since the times of the early Greek philosophers. As a result of about the last two centuries of experimentation and thought, the *atomic-molecular theory* of matter has come to be universally accepted. In this theory all elements exist in the form of particles called *atoms*, each having a structure characteristic of the particular element. The *molecule* is defined as a particle of matter capable of independent existence. Molecules of most substances consist of two or more atoms. These may be of the same kind as in O_2 and N_2 or may be of different atoms as in HCl and NH_3. A molecule, however, of any rare gas and of certain other substances, such as mercury, consists of a single atom. Such a molecule is said to be *monatomic*.

The atom may be considered to be made up of a nucleus around which are found the electrons in certain definite groupings, depending upon the particular kind of atom. The nucleus is made up of protons and neutrons, both of which are called *nucleons*. The neutron has no charge whereas the proton has a charge of plus one. Since the atom is electrically neutral, the number of electrons around the nucleus must be equal to the number of protons in the nucleus. The number of protons in the nucleus is the same for all the atoms of a given element. This number, called the *atomic number*, must be equal to the charge on the nucleus of the particular element and also equal to the number of electrons around the nucleus.

The chemical properties of a given element depend on the number and arrangement of the electrons. Although the number of protons in the nucleus is always the same for a given element, the number of neutrons may be different because of the existence of *isotopes*. For example, oxygen has an atomic number of eight since it has eight protons in the nucleus. Oxygen as we find it in air occurs in three different forms, one with eight, one with nine, and one with ten neutrons associated with the protons. These three forms are the naturally occurring isotopes of oxygen. By definition, then, we may say that the *isotopes of an element are various forms of that element having identical chemical properties but differing in their actual masses.*

It is not difficult to obtain the actual masses of atoms, but the values so obtained are so small that it would be inconvenient and cumbersome to employ them in chemical calculations. A more convenient method is to use the *atomic weight* of an element. This is the *average weight of the atoms of the elements as they occur in nature* relative to the weight of the most abundant isotope of carbon taken as 12.0000. The former standard was the weight arbitrarily set at 16.0000, of the average atom of oxygen found in nature. An interesting aspect of the new standard is that the atomic weight of carbon is given as 12.01 in the new atomic weight tables. This is due to the fact that naturally occurring carbon has more than one isotope. The atomic weights based on the new scale are given on the inside of the front cover. The molecular weight of a compound is the weight of a molecule of that compound compared to the weight of the most abundant isotope of carbon taken as 12.0000 as explained above.

The number of grams of an element numerically equal to the molecular weight is termed the *gram-molecular weight*. For example, the molecular weight of ammonia is 17.03 and 17.03 grams of ammonia is a *gram-molecular weight*. A gram-molecular weight of a substance is often referred to as a *mole*. The term, mole, will be used extensively in this book.

1e. Avogadro's Number. Since atomic and molecular weights are relative magnitudes based on the same standard, a mole of any substance contains a definite and constant number of molecules. The accepted value for this number is 6.02×10^{23} and is known as *Avogadro's number*. It is the exact number of molecules in a gram-molecular weight of any substance and the number of atoms in a gram-atomic weight of an element. It is a most important magnitude and is used extensively in chemistry.

1f. Units and Dimensions. In chemistry we deal with *measurable quantities* and *properties*. Some of these, such as length, mass, and volume are quite simple; but others, such as surface tension and viscosity, are much more complex. These quantities are expressed in terms of arbitrarily selected *units*. For example, the meter, foot, or inch could be selected as the unit of length. Since complete choice is possible, we could select an independent and a separate unit for each quantity. Thus we could have as many units as we have measurable quantities.

To simplify the situation, we select a minimum number of units and define all other units in terms of these *fundamental units*. In the *centimeter-gram-second system*, termed the *cgs system*, the *centimeter*, *gram*, and the *mean solar second* are the fundamental units. The centimeter is one hundredth of the distance between two lines on a platinum-iridium bar preserved at the International Bureau of Weights and Measures at Sèvres, near Paris, France. The meter, which contains one hundred centimeters, was originally supposed to be one ten millionth of the distance from the equator to the North Pole. The gram, the unit of mass, is one thousandth of the mass of a platinum-iridium mass preserved at the same institute. The solar second is 1/86,400 part of a mean solar day, the mean solar day being the average time of one complete revolution of the earth on its polar axis.

Now if we let L stand for length, T for time, and M for mass, we can prepare Table 1-1 for some of the more commonly used magnitudes in physical chemistry.

Table 1-1.

Quantity	Dimensions	Cgs Units
Length	L	cm
Area	L^2	cm^2
Volume	L^3	cm^3
Time	T	sec
Speed	LT^{-1}	cm per sec
Acceleration	LT^{-2}	cm per sec per sec
Mass	M	gram
Force, weight	$LT^{-2}M$	dyne
Pressure	$L^{-1}T^{-2}M$	dynes per sq cm
Density	$L^{-3}M$	grams per cm^3
Surface tension	$T^{-2}M$	dynes per cm, ergs per sq cm, grams per sec^2
Energy	$L^2T^{-2}M$	erg

Note in this table the distinction between mass and weight. Note that the *dyne* is defined as the force that gives to a mass of one gram an acceleration of one cm per second, and that the *erg* is the work done when a force of one dyne acts through a distance of one cm.

Now by introducing a unit of temperature, Table 1-1 can be expanded to include three new quantities: *heat capacity*, *specific heat*, and *entropy*.

Table 1-2.

Quantity	Dimensions
Temperature	θ
Heat capacity	$L^2T^{-2}M\theta^{-1}$
Specific heat	$L^2T^{-2}\theta^{-1}$
Entropy	$L^2T^{-2}M\theta^{-1}$

This new unit is the degree of temperature and is represented by the Greek letter theta (θ). In Table 1-2 the dimensions of the quantities are listed but not the cgs unit used for each for reasons that are explained in the next few sentences.

Heat capacity is defined as the quantity of heat required to raise the temperature of a given substance 1°C. Specific heat is the quantity of energy required to raise the temperature of 1 gram of the substance 1°C. In these two definitions we are establishing the unit of temperature as the Centigrade degree, which is equal in size to the degree on the absolute scale. The concept of entropy will be discussed in Chapter 10. This quantity has the same dimensions as heat capacity. The cgs units for the quantities in Table 1-2 were not listed because, like energy, they are seldom expressed in the cgs system.

Instead two *practical* units are used. These are the *absolute joule* and the *defined calorie*. The absolute joule by definition is equal to 10^7 ergs, and the defined calorie is 4.184 absolute joules. This calorie does not differ significantly from the 15° calorie, which is taken as the quantity of heat necessary to raise the temperature of 1 gram of water 1° at 15°C. Heat capacity is expressed in calories per degree and specific heat in calories per degree per gram. It is to be noted that, regardless of the units used for the various quantities, the *dimensions* remain the same.

The electrical units will be introduced as needed in the chapters concerned with electrochemical phenomena.

In discussing the various basic quantities, we have used both practical and absolute units. Other practical units will be introduced later in the book. For example, pressure has been given as dynes per square centimeter. Later, in Chapter 2 ("Gases"), we shall find that *atmospheres, centimeters of mercury*, and *millimeters of mercury* are practical units of great utility. Sometimes such units are called *secondary units*. The *liter* is such a unit. You will recall from your quantitative analysis that this is the volume of one kilogram of air-free water at 4°C. Its volume is 1.000028 cubic decimeters. Therefore, the milliliter (ml) is not exactly equal to the cubic centimeter (cm^3), although the difference is so slight as to have little effect in most physical chemistry calculations. Another system of units, the MKS system, is coming into extensive use in physics. Here the basic units are the meter, the kilogram, and the second. This system has not as yet come into extensive use in physical chemistry.

It is absolutely necessary to be *consistent with units* in a formula if we are to obtain an answer that has proper meaning. This necessity for consistency in the handling of units will be illustrated from time to time in the text.

REFERENCES

Daniels and Alberty, *Physical Chemistry*, John Wiley and Sons, New York, 1961, Chapter 1.

Maron and Prutton, *Principles of Physical Chemistry*, The Macmillan Co., New York, 1958, Introduction.

Daniels, Williams, Bender, Alberty, and Cornwell, *Experimental Physical Chemistry*, McGraw-Hill Book Co., New York, 1962, Chapter 18.
Crockford and Nowell, *Laboratory Manual of Physical Chemistry*, John Wiley and Sons, New York, 1956, Units and Dimensions.

REVIEW QUESTIONS

1. Discuss the scientific method and its application.

2. Discuss the terms: *law, theory,* and *hypothesis*. How are they interrelated?

3. Compare the kinetic and thermodynamic approaches to the study of physical chemistry.

4. What is the atomic theory of matter? Distinguish between atoms and molecules.

5. Discuss the general structure of the atom. How do the isotopes of a given element differ from each other?

6. Discuss the terms: *atomic number, atomic weight, gram-atomic weight, mole, gram-molecular weight*.

7. Atomic weights are based on what arbitrarily selected standard? What standard was previously used by the chemists as the basis of atomic weights?

8. What is Avogadro's number? What is its value expressed to three significant figures?

9. What are the fundamental units in the cgs system? What are the primary standards upon which they are based? Upon what units is the MKS system based?

10. Prepare a list of quantities using only L, M, and T as the dimensions. Give the dimensions of each of these quantities. Give the cgs units in which each of these quantities can be expressed. What other units are often used for these quantities? Present the information in tabular form.

11. Distinguish between *mass* and *weight*.

12. Compare the dimensions of temperature, heat capacity, specific heat, and entropy.

13. What is meant by *heat capacity* and *specific heat*?

14. Define the *erg*. What interrelationships exist among the erg, joule, and calorie? How does the defined calorie differ from the so-called 15° calorie?

15. Distinguish between the milliliter and the cubic centimeter. Why do they differ in value?

16. List the various units used in physical chemistry for expressing pressure.

TWO

Gases

The purpose of this chapter is to develop the laws that describe the behavior of matter in the gaseous state, to discuss the use of these laws, and to develop the kinetic theory of gases.

Not only must man be surrounded by an atmosphere of gas in order to survive, but also many of the vital processes within the body involve phenomena concerned with gases. Metabolism in all animals, even in marine life, requires oxygen; and photosynthesis in plants requires carbon dioxide—to cite two essential processes involving gases.

The laws of gaseous behavior form a foundation upon which rest many of the laws and theories of pure liquids and solutions.

THE GASEOUS STATE OF MATTER

2a. General Properties of Gases. In studying physical chemistry, the usual procedure is to isolate a portion of the universe by means of boundaries, which may be real or imaginary. This portion of the material world that has been isolated for study is referred to as a *system*. Matter in this system exists in one or more of the three *states of matter:* the *solid*, *liquid*, and *gaseous states*. The general characteristics of each of these states are summarized below.

In the solid state, the particles are fixed in a uniform manner in definite positions in a crystal lattice. The particles are held in their positions in this crystal lattice by the strong forces that operate between them. The resulting structure is a fairly rigid one having a definite shape and a definite volume that strongly resists compression and distortion.

In the liquid state, the particles possess a translational motion, which is sufficient to overcome the forces operating to hold the particles in their positions in the crystal lattice. The attractive forces in the liquid state, however, are still sufficient to prevent a general separation of the particles

8

from one another. The result is a state of matter that has definite volume but not definite shape. The shape assumed by a liquid, therefore, is that of the container.

In the gaseous state, the translational motion of the molecules has become sufficiently great to enable them to overcome entirely the restraining forces of attraction characteristic of the liquid state. Thus, the gaseous state is one in which the component parts or molecules of the gas are moving at high speeds in a completely random manner. The particles are relatively far apart at ordinary pressures, and the molecules exert little or no attraction upon one another. Because of the motion of the particles and the lack of restraining forces between them, they distribute themselves evenly throughout the volume of the system. Hence, a gas has neither definite shape nor definite volume.

Great distances exist between the particles and so the system consists principally of empty space. As a result gases are highly compressible. The random motion of the molecules and their high velocities result in a constant and uniform bombardment of the sides of the container or any other surface present in the gas. Thus, we say that gases exert pressure. This picture of a gas also explains why gases are infinitely diffusible and completely expansible.

THE GAS LAWS

2b. Methods for Expressing Quantity, Volume, and Pressure. The study of gases, as developed in this chapter, is concerned mainly with the relationships among the quantity, volume, temperature, and pressure magnitudes. The quantity of the gas or the gases making up the system could be expressed in terms of the number of molecules or some unit of mass such as the gram or pound. The quantity is usually expressed in moles, however, or gram-molecular-weights as explained in Chapter 1. Also, as explained, a mole contains 6.02×10^{23} molecules. The volume may be expressed in liters, cubic feet, cubic centimeters (cm^3), or milliliters (ml), as well as many other volume units. We shall use principally the liter and milliliter. Temperatures are usually expressed on the absolute scale as explained in 2d.

Pressure is defined as force per unit of area as was previously stated in Chapter 1. The unit of force in the centimeter-gram-second (cgs) system is the dyne, and the unit of pressure is the dyne per square centimeter. In chemical calculations pressure is usually expressed in *atmospheres* (atm) or *centimeters of mercury* (Hg). The significance of these units can best be understood from a consideration of the *barometer*. This is an

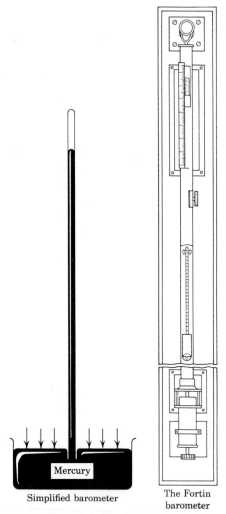

Simplified barometer

The Fortin
barometer

Figure 2-1. The barometer.

instrument used for measuring the pressure of the atmosphere. The Fortin, or mercurial, barometer consists essentially of a glass tube over 76 cm in length and closed at one end. This tube is completely filled with mercury and inverted so that the open end extends below the surface of a pool of mercury. The pressure of the atmosphere on the surface of the pool acts against the force of gravity tending to pull the mercury downward in the tube. (See Figure 2-1.) Measurements at sea level and 45° latitude show that on the average the pressure of the atmosphere will hold up a column of mercury 76 cm in height. This length is termed an atmosphere of pressure. In the above discussion we neglected the vapor pressure of the mercury in the top of the barometer tube. In most of our considerations its effect is negligible.

2c. Boyle's Law. When the pressure-volume relationships are studied experimentally for any gas at pressures that are not too high, the *volume of a given quantity varies inversely as the pressure of the gas.* In other words, the product of the pressure and volume is constant at a given temperature. This statement of behavior is known as *Boyle's law* after Robert Boyle, who first stated the law in 1661. This law may be expressed mathematically as follows:

$$\begin{matrix} (a) & (b) & (c) \\ V \propto \dfrac{1}{P} & \dfrac{V_1}{V_2} = \dfrac{P_2}{P_1} & P_1 V_1 = P_2 V_2 = K \text{ (a constant)} \end{matrix} \qquad (2\text{-}1)$$

2d. Charles's Law. When the volume-temperature relationships are studied experimentally for a given quantity of gas at constant pressure, the volume is found to increase as the temperature increases. The change in volume, however, is not directly proportional to the change in centigrade temperature. Doubling the centigrade temperature does *not* double the volume. For example, an increase in temperature from 25° to 50°C increases the volume only to $1\frac{1}{10}$ of the original volume. Experimentation shows, however, that if a new temperature scale is established by adding 273.16° to the centigrade temperature, the volume is directly proportional to this adjusted temperature. If the volume of a certain quantity of gas at 1 atm is V_1 at 0°C, it will be $2V_1$ at 273.16°C, and $3V_1$ at 546.32°C. The adjusted temperatures would be 273.16°, 546.32°, and 819.48°, thus showing a 1 to 2 to 3 ratio, the same ratio as shown by the volumes. This adjusted temperature $(t + 273.16°)$ is known as the *absolute temperature*. The expression for the relation between the volume of a gas and the absolute temperature is known as *Charles's law* after the French physicist whose experiments established it. This law may be stated as follows: *the volume of a given quantity of a gas at constant pressure varies directly with the absolute temperature.* Mathematically it may be expressed as:

$$\begin{matrix} (a) & (b) & (c) \\ V \propto T & V_1/V_2 = T_1/T_2 & V_1/T_1 = V_2/T_2 = K' \text{ (a constant)} \end{matrix} \qquad (2\text{-}2)$$

The practice of using T to indicate the absolute temperature and t to indicate the centigrade temperature is followed in this text. The letter A or K (Kelvin) after a temperature value also indicates that the absolute scale is being used.

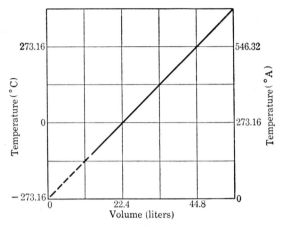

Figure 2-2. Temperature-volume relations for 1 mole of a gas at a pressure of 1 atmosphere.

(Charles's law) is represented graphically in Figure 2-2. The data plotted are for 1 mole of a gas at a constant pressure of 1 atm.

2e. The Absolute Zero. An examination of Figure 2-2 shows that if the temperature is reduced to 0°A, or −273.16°C, the volume of the gas would theoretically become zero. This temperature is termed the *absolute zero* and is the lowest temperature theoretically attainable. Actually this temperature has never been attained, although temperatures within a few thousandths of a degree of it have been reached. In practice, a gas will liquefy or solidify before the limiting temperature is reached. In reality, the volume would not approach a value of zero but rather (the volume occupied by the particles themselves) This would leave them no space in which to move and the volume occupied by the system under such conditions would be negligibly small as compared with the volume of the substance in the normal gaseous state.

Another way of approaching the concept of the absolute zero is to consider the fractional change that the volume of a gas undergoes when its temperature is changed 1°C. If the temperature of a given volume of gas at 0°C is reduced to −1°, the volume is reduced by 1/273.16 of its original value. Or if we take the same number of grams of the gas at 100°C (373.16°A) and reduce the temperature by 1°, the volume is changed by 1/373.16 of its volume at 373.16°A.

A further reduction of the temperature of the gas in the first case to −2°C reduces the volume once more by 1/273.16 of its original volume at 0°C. Successive reductions of 1° result in additional decreases by this same fractional value. If this operation is repeated 273.16 times, the total volume theoretically becomes zero at $-273.16°C$, or at the absolute zero. Again consider the same quantity of gas at $373.16°A$, or $100°C$. We stated that a decrease of $1°$ reduced the volume at $100°C$ by $1/373.16$ of its volume at this temperature. Carry out this change 373.16 times and the volume becomes zero. The temperature would again be the absolute zero. We can state in general that the volume of a gas at a given temperature, T, is reduced by $1/T$ of its volume at that temperature if T is changed $1°$. That this somewhat startling statement is true follows from Equation 2-2(c).

$$\frac{V_{373.16°}}{373.16°} = \frac{V_{273.16°}}{273.16°} = \frac{V_T}{T}$$

2f. Avogadro's Law. In addition to Boyle's and Charles's laws, it has been found experimentally that 1 mole, or 1 gram-molecular weight, of a gas at a given temperature and pressure occupies the same volume as a mole of any other gas under the same conditions of temperature and pressure. At $0°C$ and at a pressure of 1 atmosphere this volume will be 22.414 liters, and this is known as the *gram-molecular volume* at *standard* or *normal conditions* (STP or NTP). Since a mole of any substance contains the same number of molecules, it follows that *equal volumes of all gases at the same temperature and pressure contain the same number of molecules.* This is known as Avogadro's law, in honor of the Italian physicist whose researches on gases helped to establish much of our knowledge of gaseous behavior. Mathematically this law may be expressed as

$$V \propto n \quad (P, T \text{ constant}) \tag{2-3}$$

In this equation n is equal to the number of moles of gas present in the system.

It has been established by several different procedures that the number of molecules in 1 mole of a substance is 6.02×10^{23}. This number is known as Avogadro's number and is most important in many chemical calculations. Consequently in 22.414 liters of any gas at NTP the number of molecules is 6.02×10^{23}.

2g. The Ideal Gas Law. A combination of Boyle's law, Charles's law, and Avogadro's law leads to the following expressions:

$$
\begin{array}{ccc}
(a) & (b) & (c) \\
V \propto \dfrac{nT}{P} & \dfrac{PV}{nT} = R \text{ (a constant)} & \dfrac{P_1 V_1}{n_1 T_1} = \dfrac{P_2 V_2}{n_2 T_2}
\end{array}
\tag{2-4}
$$

The above equations are usually written

$$\left(PV = nRT \right) \tag{2-5}$$

and in this form the expression is termed the _general ideal gas law_. The word general is used to indicate that it applies to all gases. It is termed ideal because there is no real gas whose behavior can be completely predicted under all conditions by this equation. Nevertheless, the conditions under which we study most gases are such that the ideal equation can be used in describing their behavior with sufficient accuracy. Deviations from this equation can be accounted for by modifications in the ideal gas equation. Certain of these deviations are discussed in 2o of this chapter.

2h. The Significance of R. If Equation 2-4 is solved for R, it is equal to PV/nT. Consequently we can determine the numerical value of this constant by measuring the volume of a given number of moles of a gas at a known temperature and pressure. If one mole of gas is selected and its volume is measured under standard conditions (1 atm of pressure and 0°C), the volume as stated in 2f is 22.414 liters. Substituting these values in Equation 2-5 and solving for R gives

$$R = \frac{1 \text{ atm} \times 22.414 \text{ liters}}{1 \text{ mole} \times 273.16° \text{A}}$$

$$= 0.08205 \text{ liter-atm per mole per degree}$$

$$= 0.08205 \text{ liter} \times \text{atm} \times \text{mole}^{-1} \times °\text{A}^{-1} \qquad (2\text{-}6)$$

R is known as the _universal gas constant_, and its value is the same for a given set of pressure, volume, and quantity units whatever the gas may be. If the units for these magnitudes are changed, other values of R are obtained. For example, if the volume is expressed in milliliters rather than liters, the value would be 82.05 ml $\times$ atm $\times$ mole^{-1} $\times$ °A^{-1}.

Since pressure is force per unit of area, R may be written dimensionally as follows:

$$R = \text{liter} \times \text{atm} \times °\text{A}^{-1} \times \text{mole}^{-1}$$

$$= \text{cm}^3 \times \text{force/cm}^2 \times °\text{A}^{-1} \times \text{mole}^{-1}$$

$$= \text{distance (cm)} \times \text{force} \times °\text{A}^{-1} \times \text{mole}^{-1}$$

$$= \text{work (energy) per mole per degree} \qquad (2\text{-}7)$$

Thus, the PV product has the dimensions of work, and R may be expressed in any energy unit per mole per degree. The constant R appears in many formulas in chemistry, and the numerical value to be used depends upon the system of units employed in the equation under consideration. Its value in the centimeter-gram-second system of units can be calculated as follows. Consider the relationship (Equation 2-6).

$$R = 0.08205 \text{ liter} \times \text{atm} \times °\text{A}^{-1} \times \text{mole}^{-1}$$

In this expression the atmosphere is the force exerted by a column of mercury 76.0 cm high and 1 sq cm in cross section. Since mercury has a density at 0°C of 13.595 grams per cm^3, the mass of the mercury column is 76 × 13.595 grams. The weight of the column is the mass multiplied by the acceleration of gravity, for which a value of 980.7 cm per sec^2 will be assumed. Then

$$1 \text{ atm} = \frac{\text{force}}{\text{cm}^2} = \frac{76.00 \text{ cm}^3 \times 13.595 \text{ grams/cm}^3 \times 980.7 \text{ cm/sec}^2}{\text{cm}^2}$$

$$= \frac{1.0133 \times 10^6 \text{ grams cm/sec}^2}{\text{cm}^2}$$

Since the dyne is the force that gives to a mass of 1 gram an acceleration of 1 cm per sec^2, and the erg is the work done by a force of 1 dyne acting through a distance of 1 cm, it follows that

$$1 \text{ atm} = 1.0133 \times 10^6 \text{ dynes/sq cm}$$

and,

$$R = 82.05 \text{ cm}^3 \times 1.0133 \times 10^6 \text{ dynes/sq cm} \times {}^\circ A^{-1} \times \text{mole}^{-1}$$

$$= 8.314 \times 10^7 \text{ ergs/mole per degree}$$

From 1f it will be recalled that the joule is equal to 10^7 ergs and that the calorie is equal to 4.184 joules. Therefore, R expressed in these units has the values

$$\left(R = 8.314 \text{ joules/mole/degree} \right)$$

$$= 1.987 \text{ cal/mole/degree}$$

2i. The Use of the Gas Law in Calculations Involving Gases. Numerous types of calculations employing the ideal gas law are possible. In most of these the various magnitudes (pressure, volume, etc.) are given to only three significant figures. Therefore, the value of the absolute zero may be taken as $-273°$ and the gram-molecular volume under NTP as 22.4 liters. The more useful forms of the gas equation follow. In these w is used for the weight of a given quantity of gas, M for the molecular weight of the gas, and d for the density.

(a) $PV = nRT$ 　　　　　(b) $PV = \dfrac{w}{M} RT$

(c) $P = \dfrac{w}{V} \times \dfrac{RT}{M} = d\dfrac{RT}{M}$ 　(d) $\dfrac{P_1 V_1}{T_1} = \dfrac{P_2 V_2}{T_2}$ 　(n constant)

$$(2\text{-}8)$$

Some typical examples of gas calculations follow.

Example 2-1. A given quantity of a gas at a pressure of 730 mm and at a temperature of $-20°C$ occupies 20.0 liters. What is its volume at STP?

This can best be worked by direct substitution in Equation 2-8(d).

$$\frac{730 \text{ mm} \times 20.0 \text{ liters}}{(273 - 20)°A} = \frac{760 \text{ mm} \times V}{273°A} \qquad V = 20.7 \text{ liters}$$

Example 2-2. How many moles of gas are present in the above system? How many molecules are present?

By substituting in Equation 2-5,

$$\text{No. of moles} = \frac{\dfrac{730 \text{ mm}}{760 \text{ mm} \times \text{atm}^{-1}} \times 20.0 \text{ liters}}{0.0821 \text{ liter} \times \text{atm} \times \text{moles}^{-1} \times °A^{-1} \times 253°A}$$

$$= 0.925 \text{ mole}$$

$$\text{No. of molecules} = 0.925 \text{ mole} \times 6.02 \times 10^{23} \text{ molecules/mole}$$

$$= 5.57 \times 10^{23}$$

Example 2-3. What will be the volume of 2.006×10^{20} molecules of nitrogen at 27°C and at a pressure of 100 cm of mercury?

The number of molecules given can be converted into moles by dividing by Avogadro's number. The number of moles can then be substituted in Equation 2-5. Of course, direct substitution can be made as follows:

$$\frac{100 \text{ cm}}{76.0 \text{ cm} \times \text{atm}^{-1}} \times V = \frac{2.006 \times 10^{20}}{6.02 \times 10^{23} \text{ mole}^{-1}} \times 0.0821 \text{ liter} \times \text{atm}$$

$$\times \text{mole}^{-1} \times °A^{-1} \times 300°A$$

$$V = 0.00624 \text{ liter} = 6.24 \text{ cm}^3$$

Example 2-4. In the vapor state 0.980 gram of chloroform occupies 200 ml at a pressure of 752 mm of Hg and at 21°C. From these data calculate the molecular weight of chloroform.

This problem is an example of the use of the ideal gas law for determining molecular weights. Remembering that the mass divided by the molecular weight gives the number of moles, we can solve the problem by direct substitution in the ideal gas law.

$$\frac{752 \text{ mm}}{760 \text{ mm} \times \text{atm}^{-1}} \times 0.20 \text{ liter} = \frac{0.980 \text{ gram}}{M} \times 0.0821 \text{ liter} \times \text{atm}$$

$$\times \text{mole}^{-1} \times °A^{-1} \times 294°A$$

$$M = 119.5 \text{ grams/mole}$$

2j. Dalton's Law of Partial Pressures. This law, which gives the relationship between the total pressure in a mixture of gases and the pressure of the individual gases, was proposed by John Dalton in 1801. It states that the total pressure in a mixture of gases is equal to the sum of the *partial pressures* of the individual gases. The partial pressures are the pressures the individual gases would exert if each were present alone in the volume occupied by the whole mixture at the same temperature. The total pressure (P) for a mixture of three gases would therefore be given by the sum of the partial pressures of the three individual gases (p_a, p_b, p_c)

$$P = p_a + p_b + p_c \tag{2-9}$$

This relationship follows from a consideration of the ideal gas law. The symbol n stands for the number of moles of gas present whether they are all of one species of molecule or whether the total is made up of many gases. Consequently, these equations follow

(a)
$$PV = nRT$$

where P = total pressure, and n = total number of moles.

(b)   (c)   (d)
$$p_a V = n_a RT \qquad p_b V = n_b RT \qquad p_c V = n_c RT$$

Adding (b), (c), and (d), we get

$$(p_a + p_b + p_c)V = (n_a + n_b + n_c)RT \tag{e}$$

and since $n = n_a + n_b + n_c$, it follows that

$$(p_a + p_b + p_c)V = nRT \tag{f}$$

From (a) and (f) the total pressure P becomes

$$P = p_a + p_b + p_c \tag{g}$$

Now, dividing Equation (b) by Equation (a), it follows that

$$\frac{p_a V}{PV} = \frac{n_a RT}{nRT}$$

and hence,

$$\left(p_a = P \times \frac{n_a}{n} \right) \tag{2-10}$$

The term n_a/n is known as the *mole fraction* of a in the gas mixture. Hence, to calculate the partial pressure of a gas, it is only necessary to multiply the total pressure by the mole fraction.

Dalton's law of partial pressures is especially useful in calculations involving gases collected over water. Here the total pressure is equal to the vapor pressure of the water plus the pressure due to the gas. The handling of such data is illustrated in the following examples.

Example 2-5. Seven grams of nitrogen, 16.0 grams of oxygen, and 3.03 grams of hydrogen are introduced into an evacuated vessel of 80-liter capacity at 50°C. What is the partial pressure of each gas in the mixture? What is the total pressure?

By use of the ideal gas law the individual partial pressures can be calculated as follows:

$$p_{N_2} = \frac{7.00 \, \text{gram} \times 0.0821 \, \text{liter} \times \text{atm} \times \text{mole}^{-1} \times {}^\circ A^{-1} \times (273 + 50)^\circ A}{28.0 \, \text{gram/mole} \times 80 \, \text{liters}}$$

$$= 0.083 \, \text{atm}$$

$$p_{O_2} = 0.166 \, \text{atm} \qquad p_{H_2} = 0.498 \, \text{atm}$$

The total pressure is given by the sum of the partial pressures

$$P = p_{N_2} + p_{O_2} + p_{H_2} = (0.083 + 0.166 + 0.498) \, \text{atm}$$
$$= 0.747 \, \text{atm}$$

It should be noted that the partial pressures are equal to the total pressure multiplied by the respective mole fraction.

$$\text{Total number of moles} = \frac{7.00}{28.0} + \frac{16.0}{32.0} + \frac{3.03}{2.02} = 2.25 \, \text{moles}$$

$$\text{Mole fraction of nitrogen} = \frac{0.25}{2.25} = 0.111$$

$$p_{N_2} = 0.111 \times 0.747 = 0.083 \, \text{atm}$$

$$\text{Mole fraction of oxygen} = \frac{0.50}{2.25} = 0.222$$

$$p_{O_2} = 0.222 \times 0.747 = 0.166 \, \text{atm}$$

$$\text{Mole fraction of hydrogen} = \frac{1.5}{2.25} = 0.667$$

$$p_{H_2} = 0.667 \times 0.747 = \underline{0.498 \, \text{atm}}$$
$$\text{Total} \quad 0.747 \, \text{atm}$$

Example 2-6. Collected over water at a total pressure of 760 mm are 500 ml of oxygen. The temperature of the system is 25°C, at which temperature water has a vapor pressure of 23.8 mm. What is the partial pressure of the oxygen? How many moles of oxygen are present in the collecting tube? What would be the volume of the oxygen, free of water vapor, at STP?

$$p_{O_2} = (760 - 23.8) \, \text{mm} = 736.2 \, \text{mm}$$

$$n = \frac{\frac{736.2}{760} \, \text{atm} \times 0.500 \, \text{liter}}{0.0821 \, \text{liter} \times \text{atm} \times \text{mole}^{-1} \times {}^\circ A^{-1} \times 298^\circ A} = 0.0198 \, \text{mole}$$

$$V(\text{STP}) = 500 \, \text{ml} \times \frac{736.2 \, \text{mm}}{760 \, \text{mm}} \times \frac{273^\circ A}{298^\circ A} = 444 \, \text{ml}$$

THE KINETIC THEORY OF GASES

2k. Statement of the Kinetic Theory of Gases. The purpose of the *kinetic theory of gases* is to develop a physical picture of the nature of the gaseous state capable of explaining the various laws of gaseous behavior. The postulates of this theory follow.

1. Gases are composed of discrete particles termed molecules, which are in rapid, random motion, moving at high velocities in straight lines.

2. Upon collision with other gas molecules or with any surface, they rebound without change of velocity. In other words, all collisions are perfectly elastic.

3. Except at very high pressures, the molecules are relatively far apart and their volumes are relatively small compared to the total volume of the system.

4. The molecules exert no attractive forces upon one another.

5. The pressure of the gas results from the impacts of the molecules upon the walls of the containing vessel.

In applying the kinetic theory of gases, it is convenient to assume a common value for the velocity of all the molecules. Actually some of the molecules have high velocities compared to the average velocity and some have smaller velocities. An average velocity could be used but theoretically it is much more exact to employ what is termed the *root-mean-square velocity*. This will be represented by the symbol c and its magnitude is given mathematically by the following relationship:

$$c = \sqrt{(c_1{}^2 + c_2{}^2 + c_3{}^2 \cdots + c_N{}^2)/N}$$

wherein c_1, c_2, etc., are the individual velocities of the various N molecules.

2l. Derivation of the Kinetic Equation. From the physical picture of the gaseous state represented by the kinetic theory of gases, a mathematical expression can be derived known as the *kinetic equation of gases*. This equation can be used to derive many of the laws of gases and to draw some interesting conclusions concerning gaseous behavior.

In order to simplify the derivation of the kinetic equation, consider that the gas is contained in a square box L cm on a side as shown in Figure 2-3. Although the actual molecules are in random motion, it is assumed that a third of the molecules are moving in paths parallel to each pair of opposite faces of the box. If N is the total number of molecules in the box, the number moving along the x axis will be $N/3$. Likewise, the number moving back and forth along the y and z axes will be $N/3$ each.

The problem is to derive an expression for the force exerted on a square centimeter of the surface of the box. This is equal to the pressure exerted by the gas, since pressure is equal to force per unit area.

Consider one of the molecules that is moving back and forth along the x axis. It will collide with *one* side of the container $c/2L$ times per second, in which c is the velocity of the gas molecule in centimeters per second.

Its momentum before collision is mc (m = mass) and its momentum after collision is $-mc$. Therefore, the change of momentum per collision = $mc - (-mc) = 2mc$.

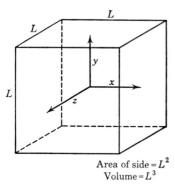

Area of side = L^2
Volume = L^3

Figure 2-3

The rate change of momentum is equal to the number of collisions per second times the change of momentum per collision = $2mc \times c/2L = mc^2/L$. It must be recalled from elementary physics that the rate change of momentum is equal to the force exerted by a moving body upon a collision or a series of collisions. This expression, mc^2/L, is the force exerted upon the side of the container by one of the molecules.

Each of the $N/3$ molecules moving in a particular direction will strike the wall with the force given by the preceding expression. It therefore follows that the force exerted on one face of the container by the $N/3$ molecules hitting that face is $N/3 \times mc^2/L = mNc^2/3L$.

Since pressure is equal to force per unit area, the pressure is equal to the above expression divided by the area of the side (L^2). Therefore

$$P = \frac{mNc^2}{3L \times L^2}$$

and since $L^3 = V$ and $PV = nRT$, it follows that

$$PV = \tfrac{1}{3}mNc^2 = nRT \tag{2-11}$$

In using this equation care must be exercised to see that all magnitudes are expressed in a consistent set of units.

2m. Graham's Law of Diffusion. If Equation 2-11 is solved for c, the following relationships are found for the root-mean-square velocity of the molecules at the temperature in question:

$$c = \sqrt{3PV/mN} = \sqrt{3nRT/mN} \tag{2-12}$$

If n is made equal to 1 mole, then N becomes Avogadro's number, and

mN becomes the molecular weight. Equation 2-12 can then be rewritten

$$c = \sqrt{3RT/M} \qquad (2\text{-}13)$$

Now consider two gases of molecular weights M_1 and M_2 and of velocities c_1 and c_2. A consideration of Equation 2-13 shows that for the same temperature the ratio of the velocities of the two gases is inversely proportional to the square roots of the molecular weights. Now according to Avogadro's law the density of a gas is proportional to the molecular weight. Furthermore, it is reasonable to assume that the rate (r) of diffusion is proportional to the velocity of the gas molecule. From these considerations it can be stated that the rate of diffusion of the gas and the speed of the gas molecules are inversely proportional to the square root of the density. This is known as *Graham's law of diffusion.* Furthermore, since the rate of diffusion is inversely proportional to the time (t) necessary for a given volume of gas to diffuse through a small opening, this series of relationships follows:

$$\frac{t_2}{t_1} = \frac{r_1}{r_2} = \frac{c_1}{c_2} = \sqrt{\frac{d_2}{d_1}} = \sqrt{\frac{M_2}{M_1}} \qquad (2\text{-}14)$$

This law, which has been derived from the kinetic equation, was first established experimentally. It has numerous applications in connection with the determinations of molecular weights and the separation of isotopes.

Example 2-7. A liter of oxygen diffuses through a pin hole in 20.0 minutes. The time necessary for a liter of ethane to diffuse through the same hole at the same temperature is 19.4 minutes. Calculate the molecular weight of ethane.

$$\frac{t_2}{t_1} = \frac{20.0}{19.4} = \sqrt{\frac{32.0}{x}} \qquad x = \frac{19.4^2 \times 32.0}{20.0^2} = 30.1$$

2n. Calculation of the Root-mean-square Velocity of Gas Molecules. Equation 2-13 can be used for the calculation of the root-mean-square velocity of the gas molecule. In using this equation, it is necessary that all units be expressed in the same system, and since velocity is best expressed in centimeters per second, all other terms must be expressed in the cgs system. Therefore, a value for R of 8.31×10^7 ergs per mole per degree is used.

Example 2-8. Calculate the root-mean-square velocity of the nitrogen molecule at 27°C.

$$c = \sqrt{\frac{3 \times 8.31 \times 10^7 \text{ ergs} \times \cancel{\text{moles}^{-1}} \times \cancel{°A^{-1}} \times 300°\cancel{A}}{28.0 \text{ grams} \cancel{\text{mole}^{-1}}}}$$

Now, since an erg is the work done when a force of 1 dyne acts through a distance of 1 cm, and a dyne is that force that gives to 1 gram an acceleration of 1 cm per sec per sec, it follows that the dimensions of the erg are gram cm^2 sec^{-2}. Consequently, the above equation becomes

$$c = \sqrt{\frac{3 \times 8.31 \times 10^7 \, \text{grams} \times cm^2 \times sec^{-2} \times \text{moles}^{-1} \times °A^{-1} \times 300°A}{28.0 \, \text{grams moles}^{-1}}}$$

$$= 5.16 \times 10^4 \text{cm per sec}$$

Example 2-9. From the value for the root-mean-square velocity of nitrogen calculated in Example 2-8, calculate the velocity of the hydrogen molecule at the same temperature.

$$\frac{c_1}{c_2} = \sqrt{\frac{M_2}{M_1}} = \frac{c_{H_2}}{5.16 \times 10^4 \text{ cm per sec}} = \sqrt{\frac{28.0}{2.02}}$$

$$c_{H_2} = 19.2 \times 10^4 \text{ cm per sec}$$

DEVIATIONS FROM THE IDEAL GAS LAW

2o. Van der Waals' Equation. It has been pointed out that the ideal gas law furnishes a satisfactory relationship for actual gases under moderate conditions of temperature and pressure. As can be seen in Figure 2-4, however, marked deviations occur at high pressures and the equation is not applicable to critical phenomena and the process of gas liquefaction. A number of equations have been developed, both empirically and theoretically, to cover a wider range of conditions than those covered by the ideal gas law and to explain the phenomena associated with the liquefaction of gases. The best known of these is the equation of van der Waals, the Dutch physicist. In the derivation of this equation, van der Waals applied corrections to both the pressure and the volume terms.

The nature of these corrections can be understood by considering the derivation of the kinetic equation. It will be recalled that the pressure of the gas was ascribed to the bombardment of the walls of the container by the gas molecules. In obtaining the expression for the pressure, it was assumed that the molecules had a common velocity that was characteristic of the temperature. It was further assumed that there were no attractive forces acting between the molecules so that this velocity was the same at the time of impact of the particle with the walls as when the particle was in the main body of the gas. In actual gases, however, attractive forces do exist, so that the velocity on impact is less than that assumed, and consequently the pressure actually exerted is less than the computed value.

Table 2-1. Van der Waals' Constants for Certain Gases

Gas	a (atm $\times$ mole^{-2} liter^2)	b (liter $\times$ mole^{-1})
Hydrogen	0.244	2.66×10^{-2}
Helium	0.034	2.37×10^{-2}
Nitrogen	1.39	3.91×10^{-2}
Carbon dioxide	3.59	4.27×10^{-2}

Van der Waals therefore added a correction term, called the *cohesion pressure*, to the experimentally determined pressure in order to obtain the so-called *thermal pressure*, the pressure term of the ideal gas law. This pressure correction term has the form an^2/V^2, in which n is the number of moles in the gaseous system, V is the volume, and a is a constant characteristic of the particular gas.

The volume term in the ideal gas law, or the volume considered in the derivation of the kinetic equation, is the volume in which the particles are free to move. In the derivation of the kinetic equation, molecules were considered as points without dimensions. If actual size is considered, they would not travel L cm in moving from one side of the container to the other but rather a distance equal to L less the diameter of the molecule. To correct for the space in which the particles are not free to move, van der Waals subtracted from the total volume as measured, a term, nb. In other words, this term is a correction for the effective volume of the molecules themselves. In this term, b is a constant characteristic of the particular gas and is the effective volume of 1 mole of the gas. The values for a and b for some typical gases are given in Table 2-1. As in the case of the gas constant R, their values depend upon the units in which they are expressed.

Van der Waals' equation in its general form follows:

$$\left(P + \frac{an^2}{V^2}\right)(V - nb) = nRT \tag{2-15}$$

If only 1 mole of gas is considered, the equation becomes

$$\left(P + \frac{a}{V^2}\right)(V - b) = RT \tag{2-16}$$

Other interesting and convenient forms are obtained by transposing terms and rearranging. For example, the following can be obtained:

$$P = \frac{RT}{V - b} - \frac{a}{V^2} \tag{2-17}$$

$$\left\{ PV = RT - \frac{a}{V} + \frac{ab}{V^2} + Pb \right\} \tag{2-18}$$

Equation 2-18 shows that the PV product given by the van der Waals equation is equal to the RT product of the perfect gas law with two positive and one negative correction terms. Since the constants a and b are small in magnitude, the correction terms in Equation 2-18 become increasingly insignificant as the volume of a given quantity of gas increases with a corresponding decrease in pressure.

Example 2-10. Calculate the expected pressure in a system consisting of 1 mole of carbon dioxide in a volume of 0.50 liter at 50°C, (*a*) using the ideal gas law, (*b*) using the van der Waals' equation.

(*a*)

$$P = \frac{1 \text{ mole} \times 0.0821 \text{ liter} \times \text{atm} \times \text{mole}^{-1} \times \text{°A}^{-1} \times (273 + 50)\text{°A}}{0.50 \text{ liter}}$$

$$= 53.0 \text{ atm}$$

(*b*) Employing Equation 2-17,

$$P = \frac{1 \text{ mole} \times 0.0821 \text{ liter} \times \text{atm} \times \text{mole}^{-1} \times \text{°A}^{-1} \times (273 + 50)\text{°A}}{0.50 \text{ liter} - 4.27 \times 10^{-2} \text{ liter} \times \text{mole}^{-1} \times 1 \text{ mole}}$$
$$- \frac{1 \text{ mole}^2 \times 3.59 \text{ atm} \times \text{mole}^{-2} \times \text{liter}^2}{0.50^2 \text{ liter}^2}$$

$$= 43.6 \text{ atm}$$

The actual value found for carbon dioxide under these conditions is 41.2 atm.

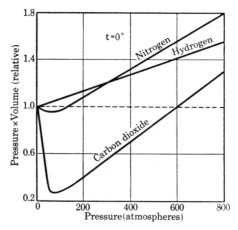

Figure 2-4. Deviation of the pressure-volume product with pressure in actual gases.

The student is referred to more advanced texts for the application of the van der Waals equation to the calculation of the critical temperature, critical pressure, and critical volume of gases.

2p. Pressure-volume Relationships in Real Gases. If the pressure-volume product of an ideal gas is plotted against P, a straight line parallel to the pressure axis is obtained. If the experimentally determined PV product is plotted, however, the departure of the curve so obtained from the ideal straight line indicates the extent to which the gas departs from the ideal. Some typical curves are shown in Figure 2-4. It should be noted that the PV product plotted is a relative value in order to make easier the comparison of the curves with the ideal, and in order to have all the curves start at the same point of origin. Observe that actual gases in most cases show first a negative and then a positive deviation from the ideal. This is in accordance with Equation 2-18, the extent and sign of the departure depending on the comparative values of the three correction terms.

REFERENCES

Daniels and Alberty, *Physical Chemistry*, John Wiley and Sons, New York, 1961, Chapters 2 and 11.

Maron and Prutton, *Principles of Physical Chemistry*, The Macmillan Co., New York, 1958, Chapter 1.

Moore, *Physical Chemistry*, Prentice-Hall, Inc., Englewood Cliffs, New Jersey, 1962, Chapter 1.

Sheehan, *Physical Chemistry*, Allyn and Bacon, Inc., Boston, 1961, Chapter 1.

Daniels, Williams, Bender, Alberty, and Cornwell, *Experimental Physical Chemistry*, McGraw-Hill Book Co., New York, 1962, Chapter 1.

Crockford and Nowell, *Laboratory Manual of Physical Chemistry*, John Wiley and Sons, New York, 1956, Experiments 1, 2, and 3.

REVIEW QUESTIONS

1. Compare the characteristics of the three states of matter.

2. Give some of the units found useful in the study of gases for expressing quantity, volume, and pressure. Distinguish between force and pressure.

3. Explain the principle of the barometer.

4. State Boyle's law in words and in the form of a mathematical expression.

5. State Charles's law in words and in the form of a mathematical expression.

6. State Avogadro's law.

7. Discuss the absolute temperature scale. What is the fractional change in volume of a given quantity of gas when the temperature is changed by one degree at constant pressure? Show the numerical value of fractional change at several temperatures.

8. By combining Charles's law, Boyle's law, and Avogadro's law, derive the expression for the ideal gas law.

9. In what sets of units may R be expressed in the usual types of gas calculations? Calculate the value of R in cgs units. Calculate the numerical value of the atmosphere in cgs units.

10. Show that the product of pressure and volume has the dimensions of work or energy.

11. Show how the ideal gas equation can be used in the determination of the molecular weights of volatile substances.

12. What is the meaning of the term *mole fraction*?

13. What is meant by the term *partial pressure*? What is the relationship between the partial pressures of the components of a gaseous mixture and the total pressure of the gas?

14. State Dalton's law in words and in the form of a mathematical expression.

15. State the postulates of the kinetic theory of gases. What is meant by the *root-mean-square velocity* of the molecules of a gas?

16. State in words the successive steps in the derivation of the kinetic equation. Show the mathematical operations involved with each of the steps.

17. Show that the kinetic equation of gases is dimensionally correct.

18. How can the kinetic gas equation be used in the calculation of the root-mean-square velocities of gas molecules?

19. State Graham's law of diffusion in words and in the form of a mathematical expression.

20. What two major factors cause the deviation of the behavior of actual gases from the behavior of an ideal gas? How are these factors accounted for in the van der Waals equation? What is meant by the terms *cohesion pressure* and *thermal pressure*?

21. In what units are the van der Waals constants usually expressed? What are the dimensions of the van der Waals constants?

PROBLEMS

I

1. A certain gas has a volume of 800 ml at 80°C and 600 mm pressure. What will be the volume under standard conditions? If the gas is oxygen, what will be its weight? How many molecules are present in this system?

2. What is the weight of 5 liters of benzene vapor at 300°C and at 380 mm pressure?

3. If the pressure of the benzene in Problem 2 is doubled, what increase must be made in the temperature in order that there be no change in volume?

4. What will be the volume of 4 grams of hydrogen at 250 mm pressure and at a temperature of 37°C? How many moles of hydrogen will be present in 40 ml of this gas at the same temperature and pressure?

5. What pressure will result if 1.05×10^{22} molecules of nitrogen at 27°C are introduced into a volume of 4 liters? What will be the pressure under these conditions of temperature and volume if the gas consists of the same number of methane molecules?

6. If 100 ml of a certain hydrocarbon in the gaseous state weigh 0.255 gram at 100°C and at a pressure of 1 atm, what is its molecular weight? How many molecules are present in the sample at the pressure and temperature given?

7. Given a sample of gas consisting of 7 grams of nitrogen, 4 grams of oxygen, and 4 grams of hydrogen. This sample is introduced into an evacuated vessel of 150-liter capacity at 50°C. What is the mole fraction of each gas in the mixture? What is the total pressure in the vessel and what is the partial pressure of each gas? How many grams of hydrogen would have to be removed in order to reduce the pressure to one half of the original value? How many grams of hydrogen would have to be introduced to double the pressure?

8. A flask contains a mixture of hydrogen and oxygen. The total pressure is 1.5 atm and the temperature is 27°C. If the oxygen is removed, the pressure falls to 0.5 atm, and the weight of the flask and contents drops by 16 grams. Calculate the volume of the flask, the weight of the hydrogen present, and the mole fraction of each gas in the original mixture.

9. How many grams of argon will occupy the same volume as 3.01×10^{22} molecules of methane at 1.5 atm pressure and at −35°C. What is the volume at the given temperature and pressure?

10. A certain quantity of nitrogen collected over water at 20°C and at a total pressure of 745 mm has a volume of 200 ml. What will be the volume of the nitrogen in a completely dry state at 780 mm pressure and at 48°C. The vapor pressure of water at 20°C is 17.54 mm.

11. Calculate the root-mean-square speed of the nitrogen molecule at (*a*) 25°C and (*b*) 0°C.

12. At what temperature will the root-mean-square speed of the nitrogen molecule be 4.0×10^4 cm sec?

13. What will be the ratio of the root-mean-square velocities of the helium and hydrogen molecules at (*a*) 30°C and (*b*) 100°C?

14. At what temperature will the argon molecule have the same speed as the oxygen molecule at 27°C?

15. What will be the ratio of the rates of diffusion of oxygen and helium at 0°C?

16. A certain volume of a gas diffuses through a small pinhole in 23.2 sec. The same volume of oxygen diffuses through the same pinhole under the same conditions in 32.8 sec. What is the molecular weight of the gas?

17. A certain volume of oxygen diffuses through a small pinhole in 40 min. How long will it take the same volume of methane at the same temperature and under the same pressure to escape through the pinhole?

18. Calculate the pressure at which 1 mole of helium at 35°C occupies a volume of 2 liters, using (*a*) the ideal gas equation and (*b*) the van der Waals equation.

19. Two liters of a certain gas at 1 atm pressure and at 273°C weigh 1.34 grams.

(a) What will be the volume of the gas at 2 atm pressure and at a temperature of −35°C?

(b) The temperature is increased to 400°C. What will be the final pressure if the volume remains the same?

(c) How many molecules are present in 10 ml of this gas when the pressure is 0.1 atm and the temperature is 50°C?

(d) What is the molecular weight of the gas?

(e) At what temperature will the root-mean-square velocity of the gas be the same as the root-mean-square velocity of the oxygen molecule at 27°C?

20. Given a system consisting of 16 grams of oxygen, 8 grams of helium, and 21 grams of nitrogen.

(a) What will be the total volume of the above gas if the temperature is 27°C and the pressure is 150 mm?

(b) If the above gaseous mixture is placed over water at 30°C and the volume remains the same, what will be the total pressure? The vapor pressure of water at 30°C is 31.82 mm.

(c) Calculate the mole fraction of each of the components in the wet gas obtained in (b).

(d) You wish to double the pressure by introducing argon gas into the original system under standard conditions. How many grams of this gas would have to be introduced? If the pressure of the original mixture was 200 mm and the temperature was 127°C, how many grams would have to be introduced to double the pressure?

(e) Calculate the number of molecules per milliliter in the original gaseous mixture under the conditions of temperature and pressure given in (a).

II

1. What is the weight of 15 liters of methane at 150°C and at a pressure of 800 mm?

2. A certain gas has a volume of 1 liter at 100°C and at 400 mm pressure. What will be the volume under standard conditions? If the gas is nitrogen, what is the weight of the sample? How many molecules are present in 500 ml under standard conditions?

3. Given two liters of nitrogen at STP. The temperature is increased to 60°C. What is the value of the final pressure if there is no change in the volume?

4. What pressure will result if 1.2×10^{21} molecules of nitrogen are introduced into a volume of 10 liters and the temperature fixed at 27°C? If twice this many molecules of oxygen are introduced instead of the nitrogen, what will be the final pressure at 27°C?

5. How many grams of helium will occupy the same volume as 1.81×10^{22} molecules of oxygen under standard conditions?

6. A sample of a substance weighing 2.200 grams in the gaseous state occupies 931 ml at 25°C at a pressure of 740 mm. What is its molecular weight?

7. Given a flask of 30-liter capacity containing 20 grams of nitrogen. How much nitrogen would have to be added to bring the total pressure to 1.2 atm at 27°C?

8. A certain flask contains a mixture of helium and nitrogen. The total pressure is 800 mm at 35°C. If the helium is removed, the pressure drops to 400 mm and the weight of the flask and contents drops by 2 grams. What is the mole fraction of each gas originally in the flask? What is the volume of the flask? How many molecules of each gas were originally present in each milliliter?

9. Given a flask of 10-liter capacity. Into the flask are introduced 2 grams each of nitrogen, oxygen, and argon. What is the total pressure and what are the partial pressures of each gas at 15°C? To double the pressure, how many additional grams of argon would have to be introduced?

10. A certain quantity of nitrogen is collected over water at 20°C. At 1 atm pressure it has a volume of 300 ml. What will be the total volume in the dry state at this temperature and pressure? What will be the volume in the dry state at 50°C and at a pressure of 900 mm?

11. A sample of gas weighing 0.400 gram is collected over water at 40°C and under a total pressure of 720 mm. The molecular weight of the gas is 32.0. What will be the volume of the wet gas? The vapor pressure of water at this temperature is 55.32 mm. How many grams of water will be present in the sample of wet gas?

12. If 0.010 gram of a gas occupies a volume of 5.8 ml at 30°C and at a pressure of 771.8 mm when collected over water, what is its molecular weight? The vapor pressure of water at this temperature is 31.8 mm.

13. Calculate the root-mean-square velocities of the krypton and hydrogen molecules at (a) −50°C, (b) 0°C, and (c) 100°C. At what temperature will the krypton molecule have the same velocity as the hydrogen molecule at −50°C? What will be the ratio of the root-mean-square velocities at (a) 0°C and (b) 100°C?

14. A sample of helium diffuses through a small pinhole in 16.4 min. How long will it take the same volume of hydrogen to diffuse through the same hole under the same conditions?

15. It requires 105.6 sec for a given volume of nitrogen to diffuse through a pinhole. Another gas under the same conditions of temperature and pressure requires 46.4 sec for the diffusion of the same volume. What is the molecular weight of the second gas?

16. Given that the root-mean-square velocity of a certain gas is 5.16×10^4 cm per sec at 27°C.
  (a) What will be the volume of 10 grams of this gas at 27°C and at a pressure of 0.5 atm?
  (b) How many molecules are present in 10 ml of this gas under standard conditions?
  (c) What is the molecular weight of the gas?

17. Two grams of a certain gas at 273°C and at 380 mm pressure occupy 1.12 liters.

(*a*) If the temperature is increased to 400°C and the pressure increased to 600 mm, what will be the new volume?

(*b*) If this quantity of gas is collected over water at 40°C and at a pressure of 800 mm, what will be the volume of the wet gas? The vapor pressure of water is 55.32 mm.

(*c*) At what temperature will the root-mean-square velocity of the molecules be the same as the velocity of the helium molecule at 35°C?

(*d*) What is the molecular weight of the gas?

18. Given a system consisting of 5 grams of argon, 5 grams of helium, and 10 grams of hydrogen at 27°C and in a volume of 100 liters.

(*a*) What is the total pressure in the system and what is the partial pressure of each gas at this temperature?

(*b*) How many molecules of each gas are present in 1 ml under the conditions stated?

(*c*) How many grams of hydrogen would have to be removed from this volume in order to reduce the total pressure to one half the original value, the temperature remaining constant?

19. Using both the ideal gas equation and the van der Waals equation, calculate the pressure exerted by 2 moles of nitrogen gas at 27°C in a volume of (*a*) 1 liter and (*b*) 20 liters.

THREE

Liquids

The purpose of this chapter is to study the vapor pressure, surface tension, and viscosity of liquids and the phenomena of fusion and evaporation. A discussion of the phase diagram for water is included. The procedures for the determination of surface tension by the more commonly used methods are given.

THE LIQUID STATE OF MATTER

3a. General Characteristics of Liquids. The essential differences among the three states of matter were discussed in Chapter 2. It was stated that the molecules of a liquid are relatively close together as compared with those in a gas and that strong attractive forces exist between the individual molecules. Unlike the particles in a solid, the molecules in the liquid state possess translational motion. This motion acts against the attractive forces but usually is not sufficient to overcome these forces. As a result, the molecules of a liquid do not distribute themselves evenly throughout the available space as do the molecules of a gas. On the other hand, because of the translational motion, the molecules do not remain fixed in rigid positions as in the solid state. A liquid, therefore, has a definite volume but not a definite shape and will take the shape of the vessel in which it is confined. The relative closeness of the molecules results in a comparatively high density as compared to the gaseous state

In the derivation of the kinetic equation of gases, a common value for the velocity of the gas molecules was assumed for a definite molecular species at a particular temperature. As a matter of fact, experimentation has shown that most of the molecules of a given gas at a specified temperature do possess velocities very close to both the average velocity and the root-mean-square velocity as discussed in the kinetic theory of gases. A small fraction of the molecules, however, have higher velocities, some very much higher, and a correspondingly small fraction have lower values. The same considerations apply to the liquid state. There is an average molecular velocity at a given temperature, but a few molecules have higher velocity values. *As the temperature increases, the fraction with the higher velocities increases.* This distribution of velocities is of extreme importance in the consideration of the vapor pressure of liquids and the phenomenon of vaporization.

THE VAPOR PRESSURE OF LIQUIDS

3b. Vapor Pressure. One of the most important of the properties of liquids is vapor pressure. Consider the system shown in Figure 3-1. A liquid is placed in an evacuated vessel so connected to a manometer that any pressure that develops in the free space above the liquid can be measured. The entire system is kept at a constant temperature. Consider the molecule *A* in the body of the liquid. It is acted upon by the attractive forces of all the molecules around it, as shown by the small arrows. Since the forces act equally in all directions, the net effect is zero, and these forces do not affect the translatory motion possessed by the molecule. But suppose the molecule moves towards the surface of the liquid, for example, to position *B*. Now the attractive forces are operating so as to pull the molecule back towards the main body of the liquid. (If the molecule has translational motion tending to move it through the surface layer into the free space above the liquid, this motion will be opposed by the attraction inward.) A particle having only the average velocity will be prevented from

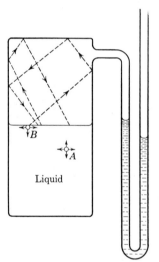

Figure 3-1

escaping. If this molecule, however, should be one with a greater than average velocity, as discussed in 3a, it may be able to break through the surface away from the forces present in the liquid and pass into the free space as a gas molecule. It will move around in this space in a path similar to one of those shown in the figure.

Eventually it will find its way back into the body of the liquid. When equilibrium is established, the number of molecules leaving the surface in a given time will be exactly equal to the number returning. Also the number leaving, and therefore the number returning, will depend upon the temperature. As noted in 3a, the higher the temperature, the greater the number of molecules with the more than average velocity, and so the greater will be the number in a unit volume of the space above the liquid. This, plus the fact that at the higher temperature the gas molecules move faster, results in a greater pressure being exerted by the gas molecules on the walls of the container. This pressure, the magnitude of which can be measured by the manometer, is spoken of as the *vapor pressure* of the liquid. Accordingly it can be stated that *the vapor pressure of a liquid at a given temperature is the pressure of the vapor in equilibrium with the liquid at that temperature.* (A gas in equilibrium with a liquid is usually spoken of as a vapor.) It should be noted that the vapor pressure is independent of the volume of the space above the liquid and of the volume of the liquid.

3c. The Change of Vapor Pressure with Temperature. An apparatus designed on the principle shown in Figure 3-1 can be used to determine the vapor pressure of liquids as a function of temperature. The pressure of the vapor is read on the manometer as the temperature is varied.

As seen in Table 3-1 and Figure 3-2, the vapor pressure at the lower temperatures changes only a small amount with rise in temperature. As the temperature increases, the vapor pressure shows a continually greater rate of change with increasing temperature and at the higher temperatures the curve becomes very steep. The vapor-pressure curve for the liquid state of water is one of the curves making up the phase diagram shown in Figure 3-4.

In a situation like the vapor-pressure-temperature relationship, we always attempt to obtain a mathematical relationship for the two variables. This can be done by plotting various functions of the two variables in order to try to obtain a simple relationship between them. For vapor pressure data it is found that if the logarithm of the pressure (log P) is plotted against the reciprocal of the absolute temperature, ($1/T$), a straight line is obtained with a negative slope. This is shown for water and benzene in Figure 3-3. This line can be represented by an equation of the form:

$$\left(\log P = -\frac{A}{T} + I \right) \tag{3-1}$$

wherein P is the vapor pressure, T is the absolute temperature, A is the slope of the line, and I is the intercept on the log P axis. In Equation 3-1 the variables must be log P and $1/T$ rather than P and T for the equation to be that of a straight line.

Table 3-1. Vapor-Pressure Data for Some Typical Liquids
(Vapor pressure in millimeters of mercury)

Temperature (°C)	Water	Ethanol	Acetone	Benzene	Acetic Acid
0	4.58	12.2	67.3	26.5	...
10	9.21	23.6	115.6	45.4	...
20	17.53	43.9	184.8	74.7	11.7
30	31.82	78.8	282.7	118.2	20.6
40	55.32	135.3	421.5	181.1	34.8
50	92.51	222.2	612.6	269.0	56.6
60	149.4	352.7	860.6	388.6	88.9
70	233.7	542.5	...	547.4	136.0
80	355.1	812.6	...	753.6	202.3
90	525.8	...	...	1016.1	293.7
100	760.0	...	...	...	417.1

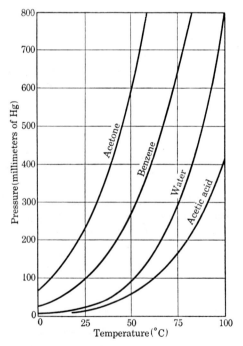

Figure 3-2. Vapor-pressure curves of some typical liquids.

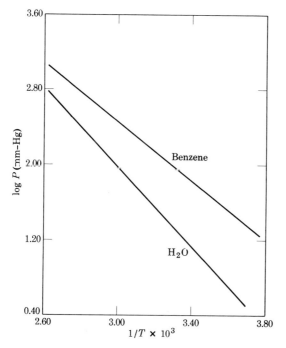

Figure 3-3. Plot of log p versus $1/T$ for water and benzene.

The problem can also be approached from a theoretical standpoint, however, and if this is done by proper thermodynamic procedures using calculus, the following equation is obtained:

$$\frac{dp}{dT} = \frac{L_v p}{RT^2}$$

In this equation dp represents the very small change in vapor pressure with a very small change in temperature at the temperature T, at which temperature the vapor pressure is p. L_v is the heat of vaporization of 1 mole of the liquid. Now if this equation is integrated, assuming that L_v is independent of temperature, the following expression is obtained.

$$\log p = -\frac{L_v}{2.303RT} + I \tag{3-2}$$

A comparison of Equations 3-1 and 3-2 shows that the slope A in Equation 3-1 is equal to $L_v/2.303R$. Hence we have in these equations a means of calculating the molar heat of vaporization of the liquid.

In order to carry out this calculation, we find it convenient to convert Equation 3-2 to a two-point equation, thus eliminating the constant I. The equation so obtained is

$$\log \frac{p_2}{p_1} = \frac{L_v}{2.303R}\left(\frac{1}{T_1} - \frac{1}{T_2}\right) = \frac{L_v}{2.303R}\left(\frac{T_2 - T_1}{T_2 T_1}\right) \tag{3-3}$$

The significance of L_v is discussed in the next section of this chapter. At this time only the calculation of its numerical value by means of Equation 3-3 is considered.

→ **Example 3-1.** Calculate the heat of vaporization of benzene from vapor pressure data.

Any two pairs of values of p-T data can be substituted in Equation 3-3 and the equation solved for L_v. It is best to select two points rather wide apart, and in this case the values for $0°$ and $60°C$ will be used. These must first be converted to the absolute temperature. Substitution in Equation 3-3 gives

$$\log \frac{388.6 \text{ mm}}{26.5 \text{ mm}} = \frac{L_v}{2.303 \times 1.99 \text{ cal mole}^{-1}\,°A^{-1}}\left(\frac{333°A - 273°A}{333°A \times 273°A}\right)$$

and

$$L_v = 8100 \text{ cal/mole}$$

It would be much more accurate to use a number of points and solve for L_v using the method of averages, or some similar mathematical procedure. The method used in this example, however, usually gives excellent values if the two points are properly selected. It should be added that L_v is not entirely independent of temperature and the value determined in this type of calculation is more precisely an average value over the temperature range covered.

3d. Boiling Point. Heat of Vaporization. If a liquid is placed in a container open to the atmosphere and slowly heated, the liquid boils when it reaches that temperature at which its vapor pressure is equal to the external atmospheric pressure. Then if heating is continued, the liquid changes to vapor without further change of temperature. If the external pressure is exactly 1 atm, the temperature of the boiling liquid is known as the *normal boiling point.* Sometimes it is convenient to boil or distill a substance at a temperature lower than the normal boiling point. This process is known as *distillation under reduced pressure.* It is often used in organic chemistry for the purification of a substance that decomposes at the normal boiling point. The fact that water boils at a lower temperature than $100°C$ on a mountain top is an example of the effect of pressure change on boiling point.

As noted above, the conversion of a liquid to vapor at the boiling point is effected by the *continued* heating of the liquid after the boiling temperature is reached. In other words, energy must be supplied not only to bring a liquid to its boiling point but also to effect the change in state. One of the things this energy does is to supply the evaporating molecules with the extra velocities necessary for them to break away from the attractive forces exerted by the molecules in the main body of the liquid. This heat supplied at the boiling point to effect the vaporization of the substance is known as the *heat of vaporization*. The quantity necessary to evaporate a gram of the substance at its boiling point is termed the *specific heat of vaporization*, and that necessary to evaporate a mole is known as the *molar heat of vaporization*. This was the magnitude assigned the symbol, L_v, in the prior section. The specific heat of vaporization of water at its normal boiling point of 100°C is 539.9 cal per gram. For benzene at its normal boiling point of 80.2°C, the value is 94.4 cal per gram. The evaporation of perspiration or other moisture from the skin produces a cooling effect because of removal from the body of the heat of vaporization.

While heat of vaporization can be measured precisely by calorimetric procedures, it can be obtained as shown in the prior section of this chapter from vapor pressure data. Later it will be shown in the section on thermodynamics that it is a special form of heat of reaction (liquid to vapor) and is classified as a change in the enthalpy, ΔH, of the system.

3e. Freezing Point. Heat of Fusion. If a liquid is cooled sufficiently, it will reach a temperature at which it changes to the solid state. If the liquid is water, if the external pressure is 1 atm, and if the water is saturated with air, the change occurs at 0°C. This temperature is known as the *normal freezing point* of water. The freezing point of a liquid is defined as that temperature at which solid, liquid, and vapor exist together at equilibrium. Freezing takes place with the evolution of heat, and, conversely, in order to melt the solid, heat must be supplied. This heat is known as *heat of fusion*. The specific heat of fusion of water has a value of 79.8 cal per gram. This heat is necessary to give the molecules sufficient energy to break away from the strong attractive forces characteristic of the solid state.

While the normal freezing point of water, as stated above, is 0°C at 1 atm external pressure and when saturated with air, the actual vapor pressure of the water at this temperature is about 4.6 mm. If an air-free water system were placed in a vacuum and allowed to seek its own equilibrium, it would be found that the freezing point at which the solid and liquid exist simultaneously in the presence of the vapor would be

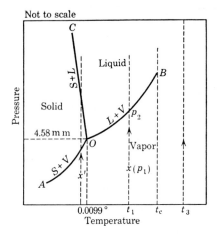

Figure 3-4. Phase diagram of water.

0.0099°C and the pressure of the vapor would be 4.58 mm. This temperature is known as the *triple point* for water and is represented by the point 0 in Figure 3-4.

Although the freezing point of water is 0°C at an external pressure of 1 atm, it can be made lower than this value by imposing a greater pressure. This is illustrated by the fact that water often runs out from under a glacier even though the temperature is well below zero. This phenomenon is due to the enormous pressure of the glacier that lowers the melting point of the ice. Another example is seen when a block of ice is subjected to a pressure at one point. The ice will melt more rapidly at the point of pressure. The lowering of the freezing point of water with increased pressure is illustrated in Figure 3-4. It should be kept in mind that (this lowering of the freezing point by pressure is characteristic only of water and a very limited number of other substances.) Most substances show the reverse effect.

3f. Sublimation. Heat of Sublimation. Solids, as well as liquids, show vapor pressures that increase with increase of temperature. If the vapor from a solid is constantly removed, the solid will pass directly into the vapor state without going through the liquid state. Such a change is known as *sublimation.* Just as in fusion and evaporation, heat is absorbed in the process. This is known as the *heat of sublimation.* The vapor-pressure, or sublimation-pressure, curve for solid water is part of the diagram in Figure 3-4. The molar heat of sublimation can be calculated from sublimation pressure data in the same manner that the heat of vaporization was calculated from vapor pressure data.

3g. The Phase Diagram of Water. Vapor-pressure curves of liquids were discussed in 3c and sublimation curves in 3f. These curves intersect at the freezing point, which was discussed in 3e. The effect of pressure on freezing point was also discussed in 3e. The facts considered in these paragraphs are shown graphically in Figure 3-4. This figure is what is called the phase diagram of water and is constructed from experimentally determined data. It should be noted that this figure is not drawn to scale. This was done in order to emphasize certain of the features of the diagram. The term *phase diagram* is used because the figure shows the various phases existing under different conditions of temperature and pressure. A *phase* is defined as a part of a system set off from the remainder of the system by a physical boundary or surface, which may or may not be continuous. In this diagram three phases are shown: a gas, a liquid, and a solid. It is possible to have more than one crystalline form

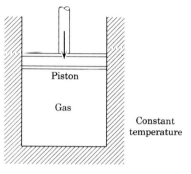

Figure 3-5

of water, and, if two of these are present, they represent two distinct phases. The diagram given covers a range of temperature and pressure in which only one crystalline form is found. That form may be in one large crystal or in many small crystals. In the latter case the phase boundary is discontinuous.

In the figure, curve *AO* is the sublimation curve, and along it the phases existing together are vapor and solid. *OB* is the vapor-pressure curve of the liquid, and along it the phases coexisting are liquid and vapor. The curves intersect at *O*, the freezing point. Here, and only here, the three phases coexist. The temperature is +0.0099°C, and the pressure is 4.58 mm. Curve *CO* is the melting-point curve of ice as a function of pressure. In the field *AOC*, the only phase is solid ice. In *AOB* it is vapor, and in *COB* it is liquid.

The phase diagram can be used to establish what happens when a quantity of water in the gaseous state is submitted to increasing pressure at constant temperature. Suppose a quantity of vapor, whose pressure and temperature is represented by the point x in the diagram, is placed in a cylinder equipped with a piston as represented in Figure 3-5. Let the pressure on the piston be p_1. Now gradually increase the pressure as shown by the ascending dotted line, keeping the temperature constant at t_1. Gas molecules will be forced closer together as the volume decreases with increasing pressure, in accordance with Boyle's law. This compression will continue until the dotted line intersects the vapor-pressure curve for water. There the pressure will be p_2, the vapor pressure of water at this temperature. The molecules will now be sufficiently close together for the attractive forces to overcome their translatory motion, and liquefaction will take place. Increase of pressure will be resisted by the condensation of the gas, and the value of the pressure will be that of the vapor pressure at t_1 until condensation is complete. The piston will now be in contact with the surface of the liquid with only one phase, liquid water, existing. Further pressure will result in compression of the liquid along the dotted line above the vapor-pressure curve. Had the original temperature been below 0°C as represented by the point x', the increase in pressure exerted by the piston would have resulted first in the formation of the solid and later in the change of solid to liquid. As before, the changes are represented by an ascending dotted line.

In each change in state brought about by increase of pressure, the system changes to a phase that occupies a smaller volume. In the second procedure, starting at x', the first change is from the gaseous to the solid state. The second change is from the solid to the liquid state. That ice occupies a larger volume than liquid water is illustrated by the fact that water pipes tend to burst on freezing.

The phase diagram for water is similar to that for many other substances, although diagrams for other systems are frequently more complicated.

3h. The Critical Temperature. The process of condensation as effected by increasing the pressure at constant temperature along the dotted line from point x in Figure 3-4 was explained on the basis that the attractive forces overcame the translational motion of the molecules at point p_2. The magnitude of the attractive forces changes little with temperature, whereas the translatory motion changes appreciably with increase in temperature. Should the temperature t_3 be employed, no amount of pressure will produce condensation. The velocity of the molecules is always able to overcome the attractive forces at such a high temperature. In other words, there is a maximum temperature, t_c, the *critical temperature*, above which liquefaction cannot be effected no matter how great the pressure. On the phase diagram, the vapor-pressure curve of the liquid ends at the critical temperature.

The critical temperature is of great importance in the commercial liquefaction of gases. In the liquefaction of air, for example, the change from the gas to the liquid does not take place until the temperature has been reduced to the critical value. Furthermore, it should be noted from Figure 3-4 that the lower the temperature is below the critical value, the smaller is the pressure necessary for liquefaction.

As stated in Chapter 2, the ideal gas law does not describe the behavior of gases under the conditions existing around the critical temperature and the critical pressure. The van der Waals equation, however, not only applies to the gas in this region but also can be used to describe in a fairly satisfactory manner the behavior of the liquid state. Also, as stated in Chapter 2, this equation can be used to evaluate the critical magnitudes, t_c, p_c, and v_c in terms of the van der Waals constants and the gas constant, R. The procedure is presented in more advanced texts in physical chemistry.

THE SURFACE TENSION OF LIQUIDS

3i. Adhesion and Cohesion. It will be recalled from Section 3b that attractive forces between molecules play an important part in the vapor pressure of liquids. A further consideration of these same attractive forces helps to explain another property of liquids, that of *surface tension*.

There are two types of attractive forces existing in liquid and liquid-solid systems. In systems of only one component, for example, those studied in the vapor-pressure discussion, attractive forces operate only between *like* molecules, and this type of attraction is termed *cohesion*. The term *adhesion* is used in connection with attractive forces operating between unlike molecules. Adhesive forces exist, for example, between water molecules and glass and between water molecules and a clean metal surface. As a result, water forms a film over glass and metal. This process is termed *wetting*. On the other hand, water does not wet a waxed surface, since there is little force of adhesion between the water molecules and the molecules of the wax.

The concepts of adhesion and cohesion should be kept clearly in mind in order to understand properly the subject of surface tension and its manifestations.

3j. Surface Tension. When a drop of liquid falls through a gas, as in the passage of rain through air, it tends to assume a spherical shape. This well-known fact may be explained by considering a drop of the liquid and the cohesive forces acting between its molecules. In the center of the drop, a molecule is attracted equally in all directions by other molecules surrounding it. As a result, all the forces acting on such a molecule cancel each other. Consider next a molecule near the periphery of the drop. The inward attractive forces are greater than the outward forces because there are a greater number of molecules towards the center. At the surface of the drop, however, there is no longer any outward force, but only those forces acting inward and sideways. As a result of this condition on the surface molecules, the drop will assume that geometric form with the *smallest surface area.* Hence the drop assumes a spherical shape. Furthermore, the surface acts as if it consisted of an elastic membrane with forces acting tangentially to the surface.

This tangential force acting in the surface of a liquid can be illustrated by the device shown in Figure 3-6. A liquid film is formed in a loop. Three sides are rigid but the fourth is movable. By applying a force to the movable side, this film can be stretched. If the force is removed, the film contracts. This tendency of the film to resist expansion is a manifestation of the tangential force in the film surface. The minimum amount of force necessary to effect a very slow stretching of the film is proportional to the length of the movable side. The magnitude of this force per *unit length* of one side of the film is termed the *surface tension* of the liquid. The surface tension of a liquid is, therefore, the force with which the surface of one side of a line 1 cm in length pulls or attracts the surface of the other side of the line. If it is expressed in cgs units, it is measured in *dynes per centimeter,* since it is force per unit length. It is usually represented by the Greek letter gamma (γ). In the loop shown, the force along the entire length (L) of the movable side would be

$$\left(\text{Force} = 2\gamma L \right)$$

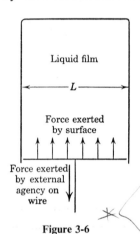

Liquid film

$\longleftarrow L \longrightarrow$

Force exerted by surface

Force exerted by external agency on wire

Figure 3-6

The number 2 is introduced because there are two sides to the film.

The tangential force, or "skin effect," in the surface of liquids manifests itself in many ways. A needle covered with a light film of oil so that it will not be "wetted" may be made to float on the surface of water. Although the needle is much denser than water, the surface tension keeps it from sinking. The needle, not being "wetted," tends to "ride" on the surface of the liquid. The liquid film curves under the needle, and the resulting concave surface exerts an upward force on the needle. This force operates against the effect of gravity, which is tending to pull the needle downward. Various types of metal gauze can be floated on a water surface in a similar manner.

Another manifestation of surface tension is shown by the manner in which water droplets tend to take a spherical shape on a waxed surface, for example, on a freshly waxed automobile body. Since the adhesive forces operating between the wax and the water molecules are small compared with cohesive forces between water molecules, the surface-tension effect produces the spherical droplets and prevents a general wetting of the surface. If the wax layer wears off or becomes coated with dirt, adhesive forces will overcome the cohesive forces and a general wetting of the surface results.

The absorption of water by blotting paper or a sponge is due to a combination of adhesive and cohesive forces. First there is a wetting of the entire surface of the sponge or paper because of adhesive forces. Thus, an enormous liquid surface is created, and the surface-tension effect then tends to reduce this surface to a minimum value. This is accomplished by the movement of water into the pores and capillaries of the sponge and blotting paper. This phenomenon will be discussed in detail in the capillary-rise method for determining surface tension.

✓**3k. Determination of Surface Tension by the Capillary-rise Method.** If a capillary tube is placed in a liquid that wets its surface, the liquid rises in the capillary. This phenomenon occurs when a glass capillary is placed in water. Adhesive forces produce a thin film of water over the entire surface of the tube as shown in Figure 3-7(a). This produces a large surface area, and the surface tension of the liquid acts to decrease its magnitude to the smallest possible value. The contraction of the surface could be effected either by the adhering film being pulled down into the main body of the liquid or by the liquid being pulled up into the capillary. The adhesive forces are sufficiently strong to prevent the former, so capillary rise takes place.

The height to which the liquid rises in the tube depends on the magnitude of the force of the surface tension pulling the liquid upward, as compared to the force of gravity pulling the liquid column downward. When the

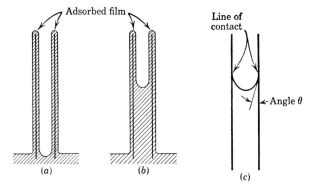

Figure 3-7. Capillary rise.

two forces are equal, further rise is prevented and a condition of equilibrium results. This equilibrium condition is represented in Figure 3-7(b). The liquid is held up by the action of the surface tension at the line of contact between the liquid column and the adsorbed film on the capillary wall. The force around the line of contact resulting from the surface tension is $2\pi r\gamma$. However, because the surface of the liquid in the capillary makes a contact with the film on the capillary wall at an angle θ [see Figure 3-7(c)], this force is not wholly effective in holding up the liquid column. Instead the resultant force must be used if an exact expression is to be obtained. The resultant force is

$$\left(\text{Upward pull} = 2\pi r\gamma \cos \theta \right)$$

where r is the radius of the capillary. If the angle of contact is very small, as it is for most liquids, then $\cos \theta$ approaches 1 in value and the upward pull reduces to $2\pi r\gamma$.

The downward pull due to gravity is equal to the mass of the liquid column multiplied by the acceleration of gravity. If the density of the liquid is d and the height to which the column has risen is h, then

$$\left(\text{Downward force} = h \times \text{area of cross section of capillary} \times d \times g \right)$$
$$\left(= h\pi r^2 \, dg \right)$$

At equilibrium

$$\text{Upward pull} = \text{downward force} = 2\pi r\gamma = h\pi r^2 \, dg$$

and
$$\left(\gamma = \tfrac{1}{2}hdgr \right) \tag{3-4}$$

In this derivation, besides the assumption that the angle of contact was zero, it was also assumed that the density of the air displaced was negligibly small as compared to the density of the liquid. Also the volume of liquid in the hemispherical meniscus [see Figure 3-7(c)] was assumed to be negligibly small compared to the volume of the liquid column. That Equation 3-4 is dimensionally correct is seen by the following example.

Example 3-2. Ethanol at 20°C rises to a height of 5.76 cm in a capillary tube whose radius is 0.010 cm. Calculate the surface tension at this temperature. The density of ethanol at 20°C is 0.789 gram per cc.

$$\gamma = \frac{\dfrac{0.789 \text{ gram}}{\text{cm}^3} \times 5.76 \text{ cm} \times \dfrac{980.7 \text{ cm}}{\text{sec}^2} \times 0.010 \text{ cm}}{2}$$

$$= \frac{0.789 \times 5.76 \times 980.7 \times 0.01 \text{ gram cm sec}^{-2}}{2 \text{ cm}} = 22.3 \text{ dynes per cm}$$

A liquid that does not wet the capillary, such as mercury in a glass capillary, produces a condition such as that shown in Figure 3-8(*a*). Here the surface is reduced to a minimum by a depression of the liquid in the capillary. At equilibrium, the downward pull of the force due to surface tension is equal to the effect of gravity in the liquid outside the capillary tending to restore the original level in the tube. The equilibrium condition is shown in Figure 3-8(*b*).

3l. Determination of Surface Tension by the du Noüy Ring Method. This method employs an instrument so constructed that the force necessary to pull a ring away from the surface of a liquid can be easily measured. The rings are made of platinum, since this metal resists chemical action and is wetted by most liquids. This instrument, termed a *tensiometer*, is shown in a highly simplified form in Figure 3-9. It was developed at

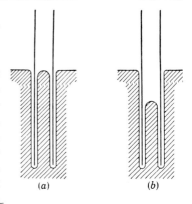

Figure 3-8. Capillary depression.

the Rockefeller Institute for Medical Research especially for use on biological fluids. Its advantages are simplicity, and ease and rapidity of handling. It is available commercially as a complete unit.

The operation of the tensiometer is essentially as follows. First the instrument is leveled by placing a small spirit level in various positions on the table, *T*, and then leveling the instrument by the screws in the legs. The dial on the face of the instrument is set at zero. By means of the adjusting screw, *E*, the torsion arm, *D*, with the ring is adjusted to the horizontal position, as shown by the indicator *F*. The liquid whose surface tension is to be measured is then brought into contact with the ring by means of the coarse and fine adjustments *G* and *G'*. A force is applied to the ring by turning the screw *A*. While this is being done, there is a tendency for the ring to lift part of the liquid surface above the general level, as shown in Figure 3-10. This tends to change the horizontal position of the torsion arm, *D*. Since the breaking force must be measured from the horizontal position, the raising of the surface must be compensated for by lowering the liquid level by means of the fine adjustment *G'*.

When sufficient force is applied, the ring breaks away from the surface. The magnitude of the force applied is indicated by the reading on the tensiometer dial. Its actual magnitude can then be determined by adding weights to the ring until the original horizontal position is restored. The actual value of the force is then equal to *mg*, where *m* is the total of the

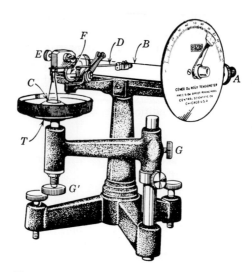

Figure 3-9. du Noüy ring tensiometer. (Courtesy of the Central Scientific Company, Chicago.)

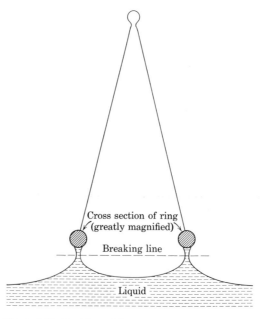

Cross section of ring
(greatly magnified)

Breaking line

Liquid

Figure 3-10. Position of du Noüy ring when about to break away from surface.

weights necessary for the restoration of the horizontal position, and g is the acceleration of gravity.

This total force is equal to the force by which the ring was originally held to the surface. This is equal to $2L\gamma$, where L is the mean circumference of the ring. The factor 2 must be used, since the liquid film that must be broken is in contact with both the inner and outer circumferences of the ring. This is illustrated in Figure 3-10. The fundamental equation for the ring method is therefore

$$\left.\begin{matrix} 2L\gamma = mg \\ \gamma = \dfrac{mg}{2L} \end{matrix}\right\} \tag{3-5}$$

Although this formula gives the apparent surface tension, it is necessary to use a correction factor, the magnitude of which depends upon the dimensions of the ring and the density of the liquid. It corrects for the effect of the small drops of liquid that adhere to the ring when it breaks away from the surface and for certain errors introduced by the liquid raised by the ring above the general surface of the liquid as a whole. Its determination and use are discussed in detail in the literature supplied with the instruments by the manufacturer.

Refinements on the instrument permit adjustments so that the dial reading will be numerically equal to the apparent surface tension. A calibration curve can be used, however, with the dial readings plotted against their surface tension values. In practice, the dial readings are usually assumed to be linear, and the value of a scale division in terms of a surface tension value is established with the weight procedure. Multiplying the dial reading after a determination by this value gives at once the apparent surface tension.

Example 3-3. In the determination of the surface tension of a liquid by the ring method, it was found that the ring broke away from the surface when the dial reading was 26. To restore the torsion arm to the original horizontal position required a weight of 0.220 gram. The ring was 4 cm in circumference, and the correction factor was 0.98. Calculate the apparent and exact surface tension from these data.

$$\text{Apparent surface tension} = \frac{0.220 \text{ gram} \times 980.7 \text{ cm/sec}^2}{2 \times 4 \text{ cm}}$$

$$= 27.0 \text{ dynes/cm}$$

Exact surface tension $= 27.0 \times 0.98 = 26.5$ dynes/cm. It will be noted that, since the dial reading was 26, each dial division was equal to 1.019 dynes/cm.

3m. Factors Affecting Surface Tension. Some of the effects of molecular structure on surface tension are brought out in Table 3-2, which gives the surface tension of a number of substances at 20°C. Water has the highest value of any of the substances shown. This value is probably due to association produced by the action of the hydrogen bonding. Glycerol and glycol also have large values, probably because of the hydroxyl groups. (The values for the four monohydroxy alcohols listed are nearly equal, a result of the chemical similarity of the molecules.)

Table 3-2. The Surface Tension of Certain Liquids Measured at 20°C at the Air–Liquid Interface*

Substance	Surface Tension (dynes/cm)	Substance	Surface Tension (dynes/cm)
Water	72.8	1-Propanol	23.8
Glycerol	63.4	Methanol	22.6
Glycol	47.7	Ethanol	22.3
Nitrobenzene	43.9	2-Propanol	21.7
Aniline	42.9	n-Hexane	18.4
Benzene	28.9	Diethyl ether	17.0

* Data from *Handbook of Chemistry and Physics*, The Chemical Rubber Co., 43rd Edition, Cleveland, Ohio.

The surface tension of all liquids *decreases with rise in temperature.* This change is so marked that highly accurate determinations must be carried out at a carefully controlled temperature. The surface tension of water between 20° and 30°C changes by an average value of 0.16 dyne per cm per degree. In the same region the change in benzene is 0.14 dyne per cm per degree. Values of the same order of magnitude are found for other substances.

The effect of an added substance on the surface tension of a liquid depends on the chemical nature of the added component. If the two substances are chemically similar, their surface tensions will probably not differ greatly, and, when mixed, the resulting solutions will probably have surface tensions that are close to a linear function of the concentrations. (Electrolytes generally increase the surface tension of water, but the effect is usually small.) On the other hand, many organic substances such as soaps, alcohols, and acids, especially the so-called surface-active substances, will, when added to water in small amounts, produce a solution that has a surface tension far below that of water. It is this lowering of the surface tension of water by soap that makes possible the stretching of the water film in the formation of a soap bubble. The action of wetting agents depends to a great extent upon the fact that they lower the surface tension of the water, thus making it possible for the adhesive forces to produce a water film over the surface of the object to be wetted. This principle is supposed to apply in the case of toothpastes, mouth washes, and certain antiseptics. Substances have been added that lower the surface tension, thus producing better tissue coverage and better antiseptic effects.

3n. Interfacial Tension. Up to this point, the discussion of surface forces has been limited to air-liquid interfaces. The same general concepts apply to liquid-liquid interfaces. The surface tension between a pair of liquids is termed the *interfacial tension*. The same techniques, with certain modifications, that were used to measure surface tension can be used for measuring interfacial tensions. The detergent action of soap and certain other cleaning agents is due to the lowering of the interfacial tension between the water and the oil or greasy material to be removed. Interfacial tension plays a very important part in certain phenomena associated with living cells.

THE VISCOSITY OF LIQUIDS

3o. Viscosity. The general concept of *viscosity* is a familiar one. Some liquids flow more readily than others. Those that flow slowly, such as castor oil, lubricating oils, and tar, are spoken of as liquids with a high viscosity. On the other hand, water, benzene, gasoline, etc., are spoken of as liquids with a low viscosity. In general, it may be stated that the viscosity of a liquid determines its rate of flow.

More exactly, the viscosity is the resistance experienced by one layer of a liquid in moving past another layer. A column of a liquid in a circular tube can be considered made up of concentric layers or cylinders of liquid. In moving through the tube, the layer nearest to the wall remains stationary if wetting of the surface takes place. Each succeeding layer moves past the one outside it with a velocity that increases as the center of the tube is approached. This is known as streamline flow and is characterized by the absence of eddies and turbulence in general. In the theoretical treatment of this type of flow the liquid is considered to have what is termed an *internal friction*, which resists the movement of the cylinders. This friction is the viscosity of the liquid. The *unit of viscosity*, (the *poise*) is defined *as such a viscosity that unit force per unit area is required to cause two parallel liquid surfaces of unit area and unit distance apart to slide past each other with unit velocity.* Mathematically this may be expressed as follows:

$$\text{Viscosity} = \frac{\text{force} \times \text{distance between surfaces}}{\text{velocity} \times \text{area}}$$

$$= \frac{\text{dynes} \times \text{cm}}{\text{cm/sec} \times \text{cm}^2} = \frac{\text{dynes} \times \text{sec}}{\text{cm}^2} = \left(1 \ poise\right)$$

Viscosity is usually represented by the Greek letter eta (η). In accordance with the above formula, a liquid has a viscosity of 1 poise if a force of 1 dyne will move a unit area of the liquid past another unit area 1 cm distant from it with a velocity of 1 cm per sec.

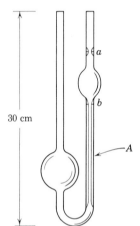

30 cm

Figure 3-11. Ostwald viscosimeter.

3p. Measurement of Viscosity. There are a number of rather diverse methods for measuring viscosity. The falling-ball method consists in determining the time necessary for a sphere of given size and weight to fall through a column of known length of the liquid. One general method employs oscillating or rotating disks, rings, or cylinders. The method most useful in measuring viscosities of the magnitudes found in most biological liquids is known as *Poiseuille's method*. It employs a type of apparatus known as an *Ostwald viscosimeter*. A simple form is shown in Figure 3-11.

The method consists in measuring the time of flow of a known volume of the liquid (that contained between the marks *a* and *b*) through a capillary, *A*, of known length and radius, under the influence of gravity. By theoretical means Poiseuille determined that the viscosity of the liquid is given by the following formula:

$$\left(\eta = \frac{r^4 pt\pi}{8vl} \right) \tag{3-6}$$

in which *p* = hydrostatic pressure on the liquid (proportional to its density),

  t = time of flow in seconds,

  r = radius of the capillary in centimeters,

  l = length of the capillary in centimeters,

  v = volume of the liquid in cubic centimeters.

The usual procedure is not to determine the absolute viscosity but the viscosity with relation to that of water. This is termed the *specific* or

(*relative viscosity.*) The times of flow for equal volumes of water and the liquid whose viscosity is being determined are measured. (Since the pressure of a liquid in a viscosimeter is proportional to its density, and since r, v, and l are constant terms for a given instrument, it follows from Equation 3-6 that for two liquids the ratio of the viscosities is equal to the ratio of their time-density products. The use of this relationship in the determination of relative and absolute viscosity is illustrated in Example 3-4.

Example 3-4. Using the same viscosimeter, it was found that the times of flow of equal volumes of water and benzene at 20°C were 120 and 88.0 seconds respectively. The density of benzene at this temperature is 0.879 gram per cm³, and that of water can be taken as 1 gram per cm³. Given that the absolute viscosity of water at this temperature is 10.05 × 10⁻³ poise, calculate the relative and absolute viscosity of benzene at this temperature.

From Equation 3-6

$$\left(\frac{\eta_1}{\eta_2} = \frac{d_1 t_1}{d_2 t_2} \right) \quad relative \ viscosity$$

and

$$\eta_1 = 10.05 \times 10^{-3} \text{ poise} \times \frac{0.879 \text{ gram} \times \text{cm}^{-3} \times 88.0 \text{ sec}}{1 \text{ gram} \times \text{cm}^{-3} \times 120 \text{ sec}}$$

Absolute viscosity = 6.48×10^{-3} poise

$$\text{Relative viscosity} = \frac{6.48 \times 10^{-3}}{10.05 \times 10^{-3}} = 0.644$$

The absolute viscosities of certain liquids are given in Table 3-3.

Table 3-3. Absolute Viscosities of Some Common Liquids at 20°C*

Liquid	Viscosity (poise)
Acetone	0.00331
Benzene	0.00647
Ethanol	0.01194
Acetic acid	0.01222
Nitrobenzene	0.01980
Water	0.01005

* Values are taken from Lange's *Handbook of Chemistry*, 10th Edition, Handbook Publishers, Inc., Sandusky, Ohio.

3q. Factors Affecting Viscosity. In general, the viscosity of a liquid depends upon the size, shape, and chemical nature of its molecules. (In liquids that tend to associate the viscosity is abnormally high.) This is illustrated by water that, in spite of its low molecular weight, has a comparatively high viscosity, due in the most part to the effect of hydrogen bonding. (For liquids of the same class, an increase in molecular weight increases the viscosity.) This is illustrated by the paraffin hydrocarbons that change from liquids of low viscosity characteristic of gasoline to the highly viscous lubricating oils.

Viscosity in general decreases rapidly with rise in temperature. In water the change is slightly over 2 per cent in the range from 20° to 30°C.

The general effect of the addition of substances on the viscosity of a liquid is illustrated in the case of blood. Blood is an aqueous solution of certain electrolytes and nonelectrolytes in which are suspended red and white corpuscles as well as some colloidal substances such as proteins. The effect of the electrolytes is to lower slightly the viscosity of the aqueous medium. On the other hand, the corpuscles and colloidal particles greatly increase the viscosity. As a result, blood serum has at 37°C a viscosity of 0.01 poise, and whole blood has a viscosity of 0.03 poise as compared with the viscosity of water, which is 0.0069 poise at this temperature. Since variations in the blood composition and changes in the number of corpuscles occur with changes in the health of the individual, considerable variations in blood viscosity are to be expected. Viscosity determinations, together with blood counts, are useful in certain diagnostic procedures.

The viscosity of the blood plays a very important part in circulatory disorders resulting from the contraction of the capillaries in arteriosclerosis and in certain types of hypertension. (The higher the viscosity of the blood, the greater the force necessary to drive it through the capillaries.) This results in a condition of high blood pressure with a greatly increased strain on the heart.

Changes in body temperature result in about a 3 per cent change in the viscosity of the blood for each change of 1 degree. In fever this results in a decrease in the viscosity of the blood, thus increasing the circulation, a desirable condition, without increasing the strain on the heart.

REFERENCES

Bull, *Physical Biochemistry*, John Wiley and Sons, New York, 1951, Chapters 10 and 13.
Daniels and Alberty, *Physical Chemistry*, John Wiley and Sons, New York, 1961, Chapters 6, 13, and 21.
Maron and Prutton, *Principles of Physical Chemistry*, The Macmillan Co., New York, 1958, Chapter 3.

Moore, *Physical Chemistry*, Prentice-Hall, Inc., Englewood Cliffs, New Jersey, 1962, Chapters 4, 17, and 18.

Sheehan, *Physical Chemistry*, Allyn and Bacon, Inc., Boston, 1961, Chapter 2.

Daniels, Williams, Bender, Alberty, and Cornwell, *Experimental Physical Chemistry*, McGraw-Hill Book Co., New York, 1962, Chapters 3, 8, 14, and 21.

Crockford and Nowell, *Laboratory Manual of Physical Chemistry*, John Wiley and Sons, New York, 1956, Experiments 4, 5, 6, and 7.

REVIEW QUESTIONS

1. What are the general characteristics of liquids?

2. Discuss the distribution of the velocities of the molecules in the liquid state. How does the distribution change with temperature?

3. What is meant by the *vapor pressure* of a liquid? How does the vapor pressure of a liquid change with temperature change? Discuss the relation between the molecular velocity-temperature distribution effect and the manner in which the vapor pressure of a liquid increases with an increase in temperature.

4. Discuss the equations that show how vapor pressure changes with temperature change. What function of vapor pressure, when plotted against the reciprocal of the absolute temperature, gives a straight line? How can the slope of this line be used in calculating the heat of vaporization of the liquid?

5. What is meant by the normal boiling point of a liquid? What is meant by distillation under reduced pressure?

6. What is meant by heat of vaporization? Distinguish between molar and specific heats of vaporization.

7. Why is it necessary to add heat to a substance at its boiling point in order to have vaporization and why is it necessary to add heat to a solid at its melting point in order to have the solid change to a liquid?

8. What is sublimation? What is meant by the heat of sublimation?

9. Distinguish carefully between the triple point of water and the normal freezing point. What is the freezing temperature in each case and why do they differ in value? Discuss the general effect of pressure change on the freezing point of a liquid.

10. What is a phase diagram? Discuss the facts concerning water and the characteristics of water as brought out by the phase diagram. List the phases existing in the various fields, along the curves, and at the various points in the diagram.

11. What does the phase diagram of water show concerning the effect of pressure change on the temperatures of sublimation, fusion, and vaporization of this substance?

12. Why can the freezing point of water, or that of any other pure substance, be used in thermometer calibration?

13. Starting with pure water at any selected temperature and pressure in the phase diagram, describe exactly what takes place when (*a*) the system is subjected to a pressure change at constant temperature and (*b*) the system is subjected to a temperature change at constant pressure. Discuss in detail any phase changes that take place, and, as far as possible, discuss the reasons for these changes.

14. Discuss the significance of the critical temperature from the standpoint of the attractive forces operating between the gas molecules and the velocities of the molecules. Discuss the location of the critical point on the phase diagram.

15. Distinguish between cohesive and adhesive forces. What is meant by "wetting"? What relation must exist between cohesive and adhesive forces for wetting to take place? Give some manifestations of the phenomenon of wetting.

16. What is meant by surface tension? Why do liquids tend to take the shape that presents the minimum surface area?

17. List some manifestations of the action of surface tension and explain fully why these take place.

18. Surface tension may be expressed in three different sets of cgs units. What are these three sets? Show that they are modifications of each other.

19. Give a detailed derivation of the mathematical expression that gives the value of the surface tension of a liquid in terms of capillary rise. Why is mercury depressed in a capillary tube?

20. Describe in detail the determination of surface tension by the capillary rise method.

21. Discuss the principle involved in the determination of surface tension by the du Noüy ring method. Describe a simplified tensiometer.

22. Derive the expression used for the determination of surface tension by the ring method. Why is it necessary to use a correction factor in determining surface tension by this method?

23. Describe in detail the experimental procedure for determining surface tension by the du Noüy method.

24. Discuss the effects of temperature change and molecular structure on surface tension. Discuss the effect of various added substances on the surface tension of a liquid.

25. What is meant by interfacial tension?

26. Explain what is meant by the viscosity of a liquid. Give an exact definition of viscosity. In what units is viscosity usually expressed?

27. Discuss the experimental determination of viscosity by means of the Ostwald viscosimeter. What data are needed and how are these data used in the calculation of the viscosity of the liquid?

28. Distinguish between relative and absolute viscosity.

29. Discuss the effect of temperature change and change in molecular structure on viscosity. Discuss the changes in the viscosity of a liquid produced by the addition of various types of substances.

PROBLEMS

I

1. Calculate the heat of vaporization of acetone from the data of Table 3-1.

2. Water (density = 1 gram per cm³) will rise to what height at 20°C in a capillary tube whose radius is 0.0140 cm? What would be the radius of a capillary in which water rises at this temperature to a height of 9.00 cm?

3. Acetone (density $= 0.792$ gram per cm^3) rises to a height of 9.39 cm at 20°C in a capillary tube which has a radius of 0.065 mm. Calculate the surface tension of acetone from these data.

4. The densities of 1-propanol and 2-propanol are 0.789 and 0.804 gram per cm^3 respectively. What is the ratio of the heights to which they will rise at 20°C in a given capillary?

5. Nitrobenzene rises to a height of 3.72 cm in a capillary tube of radius 0.02 cm. If the experiment were carried out at 20°C, what is the density of this substance?

6. In the determination of the surface tension of a liquid by the ring method, it was found that the ring broke away from the surface when the dial reading was 28.5. The circumference of the ring was 4.00 cm. It required 0.300 gram to restore the ring to its original position. Under the conditions of the experiment, the correction factor was 0.92. What is the surface tension of the liquid at the temperature of the experiment?

7. Using benzene, it was found that the ring of a tensiometer broke away from the surface at a dial reading of 29.8 at 20°C. It was found that 0.212 gram was required to restore the ring to the original position. The circumference of the ring was 4.00 cm. What correction factor was applicable to the determination?

8. With a given viscosimeter, it was found that the times of flow of water and a second liquid of density 1.22 gram per cm^3 were 155 and 80 sec, respectively. The experiment was carried out at 20°C. Calculate the absolute and relative viscosities of the second liquid at this temperature.

9. The volume of water flowing through the viscosimeter in Problem I-8 was 3.5 ml. What will be the time required for an equal volume of ethanol (density $= 0.792$ gram per cm^3) to flow through the same viscosimeter at 20°C?

II

1. Calculate the heat of vaporization per gram and per mole for (*a*) water, (*b*) acetic acid, and (*c*) ethanol from the data of Table 3-1.

2. How high will water rise at 20°C in a tube of radius 0.024 cm? How high will toluene rise in the same tube at 20°C if its surface tension at this temperature is 28.4 dynes per cm and its density is 0.866 gram per cm^3?

3. Given two solutions of ethanol in water, with densities of 0.800 and 0.900 gram per cm^3 respectively. What is the ratio of the heights to which they will rise in a given capillary? Assume ratio of surface tensions is 0.75.

4. In the determination of the surface tension of a liquid at 20°C by the ring method, it was found that the ring broke away from the surface when the dial reading was 26.0 units. To restore the arm to the original position, a mass of 0.250 gram was required. The circumference of the ring was 4.00 cm and the correction factor under the conditions of the experiment was 0.97. Calculate the surface tension of the liquid.

5. Acetone and ethanol have substantially the same densities at 20°C. What is the ratio of the times necessary for 3 cm³ of each to flow through a given viscosimeter at this temperature?

6. In an Ostwald viscosimeter the times of flow of equal volumes of ethanol and another liquid at 20°C are respectively 140 sec and 160 sec. See Problem I-9 for additional data. The density of the second liquid at the temperature of the experiment was 1.06 gram per cm³. Calculate the absolute and relative viscosity of the second liquid at this temperature.

FOUR

Basic Thermodynamics

The purpose of this chapter is to introduce some of the basic concepts of thermodynamics. Various forms of energy, with special emphasis on heat, are studied. A discussion of internal energy, enthalpy, and the idea of the reversible process form a part of the chapter. The first and second laws of thermodynamics are discussed.

HEAT, WORK, AND ENERGY

4a. Forms of Energy. Heat and Work. In Chapter 1 it was stated that the study of physical chemistry is often considered from the standpoint of thermodynamics. In this treatment the emphasis is placed on the energy changes accompanying physical and chemical processes. For this reason *thermodynamics is a study of the energy changes accompanying physical and chemical transformations.*

Energy may manifest itself in various forms. If a weight is lifted in a gravitational field, if a spring is wound, or, in general, if a force is moved through a distance, as in the movement of a piston in an internal combustion engine, *work* is performed. Mechanical work may be obtained from the energy released in a chemical reaction in an internal combustion engine. Heated gas from the burning fuel expands against an imposed pressure, and *mechanical work*, or *pressure-volume work*, is done by the moving piston. This type of work is usually expressed in calories or liter-atmospheres.

A moving piston or other object in motion, for example, a moving gas molecule, has *kinetic energy* because of its mass and speed. *Electrical energy* can be obtained from the energy released in a chemical reaction in a device such as the lead-acid storage cell. Electrical energy is usually expressed in *joules.*

An object possessing energy by virtue of its position is said to have *potential energy*. As water falls from a higher to a lower level, it loses potential energy. A coiled spring has potential energy that is lost when the spring uncoils.

Heat is a form of energy encountered in almost all physical and chemical changes. It is difficult to define heat by a simple statement, and we shall not attempt any such statement. The concept of heat is well known, however, and we know a great deal about its properties and behavior. Certainly it is a type of energy capable of raising the temperature of a substance. Experience tells us that heat always flows from a higher to a lower temperature in a spontaneous process. Some reactions take place with the evolution of heat and in other reactions heat is absorbed. One most important property of heat has to do with its relation to the other forms of energy. Heat cannot be *completely* converted to other forms of energy but all other forms of energy can be *completely* converted into heat. Heat is usually expressed in *calories* or *kilocalories*.

4b. Internal Energy. *Internal energy* constitutes one of the basic thermodynamic concepts. Every system has internal energy, E, which is a function of the chemical nature of the substance, its temperature, and at times the pressure and volume of the system. The internal energy in a given system of molecules is determined by the kinetic, rotational, and vibrational motion of the molecules and their component parts as well as by the way in which the molecules are put together and the nature of the individual atoms. The number and arrangement of the electrons contribute to E, as does the nature of the nucleus. For example, in a monatomic gas the molecules possess kinetic energy as well as energy due to the number and arrangement of the electrons, protons, and neutrons. In a diatomic gas such as nitrogen the molecules may also possess rotational and vibrational energy. The more complex the molecule, the greater may be the contributions of the rotational and vibrational effects to the internal energy.

It is impossible to determine the absolute value of the internal energy of a system. (Fortunately, however, it is the change in the internal energy accompanying a chemical or physical change that interests us) It is the change in internal energy that produces the heating or cooling when a substance undergoes a temperature change at constant volume.

Consider the heat necessary to melt a mole of benzene at its normal melting temperature. It is not the internal energy of the benzene in the solid or liquid states but rather the change in the internal energy that interests us. This difference is designated as ΔE, the symbol, Δ, being used to show that the magnitude is one concerned with a change. If E_2 is the internal energy in the liquid state and E_1 is the internal energy in the solid state, then

$$\Delta E = E_2 - E_1$$

THE FIRST AND SECOND LAWS OF THERMODYNAMICS

4c. The First Law of Thermodynamics. Man has learned by long experience that when one form of energy changes into another form, no loss or gain of energy is experienced. This constitutes the *first law of thermodynamics*, which states that energy is neither created nor destroyed. When energy in one form disappears, an equal quantity in another form must appear. Consider again the lead-acid storage cell and its use in an automobile. The change in the internal energy, ΔE, when the cell reaction takes place results in the production of electrical energy. This energy can be used to produce mechanical energy for starting the engine. The engine in turn runs the generator to recharge the battery, to operate the lights, or to produce heat energy in the heater. The potential energy in the water at the top of the dam can be used to turn a turbine, which in turn produces electrical energy for household and industrial purposes.

The first law of thermodynamics is often expressed mathematically as follows.

$$\Delta E = q - w \tag{4-1}$$

In this expression w represents the *work done*, and q is the *heat change*. Since E is a thermodynamic magnitude depending only on the state of the system, the value of ΔE is the same no matter how the transformation takes place. The path followed in going from the initial to the final state in no way affects the value of ΔE. The value of ΔE may be positive or negative depending on the magnitudes of E_2 and E_1. Heat may be evolved or absorbed in the change, and work may be done on or by the system. While the sign conventions differ from book to book, we shall follow the procedure wherein work done by the system is plus and work done on the system is minus. Heat evolved is minus and heat absorbed is plus. Any of the three magnitudes in Equation 4-1 may have a value of zero. For example, in the isothermal expansion of a gas, ΔE is zero. Heat is absorbed by the system and hence has a positive sign, and work is done by the system and according to our conventions has a positive sign. Hence the work done in this case is equal to the heat absorbed.

There is one aspect of the first law that merits some elaboration. It is possible to convert matter into energy and under certain circumstances the reverse is possible. This change of matter into energy takes place in many nuclear reactions. Therefore, under the first law matter may be considered as a form of energy.

The first law of thermodynamics merely states that the total energy in a given system remains constant. It does not state that all forms of energy can be transformed into all other forms. The restrictions on the transformation become part of the second law of thermodynamics.

4d. The Second Law of Thermodynamics. It was stated in the preceding section that the first law places no restrictions on the transformations of energy. Experience shows, however, that heat energy differs from the other forms of energy in that all other forms can be completely transformed into heat but heat cannot be completely transformed into other forms of energy. As a result, there is a continual increase in the total heat energy at the expense of other forms of energy. This is not a contradiction of the first law, since the law merely states the principle of the conservation of energy in the event that a change takes place. The *second law of thermodynamics*, among other things, gives information relating to the conditions under which heat can be converted into other forms of energy and the quantitative limitations on the conversion.

The second law of thermodynamics may be stated in several ways which may appear to be quite different but which in fact are all modifications of the same fundamental idea. Namely, all forms of energy can be completely converted into heat but no process is available for converting the heat so obtained completely to other forms of energy.

Heat energy is associated with the random motion of the molecules in a system, whereas other forms of energy have a directional aspect; for example, the movement of a piston, the flow of electrons in a wire, or the falling of water from the top of a dam. Consequently, it can be said that the universe is approaching a condition of maximum randomness. As discussed in Chapter 10, randomness is expressed in terms of entropy; the greater the randomness, the greater the entropy. Hence, another way of expressing the second law is: *the energy of the universe is constant but the entropy approaches a maximum.*

The second law may also be considered from the standpoint of the *spontaneous process.* (A spontaneous process is one that takes place without external influence.) Numerous examples of spontaneous processes can be cited. Heat flows from the hotter to the colder body. A dissolved solid diffuses from the region of higher concentration to a region of lower concentration. Two gases will diffuse into each other and will completely fill their container. Water does not spontaneously flow uphill. A coiled spring will uncoil if allowed to do so but energy from some outside source is always necessary to cause a spring to be coiled. Water will flow through a semipermeable membrane in the process of osmosis if the concentrations are different on the two sides of the membrane. In any electric cell the electrons will flow from that pole with the higher potential to the pole with the lower potential. *In all these processes there is a leveling of some intensity variable.* As the cell furnishes current, the two electrodes come to the same potential. A dissolved solid distributes itself evenly throughout the solvent. Two bodies in thermal contact at different temperatures will come to a common temperature. In all cases a final state of equilibrium is reached, and the universe has lost to a greater or lesser extent its ability to undergo spontaneous change. Consequently, in all spontaneous processes there is a running down of the universe, and although the total energy remains the same, the availability of this energy decreases.

It is the spontaneous process that is used by man to utilize the resources available in nature. Now, of course, man can effect nonspontaneous processes as, for example, the transfer of heat from the cold interior of a refrigerator to the hotter room or the decomposition of hydrochloric acid by an electric current. But in these cases he must use a spontaneous process to obtain the energy necessary to carry out the nonspontaneous process and the over-all effect is the running down of the universe to a greater or lesser extent.

No attempt will be made to place the second law of thermodynamics on a quantitative basis. To do so, it would be necessary to treat the entropy function to an even greater extent than the discussion of Chapter 10.

ENTHALPY, HEAT CAPACITY, AND HEATS OF TRANSITION

4e. Enthalpy. Most chemical and physical processes take place at constant pressure rather than at constant volume. This is true of the process of vaporization discussed in Chapter 3. While the internal energy E can be used effectively in constant volume processes, we find it very convenient in constant pressure changes to employ another thermodynamic function represented by the letter H and termed the *enthalpy.*

Enthalpy is defined in the following way:

$$H = E + PV \qquad (4\text{-}2)$$

As with internal energy, we cannot establish the absolute value of the enthalpy for a given system. But, as with E, it is the delta magnitude, ΔH, that is important. Like internal energy, the enthalpy of a system depends solely on its state and not on its prior history. Hence the value of ΔH for a given change is the same no matter what path or paths the system follows in going from state 1 to state 2.

The use of enthalpy and enthalpy change will be treated in detail in connection with heat capacities and heats of transition in this chapter and with heat of reaction in Chapter 5.

4f. Molar Heat Capacity. In this section the use of the enthalpy function and the internal energy function is discussed in connection with changes in temperature. While heat capacity was mentioned in Chapter 1 in connection with units and dimensions, let us be a little more detailed in our definitions at this time.

The molar heat capacity of a substance at constant volume, C_v, is the quantity of heat required to raise the temperature of 1 mole of the substance 1°C at constant volume and at a given temperature.

Table 4-1. Molar Heat Capacities of Gases at 25°C ± 5

Gas	C_p (cal)	C_v (cal)	Gas	C_p (cal)	C_v (cal)
Argon	4.97	2.98	Carbon dioxide	8.96	6.92
Hydrogen	6.90	4.91	Methane	8.60	6.59
Nitrogen	6.94	4.95	Ethane	12.71	10.65
Oxygen	7.05	5.05			

The molar heat capacity at constant pressure, C_p, is the quantity of heat required to raise the temperature of 1 mole of the substance 1°C at constant pressure and at a given temperature. Values for the molar heat capacities of some gases at 25°C are given in Table 4-1.

It will be noted that the heat capacities increase in numerical value with increasing complexity of the gas molecule. For a monatomic gas the only change in the internal energy, E, is associated with an increase in kinetic energy. Its numerical value is essentially 3 cal per mole per degree, a value

Table 4-2. Molar Heat Capacities at Constant Pressure as a Function of Temperature

Hydrogen	$C_p = (6.95 - 2.00 \times 10^{-4}T + 4.81 \times 10^{-7}T^2)$ cal/mole/degree
Nitrogen	$C_p = (6.45 + 1.41 \times 10^{-3}T - 8.10 \times 10^{-8}T^2)$ cal/mole/degree
Oxygen	$C_p = (6.10 + 3.25 \times 10^{-3}T - 1.02 \times 10^{-6}T^2)$ cal/mole/degree
Water	$C_p = (7.19 + 2.37 \times 10^{-3}T + 2.08 \times 10^{-7}T^2)$ cal/mole/degree

that can be calculated from the kinetic equation for gases. Kinetic considerations also show that the values of C_p and C_v for monatomic gases, besides being the same for all such gases, are also independent of temperature. For polyatomic gases heat energy is required to supply the molecules with rotational motion and vibrational motion. Since the extent of the possible vibrational effects increases with the complexity of the molecule, the value of the heat capacity shows a parallel increase. Unlike monatomic gases, the heat capacity of polyatomic gases increases with an increase in temperature. Table 4-2 gives the mathematical expressions for C_p as a function of temperature for several polyatomic gases. The use of these expressions will be discussed in Examples 4-1 and 4-2.

In Table 4-1 note that C_p differs from C_v by essentially 2 cal. As will be shown, the value is more exactly 1.99 calories and the values for C_v for the gases given in Table 4-2 can be obtained by subtracting this amount from the first term in the various expressions.

Before showing that the difference between C_p and C_v is 1.99 calories, C_p and C_v, will be identified with the change in enthalpy and change in internal energy respectively. Suppose that a gas is heated at constant volume. No work is done since there is no volume change, and the value of C_v is identified with the change in E, since only kinetic along with some possible rotational and vibrational energy is involved. In the language of the calculus, C_v is given by the expression

$$C_v = \left(\frac{\partial E}{\partial T}\right)_V \qquad (4\text{-}3)$$

If the process is carried out at constant pressure, however, there must be a corresponding increase in volume, and C_p is identified with the change in enthalpy, since by definition $H = E + PV$. Again in the language of the calculus

$$C_p = \left(\frac{\partial H}{\partial T}\right)_p \qquad (4\text{-}4)$$

It therefore follows that

$$C_p = C_v + \text{work done}$$

Since the work done is equal to the change in volume multiplied by the pressure

$$C_p = C_v + P(V_2 - V_1)$$

For one mole of a gas PV_2 is equal to RT_2 and PV_1 is equal to RT_1. Furthermore $(T_2 - T_1) = 1°C$. Therefore:

$$C_p = C_v + R(T_2 - T_1) = C_v + R \qquad (4\text{-}5)$$

In Chapter 2 it was found that R could be expressed in calories per mole per degree and in these units it has a value of 1.99 (essentially 2). Hence the difference between C_p and C_v can always be taken as R calories without introducing any appreciable error in the calculations.

In considering C_p and C_v and their use, note that ΔE is concerned with the change in temperature at constant volume, and ΔH is concerned with the change at constant pressure.

4g. Some Calculations Involving the Use of C_p and C_v.

Example 4-1. A sample of nitrogen weighing 14 grams is heated at constant pressure from 25° to 75°C. How much heat will be required for the process? What is the value of ΔH for this temperature change?

The average value for C_p for the temperature range from 25° to 75°C for nitrogen is calculated from the formula given in Table 4-2 as follows:

$$C_p(298°A) = 6.45 + 1.41 \times 10^{-3} \times 298 - 8.10 \times 10^{-8} \times 298^2$$
$$= 6.86 \text{ cal/mole/degree}$$
$$C_p(348°A) = 6.45 + 1.41 \times 10^{-3} \times 348 - 8.10 \times 10^{-8} \times 348^2$$
$$= 6.93 \text{ cal/mole/degree}$$

The average value of C_p is 6.89. Therefore,

$$\text{Heat required} = \Delta H = 14/28 \text{ mole} \times 6.89 \text{ cal/mole/degree}$$
$$\times (75 - 25) \text{ degree}$$
$$= 172.3 \text{ cal}$$

The calculation could also be carried out by integrating the heat capacity expression over the temperature range covered:

$$\Delta H = 14/28 \int_{298°}^{348°} (6.45 + 1.41 \times 10^{-3}T - 8.10 \times 10^{-8}T^2)\, dT$$
$$= 172.5 \text{ cal}$$

In this example, where the temperature range is rather restricted, the use of average value of C_p gave essentially the same answer as the more exact calculation using the process of integration.

Example 4-2. A sample of oxygen gas weighing 64 grams is heated at constant pressure from 0° to 100°C. Calculate the values of ΔE and ΔH for this process.

The average heat capacity of oxygen at constant pressure in this temperature range calculated from the datum of Table 4-2 is 7.05 cal per mole per degree.

$$\Delta H = 64/32 \text{ mole} \times 7.05 \text{ cal/mole/degree} \times (100 - 0) \text{ degrees}$$
$$= 1410 \text{ cal}$$

The value of ΔE is the same whether the process takes place at constant volume or constant pressure, since the change in kinetic, rotational, and vibrational energy is the same in both processes. Therefore,

$$\Delta E = 64/32 \text{ mole} \times 5.06 \text{ cal/mole/degree} \times (100 - 0) \text{ degrees}$$
$$= 1012 \text{ cal}$$

It is noted that ΔH and ΔE differ by almost exactly 400 calories. This difference could have been calculated by simply noting that the temperature change is 100° and that the difference in C_p and C_v is R cal, the product of these, $100R$, being 199 cal.

4h. Heats of Transition. Transitions may involve the change of one crystalline form into another, as, for example, the conversion of rhombic sulfur to monoclinic sulfur. In this discussion transitions will be limited to fusion, evaporation, and to the reverse processes, solidification and condensation. These transformations were discussed at some length in Chapter 2. *The molar heat of fusion is defined as the heat required to melt one mole of the substance at its normal melting point without change of*

Table 4-3. Some Heats of Vaporization and Fusion

Substance	ΔH_{fusion} (cal/gram)	ΔH_{vap} (cal/gram)	Melting Point	Boiling Point
Water	79.7	539.7	0°C	100°C
Acetone	23.4	124.5	−95°	56.5°
Benzene	30.3	94.3	5.4°	80.1°
Acetic acid	44.7	96.8	17°	118.3°

temperature. The molar heat of vaporization is the quantity of heat required to evaporate one mole of the substance at its normal boiling point and under a pressure of 1 atmosphere without change of temperature. Both of these processes are carried out at constant pressure so that these heats of transition are special examples of ΔH. Some heats of vaporization and condensation are given in Table 4-3.

4i. Relationship of ΔH and ΔE in Vaporization. In fusion the change in volume is vanishingly small so that ΔH and ΔE have essentially the same value. In vaporization, however, there is a large change in volume as the liquid changes to a vapor. This results in work being done against the pressure of the atmosphere. This work is given by the expression, $P \Delta V$, where ΔV is the difference between the volume of the vapor (V_v) and the volume of the liquid (V_l). Since the volume of the liquid is insignificantly small in relation to the corresponding volume of the vapor, V_1 may be neglected. Moreover, assuming that the vapor behaves as an ideal gas, PV_v may be replaced by RT. Therefore,

$$\Delta H = \Delta E + \text{work} = \Delta E + P \Delta V = \Delta E + PV_v = \Delta E + RT \quad (4\text{-}6)$$

It must be remembered that ΔE is not the heat of vaporization at constant volume, an absurd concept. Rather it is the change in the internal energy as the vaporization processes take place. Among other things this is the energy necessary to overcome the attraction of the molecules for each other in the liquid state, and the energy necessary to give the molecules the kinetic energy characteristic of the vapor state. Equation 4-6 is for one mole of the substance. If more than one mole is involved in the phase change, the work becomes nRT, wherein n is the number of moles vaporizing. The use of Equation 4-6 is demonstrated in Example 4-3.

Example 4-3. Using the data of Table 4-3, calculate the values of ΔH and ΔE and the work performed in the evaporation of two moles of benzene at its normal boiling point.

$$\Delta H = 2 \text{ moles} \times 78 \text{ grams/mole} \times 94.3 \text{ cal/grams} = 14{,}711 \text{ cal}$$

$$w = nRT = 2 \text{ moles} \times 1.99 \text{ cal/mole/degree} \times 353.1 \text{ degrees}$$

$$= 1405 \text{ cal}$$

$$\Delta E = \Delta H - \text{work} = 14{,}711 \text{ cal} - 1405 \text{ cal} = 13{,}306 \text{ cal}$$

4j. Some Calculations Involving Heat Capacity and Phase Change. Typical calculations involving both a change in temperature and phase changes are illustrated in Example 4-4.

Example 4-4. A system consisting of 9 grams of H_2O in the solid state at $-10°C$ is changed to steam at $140°C$. Calculate ΔH for this change. The heat capacity of solid H_2O is 0.5 cal per gram per degree.

The specific heats of fusion and evaporation are given in Table 4-3, and the heat capacity of steam is given in Table 4-2.

Five steps are involved in the calculations. In the fifth step an average value for the heat capacity of the steam of 8.11 cal per mole per degree can be calculated from the expression for the heat capacity. A more exact procedure would be to integrate this expression between the two temperatures of $100°$ and $140°C$.

STEP 1. The 9 grams of solid are heated from -10 to $0°C$.

$$\Delta H_1 = 9 \text{ grams} \times 0.5 \text{ cal/gram/degree} \times 10 \text{ degrees} = 45 \text{ cal}$$

STEP 2. The solid is melted at $0°C$.

$$\Delta H_2 = 9 \text{ grams} \times 79.7 \text{ cal/gram} = 717.3 \text{ cal}$$

STEP 3. The liquid is heated from $0°$ to $100°C$.

$$\Delta H_3 = 9 \text{ grams} \times 1 \text{ cal/gram/degree} \times 100 \text{ degrees} = 900 \text{ cal}$$

STEP 4. The liquid is vaporized at 100°C

$$\Delta H_4 = 9 \text{ grams} \times 539.7 \text{ cal/gram} = 4857.3 \text{ cal}$$

STEP 5. The vapor is heated from 100° to 140°C.

$$H_5 = 9 \text{ grams}/18 \text{ grams/mole} \times 8.11 \text{ cal/mole/degree} \times 40°$$
$$= 162.2 \text{ cal}$$

The over-all change ΔH is the sum of the individual ΔH values for each of the five steps.

$$\Delta H = \Delta H_1 + \Delta H_2 + \Delta H_3 + \Delta H_4 + \Delta H_5 = 6681.8 \text{ cal}$$

REVERSIBLE PROCESSES

4k. The Isothermal Reversible Expansion of an Ideal Gas. One of the most important concepts in thermodynamics is that of *reversibility*. Reversibility will be developed in this section by considering a special type of physical change, that of the isothermal expansion of an ideal gas. The principal characteristics of this process will be studied and then applied to the general case.

Consider one mole of an ideal gas confined in a cylinder having a volume of 24.4 liters and at a temperature of 298°A. Under these conditions the pressure of the gas is 760 mm or 1 atmosphere and the restraining pressure on the piston holding the gas in the cylinder must, of course, have the same value. The gas is assumed to be in contact with a heat reservoir at 298°A, and a constant temperature is maintained by having heat flow from the reservoir to the gas as the gas performs the work associated with expansion. As stated above, the pressure on the piston restraining the gas must be 760 mm. The piston is assumed to be weightless and frictionless. The pressure of 760 mm is maintained by 760 small weights, each weight exerting 1 mm of pressure. The gas will be allowed to expand by removing weights until the volume doubles. This necessitates the reduction of the pressure to 380 mm. This reduction will be effected by removing 380 weights. Now these weights may be removed in an almost limitless number of ways. All 380 could be removed at one time. Again, 190 could be removed, the gas allowed to expand to the proper volume, and then the next 190 removed. The weights could be removed one by one allowing the gas to expand to the new volume after each removal. The weights could each be divided into small subunits and the removal effected by these subunits. In the extreme case the weights could be divided into infinitely small subunits and the process of removal carried out in an infinitely large number of steps.

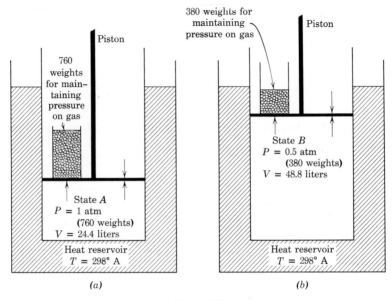

Figure 4-1

Note that the work done in any expansion is equal to the applied pressure during the expansion multiplied by the change in volume, $P\,\Delta V$. Therefore, the work performed can be illustrated with a P-V diagram. The initial and final states of the gas are represented by Figures 4-1(a) and 4-1(b). The expansion from state A to state B will be done in four ways. In the first procedure the 380 weights will be removed in two portions of 190 each. In the second procedure these weights will be removed in four portions of 95 each. In the third procedure ten steps will be used, 38 weights being removed in each step, and in the fourth procedure the weights will be subdivided into an infinitely large number of subweights and removed in an infinitely large number of steps. The work done in each case is equal to the pressure of the remaining weights multiplied by the volume change.

Consider the first procedure. The work performed is shown in Figure 4-2(a). After the removal of the 190 weights, the remaining pressure is 570 mm. The gas then expands against this pressure until the volume increases to 32.5 liters in accordance with the ideal gas law. The work done is equal to the product of $\frac{3}{4}$ atm and 8.1 liters or 6.07 liter-atm. The work done is represented in the figure by the shaded area in the first rectangle. The second 190 weights are removed and the piston again moves out and the work performed is equal to $\frac{1}{2}$ atm times 16.3 liters, or 8.15 liter-atm. This work is represented by the area in the second shaded

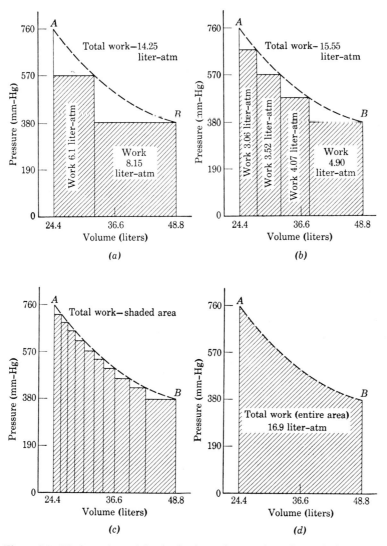

Figure 4-2. Work performed in the isothermal expansion of an ideal gas (*a*) two-step procedure; (*b*) four-step procedure; (*c*) ten-step procedure; (*d*) reversible procedure.

rectangle, and the total work performed by the gas in the two steps is equal to 14.22 liter-atm and is represented by the total shaded area.

In the second procedure the weights are removed in four portions of 95 each. After each removal the piston is moved out to a new position and the gas does pressure-volume work equal to the respective shaded area as shown in Figure 4-2(b). The total work done is given by the total of the shaded areas and its value is:

$$\tfrac{7}{8} \text{ atm} \times 3.5 \text{ liters} + \tfrac{3}{4} \text{ atm} \times 4.7 \text{ liters} + \tfrac{5}{8} \text{ atm} \times 6.5 \text{ liters}$$
$$+ \tfrac{1}{2} \text{ atm} \times 9.8 \text{ liters} = 15.55 \text{ liter-atm}$$

The important thing to note is that the work performed by the gas when the process takes place in four steps is greater than the work performed in the two-step process.

In the third process ten portions of 38 weights each will be removed. There will be ten expansions and the work performed is represented by ten rectangles, as shown in Figure 4-2(c). The work performed in this procedure is much greater than that performed in the second procedure.

Last of all, consider Figure 4-2(d). In this figure the weights were removed in an infinitely large number of steps. An infinitely large number of rectangles are necessary to represent the work, and, of course, an infinite number of steps would take an infinitely large space of time to be carried out. This infinitely large number of rectangles, each with an infinitesimally small width would essentially fill the area under the curve. The entire area under the P-V line that connects the P-V values for state A with those for state B therefore represents the work done.

If the plotting procedure was done with coordinate paper, the area under the curve evaluated from zero pressure could be determined by counting the squares on the paper and multiplying by the work value for each square. It is best done, however, by the use of integral calculus. Since the weights are removed in infinitesimally small portions, the successive volume changes will be infinitesimally small; the value is represented by the term dV. The expression for the work is then equal to

$$\text{Work} = \int_{V_1}^{V_2} P \, dV$$

In order to carry out this integration, it is necessary to reduce the number of variables to one. This is done by substituting for P its value from the ideal gas equation:

$$PV = nRT \quad \text{and} \quad P = \frac{nRT}{V}$$

Since the process is an isothermal one, the only remaining variable is V, and the integration is carried out as follows:

$$✓ \text{ Work} = \int_{V_1}^{V_2} P \, dV = nRT \int_{V_1}^{V_2} \frac{dV}{V} = \left(nRT \ln \frac{V_2}{V_1} \right) \tag{4-7}$$

$$\text{Work} = 1 \text{ mole} \times 0.082 \text{ liter-atm/mole/degree} \times 298 \text{ degrees}$$

$$\times 2.303 \log \frac{48.8 \text{ liters}}{24.4 \text{ liters}}$$

$$- 16.9 \text{ liter-atm} = 412 \text{ cal}$$

In order for the temperature to remain constant, 412 cal would have to flow from the heat reservoir into the cylinder. That this is true follows from a consideration of Equation 4-1. Since the gas under consideration is ideal, no attractive forces are present, and hence there is no change in the internal energy during the expansion. Therefore ΔE in Equation 4-1 is zero and q is equal to w.

Procedure four represents a reversible process, and the gas is said to have expanded *reversibly*. This procedure differs from the other in that (1) an infinitely large number of steps were employed, (2) an infinite amount of time was required to complete the process, (3) the pressure at any time differed only an infinitesimally small amount from the preceding pressure so that the process could have been *reversed* by an *infinitesimally small* addition of pressure, and (4) the work performed was a maximum. The first three procedures were to a greater or lesser extent *irreversible*. The first process was the most irreversible and procedure three was the nearest to reversible. Since an infinite amount of time would be required for completion, no actual process can be reversible. But processes can be made to approach the reversible by having them take place in a large number of steps, and this is brought about by keeping the applied intensity variable, in this case the pressure, fairly close to the value of the pressure of the gas.

4l. The Importance of the Reversible Process. The discussion of the reversible process in the preceding section gives no clue as to the importance of the reversible process except to show that such a process produces the maximum work. In actual processes the nearer they can be operated in a reversible manner, the greater will be the work produced.

The concept of the reversible process, however, is most important in the further study of thermodynamics. Without this concept it is impossible to understand many thermodynamic considerations, especially as they apply to such subject as free energy change and entropy change. These will be discussed in Chapter 13.

4m. Some Additional Examples of Reversible Processes. While many additional processes could be used to illustrate reversibility, only two will be considered: the discharge of an electric cell and the evaporation of a liquid.

Earlier in this chapter the methods for calculating the values of ΔH and ΔE and the work performed when 1 mole of a liquid evaporates at its boiling point against a pressure of 1 atmosphere were discussed. It was stated that it was not sufficient simply to bring a liquid to its boiling temperature in order to produce evaporation. Heat of vaporization had to be supplied. The application of this heat in a reversible manner will now be discussed. This heat is supplied by a heat reservoir similar to that used in the isothermal expansion of an ideal gas. In order for heat to flow from the reservoir into the liquid, the temperature must be at least an infinitesimal amount higher than the temperature of the liquid. If this difference is maintained at dT, the infinitesimal difference in temperature, an infinitesimally small amount of heat would flow into the liquid. This would raise its temperature very slightly and, of course, at the same time its vapor pressure would undergo an infinitesimal increase. A minute amount of liquid would evaporate and the heat of vaporization used in this process would reduce the temperature of the liquid to its original value. Another minute amount of heat would flow from the reservoir into the liquid and again the infinitely small quantity would evaporate. In this manner evaporation would take place with temperatures no more than dT apart at any time. Note that the temperature in this case plays the role of the intensity variable just as pressure did in the isothermal expansion of the gas. (Evaporation under these conditions would be reversible.) If the heat reservoir should be at a temperature varying an appreciable amount from that of the liquid, evaporation would still take place but the process would not be reversible.

The evaporation could also be carried out reversibly by keeping the heat reservoir at the temperature of the liquid and varying the external pressure by an infinitesimally small amount. This infinitesimal reduction would cause a minute amount of liquid to vaporize and this vaporization would lower the temperature a minute amount. Heat would then flow into the liquid from the reservoir, restoring the original temperature. Another minute decrease in pressure would produce another infinitesimal change, and this would continue until the liquid was completely evaporated. Irreversibility could be introduced into the process by lowering the external pressure an appreciable amount or by having the temperature of the heat reservoir an appreciable amount higher than that of the liquid.

Now consider a lead-acid storage cell, or, for that matter, any electrolytic cell. This cell could be discharged in a completely irreversible manner by simply shorting the two electrodes by means of a wire of high conductivity. No work would be done. The cell, however, could also be discharged and at the same time made to perform work by imposing across the terminals another cell, the positive pole of the external cell being connected to the positive pole of the cell being discharged. In this manner the voltage of the imposed cell would be operating against the voltage of the cell furnishing the electrical work. A reversible discharge would be effected by having the imposed voltage an infinitesimally small value below that of the operating cell. Of course, under these conditions the current supplied would be infinitely small, and it would take infinite time to complete the process. A maximum amount of work, however, would be obtained. Another angle of the situation must be considered. If the external voltage is essentially equal to the voltage of the operating cell, essentially no current will flow. Make the external voltage slightly greater and current will flow *from* the external cell into the cell under consideration. By making the external voltage slightly less, current will flow from the cell in question into the external cell. In this sense the process is *reversible*; it may be reversed by minute changes one way or the other in the opposed intensity variable, in this case the voltage.

Summarizing, it may be stated that reversible processes are those in which values of intensity variables—pressure, voltage, etc.—never differ by more than an infinitesimally small amount. Such being the case, a process can be reversed in direction by minute changes in the intensity variable. A reversible process is a hypothetical one in that an infinite number of steps are required which, in turn, would take an infinite time. The reversible process, however, is the one that will produce the most work and the amount of work produced by an actual process increases as the process approaches reversibility. All processes that occur in nature are to a greater or less extent irreversible, since all depend on finite differences in some intensity variable: the flow of heat from a body at one temperature to one at a lower temperature, the discharge of a storage battery, the flow of gas from a region of higher concentration to one of a lower concentration, the diffusion of a solute through a solution, and many spontaneous chemical reactions such as the reaction of zinc with an acid and the burning of combustible materials.

REFERENCES

Bull, *Physical Biochemistry*, John Wiley and Sons, New York, 1951, Chapter 2.
Daniels and Alberty, *Physical Chemistry*, John Wiley and Sons, New York, 1961, Chapters 3 and 5.

Maron and Prutton, *Principles of Physical Chemistry*, The Macmillan Co., New York, 1958, Chapter 2.

Moore, *Physical Chemistry*, Prentice-Hall, Inc., Englewood Cliffs, New Jersey, 1962, Chapter 2.

Sheehan, *Physical Chemistry*, Allyn and Bacon, Inc., Boston, 1961, Chapter 3.

REVIEW QUESTIONS

1. What units are usually employed to express energy? What relationships exist among these various units?

2. Name several forms of energy. In what major way does heat energy differ from the other forms of energy?

3. What factors contribute to the internal energy, E, of a substance? What is meant by vibrational and rotational energy?

4. Discuss the first law of thermodynamics. Is the conversion of matter into energy a contradiction of this law?

5. Define *enthalpy* in terms of other thermodynamic magnitudes.

6. Discuss the significance of ΔE and ΔH in physical and chemical changes.

7. Define *specific* and *molar heat capacity*.

8. Why does the heat capacity of a gas increase with increasing complexity of the gas molecules? Why is the value of the molar heat capacity of a monatomic gas independent of temperature while that of a polyatomic molecule increases with increase of temperature? In general, how does the heat capacity of polyatomic gases increase with increase of temperature?

9. Demonstrate why the difference between C_p and C_v for ideal gases is two calories.

10. Show how the values of ΔH and ΔE can be calculated for changes in temperature.

11. What are heats of transition? List the various heats of transition that may be encountered in thermochemical calculations. Discuss the significance of the difference between ΔH and ΔE for phase changes with special emphasis on evaporation.

12. Discuss the second law of thermodynamics. Discuss several spontaneous processes and give the characteristics of these processes.

13. Discuss the concept of reversibility. Discuss the importance of the reversible process. What are some of the characteristics of reversible processes?

14. Discuss the isothermal reversible expansion of an ideal gas. Show that the maximum work is obtained when such a process takes place reversibly and that the amount of work obtained decreases as the process becomes more and more irreversible.

15. Derive the equation for the work done in the reversible isothermal expansion of an ideal gas.

16. Apply the concept of reversibility to the discharge of a lead-acid storage cell.

PROBLEMS

Note: In working the following problems, average values for the heat capacities are to be used unless otherwise stated.

I

· **1.** How many calories of heat are required to raise the temperature of 48 grams of oxygen from 10° to 150°C (*a*) at constant volume and (*b*) at constant pressure?

· **2.** How many calories of heat must be removed from 56 grams of nitrogen to lower its temperature from 180° to 0°C, the volume remaining constant?

· **3.** A sample of nitrogen gas at 100°C and weighing 63 grams is placed in thermal contact with 75 grams of water at 25°C. What will be the final temperature of the nitrogen and the water, assuming that the gas remains at constant pressure during the temperature equalization process? Assume a value of 6.9 for $C_p(N_2)$.

· **4.** Given a vessel of 10 liters capacity containing 10 grams of oxygen at 100°C. Into the flask are introduced 10 grams of hydrogen at 20°C. What will be the final temperature of the mixture of hydrogen and oxygen, assuming no heat loss from the flask? Assume values of 7.0 and 7.1 for C_p of H_2 and O_2.

5. How many joules of energy will be required to heat 50 grams of oxygen at constant pressure from 20° to 120°C? If the heat is supplied by a current of 1.2 amp using a potential source of 2 volts, how long will it take to effect the temperature change?

· **6.** Calculate ΔH and ΔE for the reversible evaporation of 100 grams of benzene at its normal boiling point.

7. Using the data of Example 4-4, calculate the number of calories of heat required to change 54 grams of ice from a temperature of −20°C to steam at 1 atm pressure at 120°C.

· **8.** Assuming an average value of 0.347 cal per gram per degree for the heat capacity of acetone, calculate the heat necessary to change half a mole of acetone in its liquid state at its normal boiling point to vapor at 1 atm pressure and at 100°C.

· **9.** Calculate the value of ΔH and ΔE for the change in temperature of 10 grams of hydrogen at 25° to 125°C (*a*) using the average heat capacity of the gas and (*b*) using the heat capacity as a function of temperature and integrating this function between the initial and final temperatures.

10. Given 8 grams of oxygen at 27°C and at a volume of 5 liters. This gas expands isothermally and reversibly until the volume becomes 25 liters. What is the value of the work done? Express the answer in liter-atmospheres, ergs, calories, and joules.

11. A sample of nitrogen gas at 1 atm pressure and weighing 7 grams is compressed isothermally and reversibly until the volume is reduced to half its original value. Calculate the work that must be done on the gas to effect this compression. $T = 27°C$.

II

1. How many calories of heat are required to raise the temperature of 20 grams of hydrogen from 10° to 210°C at (a) constant volume and (b) constant pressure?

2. How many joules of energy will be required to heat 56 grams of nitrogen at (a) constant volume and (b) constant pressure from 15° to 75°C? If this energy is supplied from a potential source of 3 volts and a current of 0.5 amp is used, how long will the current have to flow to produce the required amount of energy?

3. Twenty-eight grams of nitrogen at 150°C are introduced into a vessel containing 16 grams of oxygen at 20°C. The volume of the container is 25 liters. What will be the final temperature of the gas, assuming no heat loss from the flask to the surroundings. Assume values of 6.9 and 7.1 for C_p of N_2 and O_2.

4. A sample of steam weighing 36 grams at a temperature of 150°C and at 1 atm pressure is cooled until it becomes ice at −30°C. Calculate the heat that must be removed to effect this change in temperature. See Example 4-4 for needed data.

5. Calculate the heat necessary to change 25 grams of acetone in the solid state at 15° below its normal freezing point to vapor at its normal boiling point. Assume that the specific heat of liquid acetone is 0.506 cal per gram per degree and that the specific heat of solid acetone is 0.504 cal per gram per degree.

6. Calculate the values of ΔH and ΔE for the reversible isothermal evaporation of 100 grams of water at its normal boiling point.

7. A sample of oxygen at 27°C and in a vessel of 10 liters capacity is heated until 200 cal of heat have been added to the gas. The final temperature is 50°C. How many grams of oxygen were present in the sample?

8. Work Problem II-1 by integrating the heat capacity expression rather than by using an average value for the heat capacity. How many calories of heat are required at (a) constant pressure and (b) constant volume? Compare the answers found with those of Problem II-1.

9. Twenty-five grams of an ideal gas whose molecular weight is 50 is heated from 15° to 200°C at constant pressure. Without knowing the heat capacity of the gas, calculate the difference between ΔH and ΔE for the process.

10. Twenty grams of nitrogen at a pressure of 1 atm and at a temperature of 27°C expands isothermally and reversibly until the volume is increased fivefold. Calculate the work done in calories, joules, ergs, and liter-atmospheres.

11. Calculate the work that must be done on 16 grams of oxygen at 65°C and at 1 atm pressure when it is compressed isothermally and reversibly until the volume becomes 10 liters.

FIVE

Thermochemistry

That part of thermodynamics dealing with the thermal changes accompanying chemical reactions is studied in this chapter. The relation between the heat of reaction at constant volume and constant pressure is considered, and the use of heats of formation for calculating the heat of reaction is shown. Finally, the calculation of the heat of reaction at a selected temperature from the heat of reaction at another temperature is studied.

DEFINITIONS AND CONVENTIONS

5a. Definitions. Thermochemistry is the part of thermodynamics dealing with the heat changes accompanying chemical reactions. In thermochemistry the usual balanced equation is modified to show the physical state of each of the reactants and products. The numerical value of ΔH or ΔE, the heat of reaction at constant pressure or constant volume, is given after the equation. The following are examples of thermochemical equations. The values given for the heats of reaction are for 25°C.

(a) $\quad\quad C\,(s) + O_2\,(g) \rightarrow CO_2\,(g)$ $\quad\quad\quad\quad \Delta H = -94.05$ kcal

(b) $\ CH_3OH\,(l) + \frac{1}{2}O_2\,(g) \rightarrow HCOH\,(l) + H_2O\,(l)$ $\quad \Delta H = -39.0$ kcal

(c) $\quad\quad HCl\,(g) + aq \rightarrow HCl\,(aq)$ $\quad\quad\quad\quad\quad \Delta H = -17.31$ kcal

(d) $\quad Cl_2\,(g) + 2KI\,(aq) \rightarrow 2KCl\,(aq) + I_2\,(s)$ $\quad\quad \Delta H = -52.42$ kcal

(e) $\quad\quad 2C\,(s) + 2H_2\,(g) \rightarrow C_2H_4\,(g)$ $\quad\quad\quad\quad \Delta H = +12.5$ kcal

In these equations (s) indicates that the reactant or product, as the case may be, is in its normal crystalline state. For example, carbon at 25°C would be in the form of graphite. The use of (g) shows that the substance is a gas with the pressure at one atmosphere. A pure liquid is designated by (l). The term (aq) indicates that a state of dilution has been

77

reached so that no further heat effect results when more water is added. In equation (d) KI (aq) indicates a mole of potassium iodide dissolved in such a quantity of water that no interionic attraction effects are operating between the ions, and therefore further dilution with the increased separation of the ions would produce no heat effect. Such a solution is termed an infinitely dilute one. In equations (a), (b), (c), and (d), ΔH has a negative value. From the conventions established in Chapter 4, this means that heat is evolved and that such reactions are exothermic. The last reaction (e) is endothermic and heat is absorbed when carbon reacts with hydrogen to form ethylene. Hence, by convention, the sign of ΔH is positive. The symbol ΔH indicates that the reaction takes place at constant pressure. Had the reaction taken place at constant volume, ΔE would have been used. In other words, the heat absorbed or evolved in a reaction at constant pressure is the change in enthalpy, whereas the heat absorbed or evolved when the reaction takes place at constant volume is the change in internal energy. The relation between the values of ΔH and ΔE for a given reaction are discussed later in the chapter.

5b. Classification of Reactions. Reactions are either exothermic or endothermic, depending upon whether heat is evolved or absorbed. Of course, a reaction that is exothermic in one direction will be endothermic in the reverse direction. Heat is evolved when carbon and oxygen burn to carbon dioxide, but heat is absorbed if the reverse process takes place. Equation (a) is an example of combustion, and the heat evolved in each case is termed the *heat of combustion*. Equations (a) and (e) represent the formation of a compound from its elements. In such a case the heat change is referred to as the *heat of formation*. Equation (c) represents a solution process; therefore, ΔH is the *heat of solution*. The *heat of neutralization*, another familiar thermochemical value, is the heat evolved when one mole of a strong acid reacts with one mole of a strong base in a large quantity of water, a quantity so large that the acid and the base reacting and the salt formed are all completely ionized.

Of the various heats of reaction discussed in the preceding paragraph, by far the most important is the heat of formation. In most thermochemical data tables it is the heats of formation at constant pressure that are usually listed. If the table is sufficiently complete, the heat of any reaction can be calculated, whether it actually takes place in the laboratory or whether it is a hypothetical one. The accumulation of heats of formation has been one of the major projects conducted by the Division of Thermochemistry of the National Bureau of Standards in Washington, D.C. The compilation of these data over the last several years has been partially financed by a number of industrial organizations, who find such data most

Table 5-1. Heats of Formation at 25°C
($\Delta H°$ in kcal per mole)

H_2O (l)	-68.317	CH_4 (g)	-17.890
H_2O (g)	-57.800	C_2H_4 (g)	$+12.50$
SO_2 (g)	-70.96	Ethane, C_2H_6 (g)	-20.236
H_2SO_4 (l)	-193.91	Benzene, C_6H_6 (l)	$+11.718$
NO (g)	$+21.60$	Methanol, CH_3OH (l)	-57.02
NO_2 (g)	$+8.09$	Acetic acid, CH_3COOH (l)	-116.4
CO_2 (g)	-94.052	Ethanol, C_2H_5OH (l)	-66.36
$AgCl$ (s)	-30.362		

These data have been obtained from Rossini, Wagman, Evans, Levine, and Jaffe, "Selected Values of Chemical Thermodynamic Properties," Circular of the National Bureau of Standards 500, U.S. Government Printing Office, Washington, D.C., 1952; and Rossini, Pitzer, Taylor, Ebert, Kilpatrick, Beckett, Williams, and Werner, "Selected Values of Properties of Hydrocarbons." The values given in Table 5-1 are for the substances in their standard states. A solid would be in its normal crystalline state and a gas would be at 1 atm of pressure. In the formation of the compounds the elements are assumed to be in their standard states and their enthalpies are arbitrarily assigned a value of zero.

important in their research programs. A number of heats of formation are given in Table 5-1.

THE DETERMINATION OF HEATS OF REACTION

5c. Calorimetry. Many heats of reaction can be determined by direct measurement. This is particularly true of heats of combustion. A sample of the material is burned in an atmosphere of oxygen and the heat evolved is measured by a suitable procedure. The apparatus used for this purpose is called a *calorimeter, and a calorimeter particularly suited for measuring heats of combustion is termed a combustion calorimeter. A* simple type of combustion calorimeter is shown in Figure 5-1. A weighed sample of the material is placed in a metal cup inside the bomb, which is made of corrosion-resistant metal. The sample is placed in contact with a length of fuse wire, which can be heated to red heat by an external source of current. The bomb is then charged with oxygen gas and placed in a bucket, as shown in the figure. This bucket contains a specified quantity of water, *A*. The bucket, in turn, is surrounded by an insulating air space, *B*, which prevents excess heat leakage to the surroundings. The sample is ignited by heating the fuse wire to red heat by an electric current. The

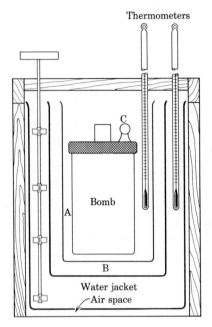

Figure 5-1. Cross section—plain calorimeter: *A*, water; *B*, air space; *C*, electrical connection. (Courtesy of Parr Instrument Company, Moline, Illinois.)

heat evolved as the sample burns causes a rise in the temperature of the water.

In this procedure it is necessary to obtain the *heat capacity* of the calorimeter system. This is found by burning a sample of material of known heat of combustion. For this purpose benzoic acid of very high purity is usually used. The temperature rise due to the sample is noted, and the number of calories of heat released in the combustion is calculated. The temperature rise obtained with the benzoic acid and the rise obtained with the sample of material permits calculation of the heat of combustion of the assigned material.

The procedure described is, of course, a greatly simplified one. In the actual process consideration must be given to the heat contributed by the burning of the wire, and corrections have to be applied in most cases for heat losses to the surroundings.

The procedure could also be modified for measuring heats of other types of reactions. Means could be employed for bringing together in the bomb a sample of acid and base or for adding zinc to a solution of copper sulfate in order to measure the heat of replacement of copper ions by zinc. In such cases the heat capacity of the calorimeter would probably be determined by electrical methods.

Since this procedure employs a closed bomb, it would give the heat of reaction at constant volume, ΔE. From this value, however, the heat of reaction at constant pressure, ΔH, can easily be calculated.

5d. The Relationship of ΔH and ΔE. From the previous chapter it will be recalled that

$$\left(H = E + PV \quad \text{and} \quad \Delta H = \Delta E + \Delta(PV) \right) \qquad \text{(5-1)}$$

Since the contributions of solids and liquids to the total volume are vanishingly small compared to the volumes of the gaseous reactants and products, the value of $\Delta(PV)$ is given by the difference in the PV-product of the gaseous products less the PV-product of the gaseous reactants. Furthermore, for a gaseous system, $PV = nRT$, in which n is the number of moles of the substances in the gaseous state. Therefore,

$$\Delta(PV) = (PV)_2 - (PV)_1 = (nRT)_2 - (nRT)_1$$
$$= (n_2 - n_1)RT = \Delta n\, RT$$

wherein Δn is the difference between the number of moles of gaseous products and the number of moles of gaseous reactants. Substituting in Equation 5-1 gives

$$\Delta H = \Delta E + \Delta n\, RT \qquad \text{(5-2)}$$

The use of this equation is illustrated in Example 5-1.

Example 5-1. Calculate the difference between the heats of combustion of benzoic acid at constant volume and constant pressure at 25°C. If the heat of combustion at constant pressure is $-771,400$ cal, what is the value of the heat of combustion at constant volume?

The equation for the combustion of benzoic acid at 25°C is

$$C_6H_5COOH\ (s) + 7\tfrac{1}{2}O_2\ (g) = 7CO_2\ (g) + 3H_2O\ (l)$$

Note that at 25°C the only gaseous substances are the oxygen and the carbon dioxide. Since the calculation is being made at 25°C, the standard state for the water would be that of the liquid.

Substituting in Equation 5-2,

$$\Delta H = \Delta E + \Delta n\, RT = \Delta E + (7 - 7\tfrac{1}{2})\ \text{moles}$$
$$\times\ 2\ \text{cal/mole/degree} \times 298\ \text{degrees}$$
$$\Delta H = -771,400\ \text{cal} = \Delta E - 298\ \text{cal}$$

and

$$\Delta E = -771,102 \text{ cal}$$

In the above example it is noted that the heat evolved at constant pressure is greater than that evolved at constant volume. An examination of the equation for the reaction shows that at constant pressure there is a diminution in volume. This means that work is done *on* the system. This work, equal to 298 calories, adds to the change in internal energy, ΔE, thus producing the evolution of more heat. Therefore, the difference in ΔH and ΔE may be positive or negative, depending on the sign of Δn.

✓ **5e. Hess's Law of Heat Summation.** The calculation of heat changes for reactions not easily carried out calorimetrically is effected by the use of *Hess's law of heat summation*. This law first proposed in 1840, is a special case of the first law of thermodynamics. Hess's law states that *the heat change in a particular reaction is always constant and is independent of the manner in which the reaction takes place*. For example, in the formation of CO_2 from C and O_2 the carbon might be burned directly to CO_2. On the other hand, the carbon might be burned to carbon monoxide and then the carbon monoxide burned to carbon dioxide. The two procedures can be represented as follows:

$$C\,(s) + O_2\,(g) \rightarrow CO_2\,(g) \qquad \Delta H = -94.052 \text{ kcal}$$

or

$$C\,(s) + \tfrac{1}{2}O_2\,(g) \rightarrow CO\,(g) \qquad \Delta H = -26.416 \text{ kcal}$$

$$CO\,(g) + \tfrac{1}{2}O_2\,(g) \rightarrow CO_2\,(g) \qquad \Delta H = -67.636 \text{ kcal}$$

adding

$$C\,(s) + O_2\,(g) \rightarrow CO_2\,(g) \qquad \Delta H = -94.052 \text{ kcal}$$

The two-step procedure evolves the same amount of heat as the one-step. That this must be true can be explained as follows. Suppose 1 mole of CO_2 is formed with the evolution of 94.05 kcal of heat. This heat is now used to decompose another mole of CO_2 into oxygen and carbon by the reverse of the two-step procedure. If the amount of heat absorbed were less than 94.05 kcal, a residual amount of heat would remain. Repetition of this cycle would result in the accumulation or creation of heat, a direct contradiction of the first law of thermodynamics.

In summary, then, it may be stated that if a reaction proceeds in several steps, the heat of the over-all reaction is the algebraic sum of the heats of the various steps, and this sum would be identical with the heat change were the reaction to take place in one step.

5f. Use of Hess's Law in Determining Heats of Formation. The problem of determining heats of formation by the use of Hess's law can best be illustrated by means of an example.

Example 5-2. Determine the heat of formation of 1 mole of benzene (l) at 25°C from the heat of combustion of benzene and the heats of formation of water and carbon dioxide. The heat of combustion of benzene (l) is -780.98 kcal at 25°C.

It should be noted that the heat of combustion of benzene and the heats of formation of water and carbon dioxide are all easily determined calorimetrically, while it is impossible to determine the heat of formation of benzene from carbon and hydrogen by direct calorimetric procedure. The heats of formation of water (l) and carbon dioxide are given in Table 5-1. The solution will be carried out in two steps.

STEP 1. Write the thermochemical equations for the three known values

$$C\ (s) + O_2\ (g) \rightarrow CO_2\ (g) \qquad\qquad \Delta H = -94.052 \text{ kcal}$$
$$H_2\ (g) + \tfrac{1}{2}O_2\ (g) \rightarrow H_2O\ (l) \qquad\qquad \Delta H = -68.317 \text{ kcal}$$
$$C_6H_6\ (l) + 7\tfrac{1}{2}O_2 \rightarrow 6CO_2\ (g) + 3H_2O\ (l) \qquad \Delta H = -780.98 \text{ kcal}$$

STEP 2. Rearrange the three equations, multiplying the first by 6 and the second by 3. Note that the third equation written in the reverse direction is an endothermic one, hence the sign of ΔH becomes positive.

$$6C\ (s) + 6O_2\ (g) \rightarrow 6CO_2\ (g) \qquad\qquad \Delta H = 6 \times (-94.052 \text{ kcal})$$
$$3H_2\ (g) + 1\tfrac{1}{2}O_2\ (g) \rightarrow 3H_2O\ (l) \qquad\qquad \Delta H = 3 \times (-68.317 \text{ kcal})$$
$$6CO_2\ (g) + 3H_2O\ (l) \rightarrow C_6H_6\ (l) + 7\tfrac{1}{2}O_2\ (g) \qquad \Delta H = 780.98 \text{ kcal}$$

adding

$$6C\ (s) + 3H_2\ (g) \rightarrow C_6H_6\ (l)$$
$$\Delta H = 6 \times (-94.052) + 3 \times (-68.317) + 780.98 = +11.720 \text{ kcal}$$

Another example of the use of Hess's law is illustrated in the calculation of the heat of formation of H_2SO_4 (l) from its elements. This is effected by the use of four reactions all easily carried out calorimetrically.

$$S\ (s) + O_2\ (g) \rightarrow SO_2\ (g) \qquad \Delta H = -70.96 \text{ kcal}$$
$$SO_2\ (g) + \tfrac{1}{2}O_2\ (g) \rightarrow SO_3\ (g) \qquad \Delta H = -23.49 \text{ kcal}$$
$$SO_3\ (g) + H_2O\ (l) \rightarrow H_2SO_4\ (l) \qquad \Delta H = -31.14 \text{ kcal}$$
$$\underline{H_2\ (g) + \tfrac{1}{2}O_2\ (g) \rightarrow H_2O\ (l) \qquad \Delta H = -68.32 \text{ kcal}}$$
$$S\ (s) + H_2\ (g) + 2O_2\ (g) \rightarrow H_2SO_4\ (l) \qquad \Delta H = -193.9 \text{ kcal}$$

5g. Use of Heats of Formation in the Calculation of Heat of Reaction. The enthalpies of formation given in Table 5-1 can be considered as the actual enthalpies of the substances for purposes of calculation, provided as stated that the enthalpies of substances in their elemental states are taken as being equal to zero. This convention is thoroughly consistent with Hess's law and makes the calculation of heats of reaction quite simple.

Example 5-3. Calculate the heat of combustion of benzene (l) at 25°C from heats of formation.

Table 5-1 gives the following heats of formation: C_6H_6 (l), +11.718 kcal; H_2O (l), −68.37 kcal; CO_2 (g), −94.052 kcal. O_2, being present in the elemental state, is considered as having an enthalpy of O.

$$C_6H_6 \ (l) + 7\tfrac{1}{2}O_2 \ (g) \rightarrow \quad 6CO_2 \ (g) \quad + \quad 3H_2O \ (l)$$
$$11.718 \qquad 0 \quad \rightarrow 6 \times (-94.052) \quad 3 \times (-68.37)$$

and

$$\Delta H = 6 \times (-94.052) + 3 \times (-68.37) - (+11.718) = -781.14 \text{ kcal}$$

Example 5-4. If a method could be devised for preparing ethanol from water and ethylene at 25°C, what would be the value of the heat of reaction?

$$C_2H_4 \ (g) + \ H_2O \ (l) \ \rightarrow C_2H_5OH \ (l)$$
$$12.5 \qquad -68.317 \qquad -66.36$$
$$\Delta H = -66.36 - (+12.5) - (-68.317) = -10.54 \text{ kcal}$$

VARIATION OF HEAT OF REACTION WITH TEMPERATURE

5h. Heat of Reaction as a Function of Temperature. The heats of formation and other heats of reaction given in most thermodynamic tables are for 25°C. With these it is possible to calculate the heat of reaction at another temperature, provided the values for the heat capacities of the reactants and products are available. The procedure is illustrated in Figure 5-2. Consider the reactants in state A at the temperature T_1 and the products in state B at the temperature T_2. We may proceed from state A at T_1 to state B at T_2 by two paths. In the first path the reactants are heated to T_2 and allowed to react at this higher temperature. In the second path the reactants are allowed to react at the lower temperature and the products heated to T_2. The value for ΔH for each of these paths follows:

$$\Delta H \text{ (path 1)} = C_p \text{ (reactants)}(T_2 - T_1) + \Delta H_2$$
$$\Delta H \text{ (path 2)} = \Delta H_1 + C_p \text{ (products)}(T_2 - T_1)$$

According to the first law of thermodynamics, the value of ΔH must be the same for both paths. Therefore:

$$C_p \text{ (reactants)}(T_2 - T_1) + \Delta H_2 = \Delta H_1 + C_p \text{ (products)}(T_2 - T_1)$$

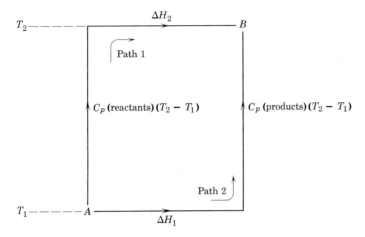

Figure 5-2.

and

$$\Delta H_2 = \Delta H_1 + [C_p \text{ (products)} - C_p \text{ (reactants)}](T_2 - T_1) \quad (5\text{-}3)$$

In this equation ΔH_2 and ΔH_1 are the heats of the reaction at the two temperatures T_2 and T_1, and C_p (products) and C_p (reactants) are the sums of the heat capacities of the products and reactants respectively. In using this equation, it is assumed that the heat capacities of the reactants and products are constant over the temperature range of the calculation. If this were not the case, it would be necessary to use the heat capacity expressions as functions of temperature and carry out the calculations for the heating processes by the use of the calculus. An inspection of Equation 5-3 shows that the change in the heat of reaction with change in temperature depends on the comparative values of the heat capacities of the reactants and products. The use of Equation 5-3 is shown in Examples 5-5 and 5-6.

Example 5-5. Calculate the heat of formation of H_2O (*l*) at 90°C from the heat of formation at 25°C.

$$H_2 (g) + \tfrac{1}{2}O_2 (g) \rightarrow H_2O (l) \qquad \Delta H_{25°} = -68,370 \text{ cal}$$

The average values of the heat capacities calculated from Table 4-2 are

$$C_p(H_2) = 6.90 \text{ cal/mole/degree}$$
$$C_p(O_2) = 7.05 \text{ cal/mole/degree}$$
$$C_p(H_2O) = 18 \text{ cal/mole/degree}$$

Substituting in Equation 5-3,

$$\Delta H_{90°} = -68,370 \text{ cal} + (18 - 6.90 - \tfrac{1}{2} \times 7.05)(90 - 25)$$
$$\Delta H_{90°} = -67,877 \text{ cal}$$

less than $\Delta H_{25°}$ because more energy
at 90°

Example 5-6. Calculate the heat of formation of ethane at 200°C.

$$2C (s) + 3H_2 (g) \rightarrow C_2H_6 (g)$$

Data needed:

$$C_p(C) = 2.70 \text{ cal/mole/degree}$$

$$C_p(H_2) = 6.90 \text{ cal/mole/degree}$$

$$C_p(C_2H_6) = 15.4 \text{ cal/mole/degree}$$

$$\Delta H_{25°} = -20.24 \text{ kcal}$$

Substituting in Equation 5-3,

$$\Delta H_{200°} = -20{,}240 \text{ cal} + (15.4 - 2 \times 2.70 - 3 \times 6.90)(200 - 25)$$

$$\Delta H_{200°} = -22{,}112 \text{ cal} = -22.11 \text{ kcal}$$

REFERENCES

Bull, *Physical Biochemistry*, John Wiley and Sons, New York, 1951, Chapter 2.

Daniels and Alberty, *Physical Chemistry*, John Wiley and Sons, New York, 1961, Chapter 4.

Maron and Prutton, *Principles of Physical Chemistry*, The Macmillan Co., New York, 1958, Chapter 9.

Moore, *Physical Chemistry*, Prentice-Hall, Englewood Cliffs, New Jersey, 1962, Chapter 2.

Sheehan, *Physical Chemistry*, Allyn and Bacon, Boston, 1961, Chapter 3.

Daniels, Williams, Bender, Alberty, and Cornwell, *Experimental Physical Chemistry*, McGraw-Hill Book Company, New York, 1962, Chapter 2.

Crockford and Nowell, *Laboratory Manual of Physical Chemistry*, John Wiley and Sons, New York, 1956, Experiments 21, 13, 14, and 15.

REVIEW QUESTIONS

1. What additional information, over that given in the usual equation for a chemical reaction, is given in a thermochemical equation. How is the physical state of each reactant and product indicated?

2. What convention is followed for showing that a given reaction is endothermic or exothermic and for showing how much heat is evolved or absorbed?

3. What is meant by the terms *heat of combustion, heat of neutralization*, and *heat of formation*?

4. Describe the construction and use of a simple calorimeter. What is meant by the heat capacity of the calorimeter system? How is its value determined? How is it used in a calorimetric experiment?

5. Discuss the difference between ΔE and ΔH for a chemical reaction. Derive the mathematical expression that gives the relationship between these terms.

6. What is *Hess's law* of heat summation? How is it used in the calculation of heats of reaction?

7. Describe the use of heats of formation in the determination of the heat change in a typical reaction.

8. Discuss the relationship of heat of reaction to change in temperature. Derive a mathematical expression for heat of reaction as a function of temperature. If you have the value of the heat of reaction at one temperature, what data do you need to calculate the heat of reaction at another temperature?

PROBLEMS

I

1. Calculate the heat of combustion of methanol at (*a*) constant pressure and (*b*) constant volume for a temperature of 25°C.

2. Calculate ΔH for the following reaction at 25°C:

$$SO_2\,(g) + \tfrac{1}{2}O_2\,(g) + H_2O\,(l) \rightarrow H_2SO_4\,(l)$$

3. The enthalpy change for the following reaction

$$CH_3COOH\,(l) + C_2H_5OH\,(l) \rightarrow CH_3COOC_2H_5\,(l) + H_2O\,(l)$$

has a value of zero over a wide range of temperature. Calculate the heat of formation of ethyl acetate at 25°C.

4. The heat of formation of $PCl_3(l)$ from phosphorus and chlorine is $-151,800$ cal at 25°C. When 1 mole of chlorine reacts with 1 mole of $PCl_3(l)$ at 25°C, 32,810 cal of heat are evolved. From these data calculate the heat of formation of $PCl_5(s)$.

5. Calculate the heat of formation of acetaldehyde (*g*) at 25°C from the value of ΔH for the following reaction:

$$C_2H_5OH\,(l) + \tfrac{1}{2}O_2\,(g) \rightarrow CH_3COH\,(g) + H_2O\,(l) \qquad \Delta H = -31.72\ \text{kcal}$$

6. The heat of combustion of 1 mole of cyclohexane (*l*), is $C_6H_{12}, -936.9$ kcal per mole at 25°C. Calculate its heat of formation at this temperature.

7. Calculate the heat of formation of ethane (*g*), C_2H_6, at 200°C. The molar heat capacity of ethane may be taken as 14.6 cal per mole per degree over the temperature range covered in the problem. The heat capacity of carbon may be taken as 2.70 cal per mole per degree, and the average heat capacity of hydrogen may be calculated from the data of Table 4-2.

8. Calculate ΔH for the formation of 1 mole of ammonia at 120°C. Assume a value of 0.523 cal per gram per degree for the heat capacity at constant pressure of ammonia. The necessary heat capacity data for nitrogen and hydrogen are given in Table 4-2. The heat of formation of NH_3 at 25°C is -11.04 kcal.

II

1. Calculate the heat of combustion of ethanol at 25°C at (*a*) constant pressure and (*b*) constant volume.

2. Calculate ΔH and ΔE for the combustion of 2 moles of acetic acid at 25°C.

3. The heat of combustion of 1 mole of propylene (g) at 25°C at constant pressure is 492 kcal. Calculate the heat of formation of propylene at this temperature.

4. Calculate the standard enthalpy of formation of formaldehyde at 25°C from the value of ΔH for the following reaction at this temperature.

$$CH_3OH\ (l) + O_2\ (g) \rightarrow HCOH\ (l) + H_2O\ (l) \qquad \Delta H = -39,000\ cal$$

5. What would be the heat of formation of cyclopentane at constant volume and at constant pressure at 25°C? The heat of combustion for 1 mole at 25°C and at constant pressure is 786,540 cal.

6. Calculate the heat of formation of propane (g), C_3H_8, at 200°C. The value of ΔH for the formation of 1 mole at 25°C is $-24,820$ cal. Assume that C_p for propane over the range of temperature given in the problem is 24.3 cal per mole per degree. The heat capacity of carbon is 2.70 cal per mole per degree, and the heat capacity of hydrogen can be calculated from the data of Table 4-2.

7. Calculate the heat of formation of 1 mole of $H_2O\ (l)$ at 95°C. See Table 4-2.

8. Calculate the heat of formation of 1 mole of $H_2O\ (g)$ at 130°C. See Table 4-2 for necessary heat-capacity data.

SIX

Solutions I:
Nonelectrolytes

The purpose of this chapter is to acquaint the student with the nature and properties of solutions and to develop the laws that describe their behavior. The chapter includes methods of expressing concentration, solutions of gases in liquids, solubility relationships in partially miscible systems, vapor-pressure relationships in solutions, distillation phenomena, and the determination of molecular weight by the freezing-point-lowering and boiling-point-elevation methods.

FUNDAMENTAL CONCEPTS

6a. Solutions and Solubility. A *solution* may be defined as a homogeneous dispersion of two or more substances in each other. If a sugar lump is dropped into a beaker of water, the lump disintegrates and within a short time disappears into the liquid phase. In this process, the molecules of the sugar leave the crystal structure of the solid and become uniformly dispersed throughout the water, thus producing a complete molecular mixing of the two substances. A sugar-water solution is an example of a two-component system consisting of one liquid phase. The component that is considered the dissolving medium is called the *solvent*, and the dissolved substance is called the *solute*. There is no theoretical distinction between the terms *solvent* and *solute*, since the molecules of both are uniformly distributed throughout the solution. Consider, for example, a solution made by mixing equal volumes of ethyl alcohol and water. Either may, with equal justification, be considered to be dissolved in the other. Ordinarily, however, the component present in the larger amount is called the solvent. A three-, four-, or five-component solution may be prepared by dissolving a second, third, or fourth solute in a solvent or a mixture of solvents.

Since there are three states of matter, there are theoretically nine possible classes or types of solutions. Three types are possible when a liquid is the solvent, since the solute may be a gas, another liquid, or a solid. Similarly, three classes are possible when the solvent is a gas, and three when the solvent is a solid. It is questionable, however, whether true solutions of solids and liquids in a gas exist or whether such dispersions are colloidal system as discussed in Chapter 18.

The solubility of one gas in another is unlimited because gases mix in all proportions to form true solutions. This particular type is the simplest of solutions, and, in general, gaseous solutions obey the gas laws studied in Chapter 2. Of the eight remaining types of solutions, the three most important are: solutions of gases in liquids, liquids in liquids, and solids in liquids. These will be the three types discussed in detail in this chapter. First, however, several familiar definitions should be recalled. A *saturated solution* is a solution that contains as much dissolved solute as the solvent can hold when in contact with undissolved solute. A *saturated solution is defined*, therefore, *as a solution in which dissolved and undissolved solute are in equilibrium with one another.* The *solubility* of a substance at a given temperature is the *concentration of solute* in the solvent in a saturated solution.

6b. Methods of Expressing Concentration. The use of the *mole-fraction* methods for expressing concentration was discussed in Chapter 2. In addition to this method, the concentration of a solution may be expressed by stating either (*a*) the *quantity of solute* per unit volume of solution, or (*b*) the *quantity of solute* per unit quantity of *solvent*. The former method finds its greatest usefulness in analytical procedures, where the *volume* of a standard solution is the essential factor in the experimental procedures and calculations. In physical chemistry, however, it is often more convenient to express concentration in terms of the amount of solute per unit quantity of solvent. A discussion of the more familiar concentration units in each of the two general classifications follows.

Quantity of Solute per Unit Volume of Solution

1. WEIGHT PER UNIT VOLUME. In this method, the concentration is usually expressed in terms of the number of *grams* of solute per *liter* of solution. Sometimes, when the concentration of solute is small, as for example the concentration of glucose in blood, it is convenient to employ milligrams per 100 ml, or even other weight-volume units. Although this general method is simple, it does not lend itself readily to the stoichiometric calculations characteristic of analytical chemistry.

2. MOLARITY. A 1 molar (1*M*) solution contains 1 gram-molecular

weight of solute per liter of solution. *The molarity of a solution is,* therefore, *the number of gram-molecular weights of solute per liter of solution.* It should be understood that a 1 molar solution is *not* prepared by dissolving a gram-molecular weight in a liter of solvent. Such a solution probably would not occupy a volume of exactly 1 liter and would not, therefore, be exactly $1M$.

In the methods just given, there is the disadvantage of a concentration change with change in temperature. For example, a $1M$ solution prepared at 20°C becomes somewhat less than $1M$ if the temperature rises because the weight of solute remains unchanged, whereas the volume of the solution increases.

Quantity of Solute Per Unit Quantity of Solvent

1. PER CENT BY WEIGHT. *The weight-percentage method gives the number of grams of solute per 100 grams of solution.* A 10 per cent glucose solution contains 10 grams of glucose in 90 grams of water.

2. MOLALITY. A 1 molal ($1m$) solution contains 1 gram-molecular weight of solute per 1000 grams of solvent. *Molality is,* therefore, *the number of gram-molecular weights of solute per 1000 grams of solvent.* Since the amount of both solute and solvent is expressed in grams, there is no change in the molality of a solution with change in temperature.

In connection with both molarity and molality, it would be more meaningful to use the words *gram-formula weight* in place of gram-molecular weight because sometimes there may be association, even with nonionized solutes. Two or more molecules may be bound together more or less tightly to form a larger "molecule" than that usually considered to be the molecule. The term *formula weight* would tend to eliminate possible confusion in such cases. We, however, prefer the more familiar notations, molecular and gram-molecular weight.

Although the *mole-fraction* method of expressing concentration does not fit properly into either of the general methods of expressing concentration just discussed, it is extremely useful in many types of calculations, for it gives directly the relative numbers of molecules of the components of the solution. If the mole fraction of solute in a glucose-water solution is 0.05, the solution contains 0.05 mole of glucose per each 0.95 mole of water. Sometimes concentrations are expressed in mole per cent. This is simply 100 times the mole fraction. Thus, in the glucose-water solution the mole per cent of glucose would be 5.0 per cent.

Example 6-1. A solution of acetic acid is prepared by adding 164.2 grams of the acid to sufficient water to make 800.0 ml of solution at 20°C. The density at this temperature is 1.026. Calculate (*a*) the molarity, (*b*) the molality, (c) the mole fraction of the solute, (d) the mole fraction of the solvent, (e) the mole per cent of solute and solvent, and (f) the per cent acetic acid by weight. The molecular weight of acetic acid is 60.0.

(a) *Molarity*

$$\text{Moles of acetic acid} = \frac{164.2}{60.0} = 2.737$$

$$M = \frac{\text{number moles of solute}}{\text{liters of solution}} = \frac{2.737}{0.8000} = 3.421M$$

(b) *Molality*

Grams of solution = volume × density = 800.0 × 1.026 = 820.8 grams

Grams of solvent = 820.8 − 164.2 = 656.6 grams

$$m = \frac{\text{number moles of solute}}{\text{kilograms of solvent}} = \frac{2.737}{0.6566} = 4.168m$$

(c) *Mole Fraction*

$$\text{Moles of water} = \frac{656.6}{18.02} = 36.44$$

$$\text{Mole fraction solute} = \frac{\text{moles solute}}{\text{total moles}} = \frac{2.737}{2.737 + 36.44} = 0.0699$$

$$\text{Mole fraction solvent} = \frac{\text{moles solvent}}{\text{total moles}} = \frac{36.44}{2.737 + 36.44} = 0.9301$$

(d) *Mole per cent of Solute*

Mole per cent of solute = 100 × mole fraction = 100 × 0.0699
$$= 6.99\%$$

Mole per cent of solvent = 100 × mole fraction = 100 × 0.9301
$$= 93.01\%$$

(e) *Per Cent Acetic Acid by Weight*

$$\text{Per cent by weight} = \frac{\text{grams acetic acid}}{\text{grams solution}} \times 100 = \frac{164.2}{820.8} \times 100$$
$$= 20.00\%$$

SOLUTIONS OF GASES IN LIQUIDS

6c. The Effect of Pressure on the Solubility of Gases. A gas in contact with a liquid at a given temperature will dissolve to a certain extent, depending upon the natures of the solvent and the gas. The most soluble gases are those that react with the solvent. Water, for example, "dissolves" enormous quantities of hydrogen chloride and ammonia because of the reaction of these substances with water. Where the solubility process is wholly physical, as in the solution of nitrogen and oxygen in water, the gas dissolves to a much smaller extent. The fact that oxygen is more soluble in water than is nitrogen, however, indicates that factors other than chemical reaction between the gas and the solvent are involved. But no adequate law has been discovered to correlate the nature of the gaseous solute with its solubility.

It has been found experimentally that the solubility of a gas over a given solvent increases with an increase in the partial pressure of the gas over the solution. The law that relates the solubility of a gas to its pressure was proposed in 1803 by the English physician and chemist, William Henry. Henry's law states that *the concentration of dissolved gas in a given solvent is directly proportional to the partial pressure of the gas, temperature remaining constant.* From this simple statement it follows that, if the pressure of undissolved gas is doubled, the concentration of dissolved gas also doubles. Mathematically this law may be written

$$c = kp \qquad (6\text{-}1)$$

where c is the concentration of dissolved gas, p is the partial pressure of the gas, and k is a constant whose value depends on the particular gas-liquid system and the temperature. The value of k also depends on the units chosen for expressing concentration and pressure.

The concentration may be expressed in any of the usual units, such as weight per unit volume of solvent or solution or mole fraction of solute. The solubilities of certain gases in water at 25°C are given in Table 6-1.

Example 6-2 illustrates the application of Henry's law. Since the solubility of most gases is very slight, it is assumed in this example and in subsequent problems that the volume of the solution containing a given quantity of solvent is identical with the volume of the pure solvent.

Example 6-2. If 0.0346 gram of oxygen dissolves in 800 ml of water at an over-all pressure (oxygen and water vapor) of 1 atm and at a temperature of 20°C, calculate (*a*) the concentration of oxygen in grams per liter under the above conditions, (*b*) the concentration of oxygen in grams per liter and moles per liter dissolved at this temperature when the pressure of the gas is 1 atm, and (*c*) the grams of oxygen dissolved by a liter of water at 20°C but with the oxygen at a pressure of 400 mm of Hg. The vapor pressure of water at 20°C is 18 mm.

(*a*) $c = $ grams per liter $= \dfrac{0.0346}{0.800} = 0.0433$ gram per liter

Table 6-1. Solubilities of Some Gases in Water, at 25°C and 1 Atm Pressure of the Gas

Gas	Moles of Gas Dissolved in 1 Liter of Water
Nitrogen	6.38×10^{-4}
Hydrogen	7.36×10^{-4}
Oxygen	1.26×10^{-3}
Carbon dioxide	3.39×10^{-2}
Hydrogen sulfide	1.02×10^{-1}
Sulfur dioxide	1.47
Hydrogen chloride	10.9

Most of the values in this table are taken from *Handbook of Chemistry and Physics*, 42nd Edition, Chemical Rubber Publishing Company, Cleveland, Ohio.

(b) Since the combined pressure of the oxygen and the water vapor is 1 atm, the partial pressure of the oxygen = 760 mm − 18 mm = 742 mm. Therefore:

$$\text{Grams dissolved} = 0.0433 \times \frac{760 \text{ mm}}{742 \text{ mm}} = 0.0443 \text{ gram}$$

$$\text{Moles dissolved} = \frac{0.0443 \text{ gram}}{32 \text{ grams per mole}} = 0.00139 \text{ mole}$$

(c) As seen in (b), the partial pressure of the oxygen is 742 mm. Substituting in Equation 6-1 gives the value of the Henry's law constant.

$$k = \frac{c}{p} = \frac{0.0433}{742} = 5.83 \times 10^{-5}$$

Then

$$5.83 \times 10^{-5} = \frac{c'}{400}$$

$$c' = 0.0232 \text{ gram per liter}$$

It should be noted that it is not necessary to solve for k. Instead, Henry's law may be written

$$\frac{c}{p} = \frac{c'}{p'} \quad \text{and} \quad \frac{cp'}{p} = 0.0433 \times \frac{400}{742} = 0.0232 \text{ gram per liter}$$

Henry's law may be applied to slightly soluble gases over a considerable range of temperatures and up to several atmospheres of pressure. Moderately soluble gases show deviations, so that Henry's law may be used with only moderate success, and the range of pressures and temperatures where it is valid is limited. The law breaks down completely when an attempt is made to apply it to an extremely soluble gas such as hydrogen chloride. Here a large portion of the dissolved gas is converted by reaction with water into ions. Henry's law could not be expected to hold for this dissociated portion of the gas because the properties of the ions would be altogether different from those of neutral molecules of hydrogen chloride. Thus, the concentration-pressure relationships between dissolved and undissolved gas cannot be predicted by this law.

If a mixture of gases, all obeying Henry's law, is brought into contact with a liquid, each gas dissolves as if it alone were present at a pressure equal to its partial pressure in the mixture. For example, if the gas space above a given volume of liquid water is occupied solely by nitrogen and the pressure of this gas is 1 atm, 6.38×10^{-4} mole of gas will dissolve in each liter of water at 25°C, as shown in Table 6-1. Now if into this space, previously containing only nitrogen, oxygen is introduced until its partial pressure is 1 atm, then, according to Dalton's law of partial pressures, each gas would have a partial pressure of 1 atm. The solubility of the nitrogen would be unaffected and would still be 6.38×10^{-4} mole per liter. In accordance with Table 6-1 the solubility of the oxygen would be 1.26×10^{-3} mole per liter.

The presence of dissolved substances, particularly electrolytes, usually lowers the solubility of a gas, probably because of the fact that dissolved substances orient solvent molecules around them and hence leave fewer completely free sovent molecules for the gas to dissolve in. There are, however, certain exceptions to this rule.

One of the most important functions of the blood is to transport oxygen from the lungs to the body tissues and carbon dioxide from the tissues to the lungs. Whole blood dissolves large quantities of oxygen because of the fact that oxygen reacts chemically with the hemoglobin of the red blood cells. Henry's law cannot, therefore, be used to predict this solubility. The solution of oxygen in blood plasma—the fluid medium in which the blood cells float—approximates the solubility of oxygen in water, being, however, somewhat less as a result of the presence of dissolved substances in the plasma. Carbon dioxide is likewise transported principally in a combined form. Nitrogen shows somewhat the same solubility in both whole blood and plasma. Deep-sea divers and caisson workers who are exposed to air at high pressures absorb considerably more than the normal quantities of the components of the air. If these workers are returned too quickly to normal pressures, the sudden release of gas bubbles in the blood stream may result in rupture or clogging of the capillaries. This painful and dangerous condition is termed the "bends."

Nitrogen is the chief offender in this respect because, while the red blood cells can take care of a greater than normal supply of oxygen, there is no mechanism to alter the application of Henry's law insofar as nitrogen is concerned. Hence, if the partial pressure of nitrogen is suddenly reduced, say, by one third, by a rapid return to atmospheric pressure, its solubility is also lessened by one third. The danger is minimized by a slow return to atmospheric conditions, a process termed decompression, thereby allowing time for expelling the excess nitrogen between successive pressure changes. By using a mixture of oxygen and helium in place of air, the time required to expel unwanted gas may be shortened, since helium is less soluble than nitrogen. This application has been used with success in recent years.

6d. The Effect of Temperature on the Solubility of a Gas. In general, the solubility of a gas decreases markedly with increase in temperature, undoubtedly because of the increased translatory motion of the solute molecules in the liquid and the resulting increase in their ability to escape. The decrease in solubility with temperature is not linear, however; and the solubility curve will in some cases pass through a minimum. Minor variations of this type, however, do not invalidate the general idea of decreased gas solubility with increased temperature.

Most gases may be almost completely expelled by *continuous* heating at the boiling point. This is true of the slightly soluble gases, the moderately soluble gases such as carbon dioxide, and even ammonia. The hydrogen halides, however, form constant-boiling mixtures so that their behavior does not fit into this generalization.

SOLUTIONS OF LIQUIDS IN LIQUIDS. DISTILLATION PHENOMENA

6e. The Classification of Liquid Pairs from the Standpoint of Solubility. Unlike gases, which show complete solubility in each other in all cases, liquid pairs show all variations of solubility or miscibility, ranging from complete miscibility to essentially complete immiscibility. For purposes of study, liquid pairs are divided into three classes as follows: (1) completely immiscible liquids, (2) partially immiscible liquids, and (3) completely miscible liquids.

6f. Completely Immiscible Systems. Steam Distillation. Although there is probably no such thing as complete immiscibility, many liquid pairs show such slight miscibility that they may be considered immiscible. In Chapter 3 the vapor pressure of pure liquids was studied as a function of temperature. If two immiscible liquids are brought into contact with each other in such a way that neither completely covers the other, each continues to exert its own individual pressure. Furthermore, the vapor pressure of each liquid varies with temperature as if it were present alone. Consequently, at a given temperature the total pressure over the two liquids is the sum of the two individual vapor pressures at that temperature. The individual vapor pressures do not depend on the amounts of the two components; hence, the total pressure is independent of the relative amounts. Water exerts a vapor pressure of 760 mm at 100°C, and if it is placed in contact with bromobenzene at this temperature, there will be an additional pressure of 141 mm due to the bromobenzene, or a total vapor pressure of 901 mm. Consequently, if steam is passed into a mixture of bromobenzene and water, the mixture boils at a temperature less than 100°C, and water and bromobenzene distill over in a proportion determined by their vapor pressures. The mixture is agitated by steam bubbles so that each liquid has an exposed surface and may exert its vapor pressure independently of the other. A study of the individual vapor-pressure curves shows that the mixture should boil at 95.5°C, a finding that is in accord with the experimental value. This is an example of *steam distillation*, a process that makes possible the purification of many water-insoluble substances at temperatures well below their boiling points, thus avoiding decomposition that might take place at a higher temperature. Bromobenzene can be steam distilled at 61°C and chlorobenzene at 40°C below their normal boiling points.

Steam distillation is used to obtain certain volatile oils from plant bodies and in perfume manufacture from flowers. The production of benzoin fumes by heating this substance with water for the treatment of certain respiratory ailments depends upon the principle of steam distillation.

As stated above, the distillate from steam distillation has a composition that depends upon the two vapor pressures. The combined vapor pressure is, of course, equal to the two partial pressures in the vapor in equilibrium with the mixture. In 2j it was shown that the partial pressure of a component in a gaseous system is equal to the mole fraction of the component multiplied by the total pressure. Let the substance being steam-distilled be represented by A. Since the number of moles of a substance is equal to the weight divided by the molecular weight, the following relationships are obtained:

$$P_{H_2O} = x_{H_2O} \times P_{total} = \frac{\text{moles } H_2O}{\text{total moles}} \times P_{total} \qquad (a)$$

$$P_A = x_A \times P_{total} = \frac{\text{moles A}}{\text{total moles}} \times P_{total} \qquad (b)$$

Dividing (a) by (b),

$$\frac{P_{H_2O}}{P_A} = \frac{\text{moles } H_2O}{\text{moles } A} = \frac{\text{grams } H_2O \times M_A}{18 \times \text{grams } A}$$

hence

$$\frac{\text{Grams } H_2O}{\text{Grams } A} = \frac{P_{H_2O} \times 18}{P_A \times M_A} \tag{6-2}$$

This formula shows that because of the comparatively high vapor pressure of the water and the fact that the molecular weight of the water is small compared with that of the substance being distilled, it is possible to purify the substance without having to distill over an excessively large quantity of water. The application of Equation 6-2 is illustrated in the following example.

Example 6-3. Chlorobenzene distills with steam at 91°C when the external pressure is 1 atm. At this temperature its vapor pressure is 214 mm. Calculate the quantity of water that would have to be distilled to effect the purification of 10 grams of this compound.

$P_{H_2O} = 760 \text{ mm} - 214 \text{ mm} = 546 \text{ mm}$ Mol. wt. chlorobenzene $= 112.5$

$$\frac{\text{grams } H_2O}{10 \text{ grams}} = \frac{546 \text{ mm} \times 18.0}{214 \text{ mm} \times 112.5} \qquad \text{Grams } H_2O = 4.08$$

6g. Partially Miscible Systems. The best-known examples of partially miscible liquids are phenol, cresol, or similar substances in water. Certain of these constitute some of the more widely used disinfectants. As an example of such a pair, the system of phenol and water will be considered. Figure 6-1 shows the solubility relationships in this system. At 20°C it has been found that water will dissolve in phenol to the extent of 27.8 weight per cent of water. On the other hand, phenol will dissolve in water until the water percentage is reduced to 91.6 per cent. These phases are represented by the points A and B in the figure. When the temperature is raised to 30°C, the solubility of each component in the other is increased. This is shown by the points C and D. Further examination of the figure shows that the composition of the two phases becomes equal at 65.85°C, and above this temperature phenol and water are miscible in all proportions. This temperature is known as the *consolute temperature* or the *critical solution temperature*. Any mixture outside the enclosed area forms a single liquid phase. But any mixture within the enclosed area forms two liquid phases whose compositions are functions of the temperature. The relative amounts of the phases, however, depend on the composition of the

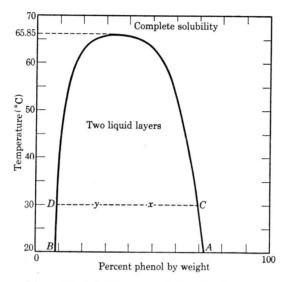

Figure 6-1. Solubility curve of phenol and water.

original mixture. For example, mixtures x and y will both resolve themselves into two phases of composition C and D, but the quantity of C will be greater in the case of x.

Nicotine and water form a liquid pair with both an upper and a lower consolute temperature. Between these two temperatures certain mixtures result in two liquid layers, but above and below these consolute temperatures there is complete miscibility.

6h. Vapor-pressure Relationships in Ideal Solutions. Raoult's Law. In considering the vapor pressure of a pure substance, it will be recalled that its magnitude is determined by the number of molecules that can escape from the surface of the liquid in a unit of time. The number escaping is a function of the number having velocities sufficiently high to escape from the surface against the attractive or cohesive forces exerted by the main body of the liquid. If the temperature is kept constant, the vapor pressure can be lowered by reducing in the surface layer the number of molecules having these high velocities. This can be done by a process of dilution of the solvent molecules. Of course, the solute molecules used for this purpose also have attractive forces, but for the present it will be assumed that the solvent and solute are sufficiently similar in their structure and properties so that the attraction between the solute particles and solvent particles is the same as that between the solvent particles alone. Hence, the dilution will not result in any change in the attractive forces, and the vapor pressure of the solvent will therefore be directly proportional to its mole fraction. This can be expressed by Equation 6-3, in which $p°$ is the vapor pressure of the pure solvent at the given temperature, p its vapor pressure over the solution at the same temperature, and x_1 its mole fraction.

$$p = p°x_1 \tag{6-3}$$

This quantitative relationship between the vapor pressure of a component and its mole fraction in the solution was discovered experimentally by F. M. Raoult, the French chemist, as a result of a large number of experiments with a great variety of solutions. This law, termed *Raoult's law*, states that *the vapor pressure of a component in a solution is directly proportional to its mole fraction and is equal to its mole fraction multiplied by the vapor pressure in the pure state at that temperature.* Although this law holds quite well for many solutions, it could be expected to prevail only if the substances are very similar chemically. For example, it applies quite well to all concentrations of solutions of toluene-benzene, chloroform-carbon tetrachloride, and other similar pairs. Frequently it adequately predicts the behavior of dilute solutions but does not hold so well for concentrated solutions.

When Raoult's law is considered for both the components, it can be seen that the total pressure over the solution is given by the following relationship:

$$P_{total} = x_1 p°_1 + x_2 p°_2 \tag{6-4}$$

If the solute is nonvolatile, the total pressure becomes equal to the partial pressure of the solvent alone.

Raoult's law may be expressed in another form which is more convenient for many calculations than Equation 6-3. Remembering that $x_1 + x_2 = 1$, Equation 6-3 may be written

$$p_1 = p°_1 x_1 = p°_1(1 - x_2)$$

and

$$\frac{p°_1 - p_1}{p°_1} = x_2 = \frac{\Delta p_1}{p°_1} \quad \text{or} \quad \Delta p_1 = p°_1 x_2 \tag{6-5}$$

In words, Equation 6-5 states that the vapor-pressure lowering is equal to the vapor pressure of the solvent in the pure state multiplied by the mole fraction of solute. The use of Raoult's law is shown by the following examples.

Example 6-4. The vapor pressure of pure water at 20°C is 17.4 mm. What is the vapor pressure of a solution in which 2 moles of a nonvolatile solute are dissolved in 1000 grams of water?

Using Equation 6-3,

$$p = 17.4 \text{ mm} \times \frac{1000/18}{(1000/18) + 2} = 16.79 \text{ mm}$$

Using Equation 6-5,

$$\Delta p = 17.4 \text{ mm} \times \frac{2}{(1000/18) + 2} = 0.60 \text{ mm}$$

$$p = (17.40 - 0.60) \text{ mm} = 16.80 \text{ mm}$$

Example 6-5. At 30°C benzene and toluene have vapor pressures in the pure state of 119.6 mm and 36.7 mm, respectively. What are the partial vapor pressures of each of these components and the total pressure over a solution consisting of equal weights of these two components at 30°C? What is the composition of the vapor in equilibrium with the solution at this temperature?

In this problem any weights of the components may be used just so that the two values are equal. For convenience 92.06 grams will be used, since this is the gram-molecular weight of toluene. Then:

Moles of toluene in liquid $= 1$

Moles of benzene in liquid $= \dfrac{92.06}{78.05} = 1.18$

Mole fraction of toluene in liquid $= \dfrac{1}{1 + 1.18} = 0.459$

Mole fraction of benzene $= 1 - 0.459 = 0.541$

$P_{benzene} = 0.541 \times 119.6 \text{ mm} = 64.7 \text{ mm}$

$P_{toluene} = 0.459 \times 36.7 \text{ mm} = 16.9 \text{ mm}$

Total pressure $= 64.7 + 16.9 \text{ mm} = 81.6 \text{ mm}$

The vapor composition is calculated from Equation 2-10 as follows:

$P_{benzene} =$ mole fraction of benzene in vapor $\times$ total pressure

$64.7 \text{ mm} =$ mole fraction of benzene $\times$ 81.6 mm

Mole fraction of benzene $= 0.793$

Mole fraction of toluene $= 1 - 0.793 = 0.207$

Example 6-5 shows that the vapor is richer in the more volatile component than the liquid with which it is in equilibrium.

The term *ideal solution* is used for those systems in which the vapor pressure can be calculated by Raoult's law. Such solutions are characterized by the fact that the tendency of the molecules of each of the components to escape into the vapor phase is altered only by the number of each present in unit volume. Their escaping tendency is in no way changed by the

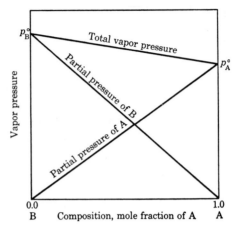

Figure 6-2. Vapor-pressure relations in an ideal liquid pair.

presence of the other molecular species making up the system. The vapor-pressure relationships in an ideal binary system are shown in Figure 6-2. Since the two pressures of the pure substances vary with temperature, this diagram is for the relationships at one temperature only. Similar diagrams may be constructed for other temperatures, the essential differences being that the higher the temperature, the higher the pressures. In this diagram the composition is plotted in terms of the mole fraction of A. Since the sum of the mole fractions is always equal to 1.0, the left-hand end of the composition line represented by a mole fraction of A equal to 0.0 corresponds to pure B. A solution in which the mole fraction of B is 0.75 would be represented by a mole fraction of A equal to 0.25. This method of plotting concentration will be used in Figures 6-2 through 6-10.

6i. Vapor-Pressure Relationships in Nonideal Solutions. In some binary solutions the attractive forces between the molecules of component A and component B are less than the attraction of A for A and B for B. As a result, the partial pressures are greater than those calculated from Raoult's law. This type of solution is said to exhibit *positive deviation.* If the positive deviation is sufficiently great and extends over a sufficiently wide range of concentrations, the total vapor-pressure curve shows a maximum. The vapor-pressure relationships in such a system are shown in Figure 6-3.

In the second type of nonideal solution, the attractive forces between the molecules of component A and component B are greater than the attractive forces of A for A and B for B. As a result, the partial pressures are less than those calculated from Raoult's law and the solution is said to exhibit *negative deviation.* If this deviation is sufficiently great and

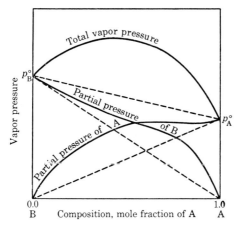

Figure 6-3. Vapor-pressure relations in a liquid pair having a maximum in the vapor-pressure curve.

extends over a sufficiently long concentration interval, the vapor-pressure curve shows a minimum. The vapor-pressure relationships in such a system are shown in Figure 6-4.

It must be kept in mind that just because a solution is nonideal in behavior it does not follow that there will be a minimum or maximum in the total vapor-pressure curve. There can be limited positive deviation without a maximum and limited negative deviation without a minimum.

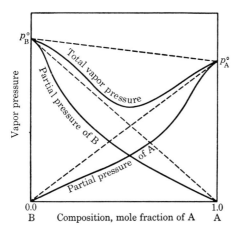

Figure 6-4. Vapor-pressure relations in a liquid pair having a minimum in the vapor-pressure curve.

6j. Boiling-point Diagrams. Distillation phenomena can best be studied by *boiling-point diagrams*. They consist of two curves, one showing the boiling temperature of various solutions at a selected pressure, usually 1 atm, and the other showing the composition of the vapor in equilibrium with the various solutions at their boiling points. One method for compiling the data for a boiling-point diagram of an ideal solution is shown in Figure 6-5. Here the total-pressure curves are plotted for a number of temperatures. The curves shown approximate, in their relative positions, the curves for benzene and toluene. Since the boiling point of a solution is defined as that temperature at which the vapor pressure is 760 mm, the compositions of various mixtures boiling at selected temperatures can be obtained from the intersections of the total-pressure curves with the 760-mm pressure line. Thus from the figure the compositions of the solutions boiling at the temperatures T_1, T_2, T_3, T_4, and T_5 can be determined. These compositions are obtained by dropping a perpendicular to the base of the diagram at the point of intersection of the 760-mm pressure line with the total-vapor-pressure curve at the particular temperature. The

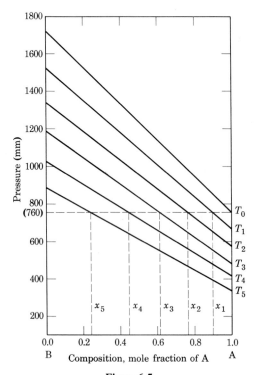

Figure 6-5.

temperature T_0 would be the boiling temperature of pure A under a pressure of 1 atm. The compositions so obtained—x_1, x_2, x_3, x_4, and x_5—are then plotted on a temperature-composition diagram, and in this way the lower curve of Figure 6-6 is obtained. This lower curve thus gives the boiling temperatures of all mixtures of A and B under 1 atm pressure. To obtain the boiling temperature of any mixture, it is necessary only to determine the temperature at which a perpendicular to the base at the given concentration intersects the boiling-point curve.

The composition of the vapor in equilibrium with any given con- centration of A and B can be calculated from Raoult's law by means of Equation 6-3. The plotting of the various vapor compositions against the temperature at which they are produced establishes the upper curve. To obtain the composition of the vapor in equilibrium with any particular solution, a line is drawn parallel to the base from the composition on the lower curve. The intersection of this line with the vapor-composition curve gives the composition of the vapor. For example, the vapor in equilibrium with solution x_2 in Figure 6-6 is x_2', and with x_3 is x_3'. It should be noted that the vapor is always richer in the more volatile com- ponent than the liquid with which it is in equilibrium. It is emphasized that the upper curve in Figure 6-6 has been drawn considerably higher in position than is justified by the data of Figure 6-5. This was done to spread the curves farther apart in order to make it easier to discuss the process of fractional distillation in 6k.

For nonideal solutions it is impossible to calculate the necessary data

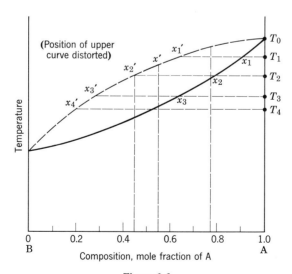

Figure 6-6.

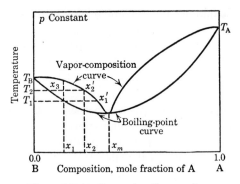

Figure 6-7. Boiling-point diagram for a mixture whose vapor-pressure curve shows a maximum.

because of the failure of Raoult's law. Consequently, experimental procedures must be used. The boiling points of various mixtures are determined in an apparatus so constructed that a sample of the distillate in equilibrium with the various mixtures can be obtained and analyzed. The systems in which a *maximum* occurs in the *pressure-composition curve* (see Figure 6-3) show a *minimum* in the boiling-point curve. This is illustrated in Figure 6-7. Note that the vapor-composition curve is continuous throughout the range of composition and becomes tangent to the boiling-point curve at its minimum.

In the same way experimental results show that the boiling-point diagram for mixtures showing *negative* deviation from Raoult's law and also a *minimum* in the total-pressure curve (see Figure 6-4) shows a *maximum* boiling mixture and a vapor-composition curve tangent to the boiling-point curve at its maximum point. (See Figure 6-8.)

Thus binary systems consisting of two volatile and completely miscible components fall into three classes: (1) those in which the boiling points of mixtures *increase continuously* and lie *between* the values for the pure components; (2) those in which there is a *minimum* in the boiling-point curve; and (3) those in which there is a *maximum* in the boiling-point curve. From the standpoint of the vapor-pressure curves, in Class 1 the vapor pressure of mixtures is intermediate between the vapor pressures of the pure substances; in Class 2 there is a maximum in the vapor-pressure curve; and in Class 3 there is a minimum in the vapor-pressure curves. Substances in Class 1 may be ideal in behavior and the vapor-pressure relationships will in such cases follow Raoult's law. On the other hand, there may be deviation, either positive or negative, from this law but not sufficient deviation to produce a maximum or a minimum. Figures 6-2 through 6-8 are for hypothetical systems. The boiling-point diagram for

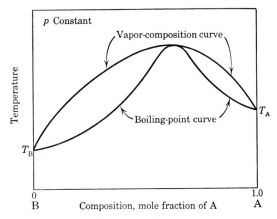

Figure 6-8. Boiling-point diagram for a mixture whose vapor-pressure curve shows a minimum.

an actual system in Class 2 is shown in Figure 6-9. Figure 6-10 is for the actual system: benzene-*n*-hexane. This is an example of Class 1 in which the behavior is nonideal.

6k. The Distillation of Liquid Pairs. Fractional Distillation. What takes place in the distillation of binary mixtures of Class 1 can be seen from a consideration of Figure 6-6. If a solution of composition x_2 is heated, the first drop of distillate will appear at T_2. This drop of distillate will have the composition x_2'. If the heating is continued to T_1, the residue will have the composition x_1 and the distillate forming at this temperature will have the composition x_1'. Note that the compositions of the residue and the distillate in equilibrium with it are joined by a line

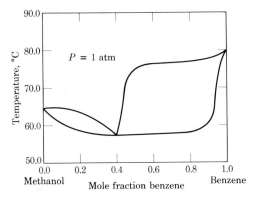

Figure 6-9.

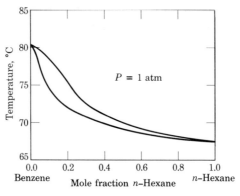

Figure 6-10.

parallel to the base of the diagram. The composition of the *accumulated* distillate at T_1 is about half way between x_1' and x_2', the value being approximately x' as shown in the figure. It is seen that the accumulated distillate is richer in B, the more volatile of the two components. The residue is richer in the less volatile component. Thus, a partial separation of the two components has been effected.

Now, if the heating process is stopped and the accumulated distillate cooled below T_4 and then reheated, it in turn can be separated into two phases of different composition. For example, if it is reheated to T_3 a residue x_3 is obtained, and the distillate has a composition about half way between x_4' and x_3'. If the various fractions of distillate and residue that can be obtained are properly recombined and redistilled a sufficient number of times, a complete separation of the two components can be effected. This process is termed *fractional distillation*. In the laboratory and in industry the process is effected by distilling columns rather than by manual recombination followed by redistillation of the various fractions. Distilling columns vary greatly in type and efficiency. The general principle in their operation is a series of evaporations and condensations produced by having the rising vapors come in contact with the downflow of cooler liquid produced by partial condensations of the vapor.

In mixtures of Class 2, reference to Figure 6-7 shows that a mixture of composition x_1 when heated to T_2 will produce a residue of composition x_3 and an accumulated distillate of composition about midway between x_1' and x_2'. Fractional distillation of x_1 will not, however, produce a complete separation of the two components as was the situation in solutions of Class 1. Instead a residue of pure B is obtained, but the ultimate distillate has the composition x_m. This mixture will distill unchanged, since the residue and distillate have the same composition, as is shown by the intersection of the liquid-composition and vapor-composition curves. Any mixture of composition between x_m and pure A can be separated into an ultimate residue of pure A, but the distillate will have the composition x_m. The solution x_m constitutes what is known as a *minimum constant-boiling solution*. Thus, solutions of Class 2 cannot be completely separated by fractional distillation into the two pure components. Instead pure A and the constant-boiling mixture will be obtained or pure B and the constant-boiling mixture, depending upon whether the mole fraction of A is greater or less than x_m.

Table 6-2. Boiling Points and Composition of Azeotropic Mixtures*

Type	A	B	B.P. of A (°C)	B.P. of B (°C)	Azeotropic Mixture	
					B.P. (°C)	Wt. %A
Minimum boiling point	Benzene	Ethanol	80.2	78.3	68.2	67.6
Minimum boiling point	Chloroform	Methanol	61.1	64.7	53.5	87.4
Minimum boiling point	Ethanol	Water	78.4	100.0	78.1	95.5
Minimum boiling point	Isobutyl alcohol	Toluene	107.9	110.8	100.9	44.5
Maximum boiling point	Acetone	Chloroform	56.5	61.2	64.7	80.0
Maximum boiling point	Formic acid	Water	100.8	100.0	107.3	77.5
Maximum boiling point	Hydrogen chloride	Water	−84.0	100.0	110.0	20.2
Maximum boiling point	Chloroform	Methyl acetate	61.2	57.1	64.5	22.0

* Most of the values in this table are taken from Lange's *Handbook of Chemistry*, 10th Edition, Handbook Publishers, Inc., Sandusky, Ohio.

A similar analysis of distillation processes in solutions of Class 3 shows again that complete separation of the two components is impossible. Solutions of composition between x_m and pure A can be separated into an ultimate distillate consisting of pure A, but the residue will be the constant-boiling mixture. If the composition is between x_m and pure B, the residue will again be the constant-boiling mixture and the ultimate distillate pure B. In this case x_m is a *maximum boiling mixture*.

Some examples of liquid pairs that have constant-boiling mixtures are given in Table 6-2. These mixtures are sometimes termed *azeotropic mixtures*, from the Greek word meaning "to boil without change." They have the characteristics of a pure substance in that they show a constant boiling point. Industrially they are most important, for their occurrence prevents the separation of their pure components by fractional distillation. Instead, more costly chemical or other methods must be employed.

Ninety-five per cent ethyl alcohol is an azeotropic mixture; hence the great difference in the costs of 95 per cent and absolute alcohol.

SOLUTIONS OF SOLIDS IN LIQUIDS

6l. Solubility Relationships. In 6e it was stated that in liquid-liquid systems solubility varies from complete miscibility to complete immiscibility, depending upon the individual natures of the two components. In systems of solids in liquids, again there is a wide range of solubility, which varies from complete insolubility to very large solubilities. No solid, however, is completely soluble in a liquid. In most cases the solubility of a solid increases with increase of temperature, although there are certain systems in which the reverse is true.

6m. Vapor-pressure Relationships. Just as there are ideal solutions of liquids in liquids in which partial pressures may be calculated by Raoult's law, many solutions of solids in liquids also show ideal behavior. Although in many liquid-liquid systems the ideality extends over a wide range of concentrations, the region of ideality for solid solutes is often restricted to rather dilute solutions. At the low concentrations, Raoult's law can be used in many cases to calculate the vapor pressure if the solute is nonvolatile. In two solutions of the same solvent, the vapor-pressure lowering in each is directly proportional to the mole fraction of the solute (see Equation 6-5). Thus the ratio of the two vapor-pressure lowerings, $\Delta p'$ and $\Delta p''$, is equal to the ratio of the mole fractions of the solute in the two solutions. Mathematically this may be expressed as follows:

$$\frac{\Delta p'}{\Delta p''} = \frac{x_A'}{x_A''} \tag{6-6}$$

It should be noted that since Raoult's law does not depend upon the individual nature of the solute but only on its mole fraction, Equation 6-6 does not demand that the solute in the two solutions be of the same molecular species.

The effect of added solute on the vapor pressure of a pure solvent at various temperatures is shown in Figures 6-11 and 6-13. At any given temperature the vapor pressure of the solution will be less than that of the pure solvent. The extent of the lowering is proportional to the mole fraction of solute, as shown in Equation 6-6. Consequently, for a solution in which the mole fraction of solute is x_A', the vapor-pressure curve will fall below that of the pure solvent. How far below it will fall will depend upon the concentration. In the figure x_A'' is greater than x_A'. The representation in Figure 6-11 is schematic and covers only a small temperature

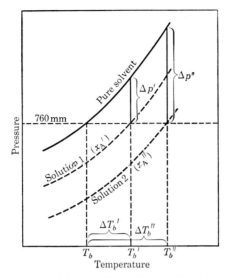

Figure 6-11. Boiling-point relations in pure solvent and solutions.

range. Over a small range the vapor-pressure curves for the pure solvent and for various solutions are essentially parallel, and they will be so treated in the discussion that follows.

6n. Molecular Weight by Boiling-Point Elevation. Figure 6-11 shows that at the normal boiling point of the solvent the solutions shown have vapor pressures below 760 mm. In order to bring them to the boiling point, it is necessary to heat them to T_b' and T_b'', respectively. In other words, the boiling point of a solvent is raised by the addition of a non-volatile solute. If the various vapor-pressure curves are considered as straight lines over the small temperature range involved, the $\Delta p - \Delta T_b$ pairs make up corresponding sides of similar triangles. Therefore

$$\frac{\Delta p'}{\Delta p''} = \frac{\Delta T_b'}{\Delta T_b''} \qquad (6\text{-}7)$$

Since the ratio of the vapor-pressure lowerings in two solutions of the same solvent is equal to the ratio of the mole fractions of the solute, if the same quantity of solvent is used in both solutions, it follows that

$$\frac{\Delta T_b'}{\Delta T_b''} = \frac{\dfrac{\text{moles of A in solution 1}}{\text{moles of A in solution 1 + moles of solvent}}}{\dfrac{\text{moles of A in Solution 2}}{\text{moles of A in Solution 2 + moles of solvent}}}$$

Let us assume that we have 1000 grams of water in both solution 1 and in solution 2. This represents 55.56 moles of water. If the solutions are sufficiently dilute, the number of moles of solute in the denominators of the two right-hand terms is negligibly small in relation to the moles of solvent, and the above relationship reduces to

$$\frac{\Delta T_b'}{\Delta T_b''} = \frac{\text{moles of A in solution 1}}{\text{moles of A in solution 2}} = \frac{m_A'}{m_A''} \qquad (6\text{-}8)$$

In words, this equation states that the rise in the boiling point is proportional to the molality of the solution. Mathematically,

$$\Delta T_b \propto m_A \quad \text{and} \quad \Delta T_b = K_b m_A \qquad (6\text{-}9)$$

The constant K_b is termed the *molal boiling-point constant*. It is seen from Equation 6-11 that K_b is numerically equal to the increase in the boiling point of the solvent produced in an ideal solution by dissolving 1

Table 6-3. Molal Boiling-Point Constants for Some Commonly Used Solvents

Solvent	B.P. (°C)	K_b (°C)
Acetone	56.0	1.71
Benzene	80.2	2.53
Water	100.0	0.51
Chloroform	61.2	3.63

mole of solute in 1000 grams of solvent. Its numerical value varies with the nature of the solvent and can be calculated from theoretical considerations. This calculation, however, is beyond the scope of this textbook. The molal boiling-point constants for certain solvents are given in Table 6-3.

Equation 6-9 may be used for the determination of molecular weights by the boiling-point-rise method. A modified Cottrell apparatus, such as that shown in Figure 6-12, can be used. G grams of the solvent are placed in the boiler, and the boiling point determined with a thermometer so graduated that readings can be made to 0.002°C. Then g grams of solute are added, and the boiling point of the solution determined. The difference between the two readings is the boiling-point rise. In determining these boiling points, a percolator device is used to pump the boiling liquid over the thermometer bulb. In this way difficulty from superheating is eliminated. To express the molality, g is divided by the molecular weight

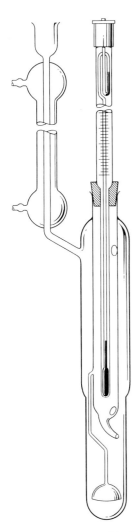

Figure 6-12. A modified Cottrell apparatus for the determination of molecular weight by boiling-point rise.

of the solute. This in turn is divided by G, and the result is multiplied by 1000. Equation 6-9 then takes the form

$$\Delta T_b = K_b m_A = \frac{K_b \times g/M_{\text{solute}} \times 1000}{G}$$

$$= \frac{K_b \times g \times 1000}{M_{\text{solute}} \times G}$$

$$M_{\text{solute}} = \frac{K_b \times g \times 1000}{\Delta T_b \times G} \qquad (6\text{-}10)$$

The assumptions that the vapor-pressure curves are parallel and that they can be treated geometrically as straight lines are made only for purposes of simplification in the derivation of Equation 6-10. A rigorous mathematical procedure could be used, but for dilute solutions the result would be the same.

60. Molecular Weight by Freezing-Point Depression. By definition the freezing point of a solution is the temperature at which the solution exists in equilibrium with the solid solvent. In such an equilibrium the solvent must have the same vapor pressure in both the solid and liquid states. Consequently the freezing point is the temperature at which the vapor-pressure curve of the solution intersects the sublimation curve of the solid solvent. Thus in Figure 6-13 the freezing points of the two solutions are $T_f{'}$ and $T_f{''}$. This figure includes the vapor-pressure and sublimation-pressure curves for a phase diagram of a pure substance such as water. (See Figure 3-4.) Again, on the assumption that the vapor-pressure curves are parallel and that for the concentration range considered they are straight lines, the relationship between the freezing-point lowering and the molality of the solution can be derived as follows. Since triangles afc and age are similar, and bfc and dge are similar, then

$$\frac{ac}{fc} = \frac{ae}{ge} \quad \text{and} \quad \frac{bc}{fc} = \frac{de}{ge}$$

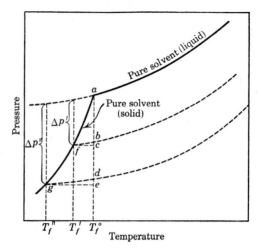

Figure 6-13. Freezing-point relations in pure solvent and solutions.

From these expressions it follows by the laws of proportion that

$$\frac{ac}{fc} - \frac{bc}{fc} = \frac{ae}{ge} - \frac{de}{ge} = \frac{ac - bc}{fc} = \frac{ae - de}{ge} = \frac{ab}{fc} = \frac{ad}{ge}$$

Since the vapor-pressure curves are parallel, $\Delta p' = ab$ and $\Delta p'' = ad$. Then

$$\frac{\Delta p'}{\Delta p''} = \frac{\Delta T_f'}{\Delta T_f''} \tag{6-11}$$

since *cf* and *eg* are the freezing-point lowerings for solutions 1 and 2.

This equation is similar in form to 6-7. By a series of substitutions similar to those made in the derivation of the equation for molecular weights by the boiling-point method, an expression similar to Equation 6-10 is obtained. Its final form is

$$M_{\text{solute}} = \frac{K_f \times g \times 1000}{\Delta T_f \times G} \tag{6-12}$$

For the determination of molecular weight by the freezing-point or, as it is often called, the *cryoscopic* method, an apparatus similar to that shown in Figure 6-14 is used. *G* grams of the pure solvent are placed in the

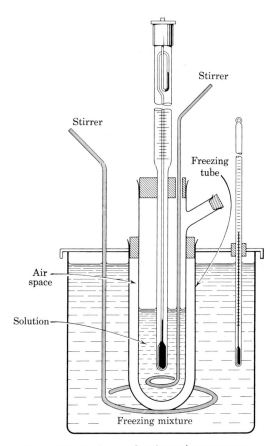

Figure 6-14. Beckmann freezing-point apparatus.

freezing tube, and the freezing point is determined. Then *g* grams of solute are added, and the freezing point of the solution is determined. With these two weights and with the freezing-point lowering, substitution in Equation 6-12 gives the desired molecular weight. The purpose of the air bath is to keep the drop in temperature in the solution from becoming too rapid.

K_f is termed the *molal freezing-point constant.* Like the molal boiling-point constant, it is the lowering produced in an ideal solution when 1 mole of solute is added to 1000 grams of solvent. It can be calculated from theoretical considerations or by means of Equation 6-12 by using a solute of known molecular weight. The values of this constant for a number of solvents are given in Table 6-4.

Besides offering methods for determining the molecular weight of solutes, the freezing-point depression and boiling-point rise can also be used to determine the molality, or concentration, of solutions. In biological work, where chemical analysis is often difficult or even impossible, the cryoscopic method is often employed. This method is more satisfactory than the boiling-point method, as the higher temperature is likely to alter the chemical nature of the solutions.

Table 6-4. Molal Freezing-Point Constants for Some Commonly Used Solvents

Solvent	Freezing Point (°C)	Freezing-point Constant (°C)
Water	0.00	1.86
Benzene	5.5	5.12
Acetic acid	16.7	3.90
Camphor	178.0	37.7

6p. Colligative Properties in General. The lowering of the vapor pressure, rise of the boiling point, and depression of the freezing point are all properties that depend solely on the number of moles of solute present in a given quantity of solvent. The individual nature of the solute makes no difference just as long as its action is ideal. Since the number of solute molecules present is equal to the number of moles multiplied by Avogadro's number, it follows that these properties are due to the number of *particles of solute* present in a given quantity of solvent. Such properties are termed *colligative properties*. In addition to the three studied in this chapter, an additional colligative property of solutions, *osmotic pressure*, will be studied in the next chapter.

REFERENCES

Bull, *Physical Biochemistry*, John Wiley and Sons, New York, 1951, Chapter 12.
Daniels and Alberty, *Physical Chemistry*, John Wiley and Sons, New York, 1961, Chapters 7 and 8.
Maron and Prutton, *Principles of Physical Chemistry*, The Macmillan Co., New York, 1958, Chapters 5 and 6.
Moore, *Physical Chemistry*, Prentice-Hall, Englewood Cliffs, New Jersey, 1962, Chapter 5.
Sheehan, *Physical Chemistry*, Allyn and Bacon, Boston, 1961, Chapter 5.
Daniels, Williams, Bender, Alberty, and Cornwell, *Experimental Physical Chemistry*, McGraw-Hill Book Co., New York, 1962, Chapter 4.
Crockford and Nowell, *Laboratory Manual of Physical Chemistry*, John Wiley and Sons, 1956, New York, Experiments 8, 9, 10, and 11.

REVIEW QUESTIONS

1. Give a suitable definition for each of the following terms: *solution, solvent, solute, solubility, saturated solution.*

2. Define and show the interrelationships among the following methods of expressing concentration: mole fraction, molarity, molality, weight per cent, mole per cent.

3. Explain the relationship between the solubility of a gas in a liquid at a given temperature and the pressure of the gas over the solution. State Henry's law both in words and in the form of a mathematical equation. What are the limitations of the law?

4. How does Henry's law apply to the solubility relationships in a mixture of gases?

5. In general, how does gas solubility vary with the nature of the gas? Discuss the change in the solubility of gases with change in temperature.

6. Discuss the vapor-pressure relations in systems composed of immiscible components.

7. Explain the principle of steam distillation. Give the mathematical relationship that exists among the partial pressures, molecular weights, and the relative quantities of components distilling over in steam distillation.

8. Interpret the diagram that shows the solubility relations in the phenol-water system. What is meant by the consolute temperature?

9. State Raoult's law in words. Give two alternate mathematical expressions for this law. What are its limitations? Explain how Raoult's law can be used to calculate the composition of the vapor existing over a solution composed of components showing ideal behavior.

10. Discuss the vapor pressure relationships in nonideal systems of completely miscible liquids. Explain the positive and negative deviations found in such systems. Does a positive deviation necessarily mean that there will be a minimum-boiling azeotropic mixture? Explain your answer.

11. What is a boiling-point diagram? Show how data for such a diagram for a pair of ideal components can be calculated from the vapor pressures of the pure components.

12. Discuss the shapes of the boiling-point diagrams for the following: (*a*) a pair of ideal components, (*b*) a pair of liquids showing positive deviation in the vapor pressure-composition diagram but without a maximum in the vapor pressure curve, (*c*) a system with an azeotropic mixture with a maximum boiling point, and (*d*) a system with an azeotropic mixture with a minimum boiling point.

13. Draw approximate boiling-point diagrams for the systems given in Table 6-2.

14. Give a clear explanation of exactly what takes place when various mixtures, both ideal and nonideal, are subjected to fractional distillation.

15. In what respects do azeotropic mixtures resemble pure compounds and in what respects are they different?

16. By means of vapor pressure diagrams show why the boiling point of a solvent is raised and the freezing point lowered by the addition of a nonvolatile solute.

17. From the vapor pressure curves derive the mathematical expressions for the molecular weight of a nonvolatile solute from the lowering of the freezing point and the rise in the boiling point of a solvent.

18. What is meant by the terms *molal freezing-point constant* and *molal boiling-point constant*?

19. Discuss the experimental determination of molecular weights by the boiling-point rise and freezing-point lowering methods.

PROBLEMS

I

1. Complete the following table:

Solute	Weight Per Cent	Density	Molality	Molarity	Mole Fraction Solute
(a) Sodium hydroxide	10.00	1.109	—	—	—
(b) Sulfuric acid	25.00	1.178	—	—	—
(c) Sodium carbonate	14.00	1.146	—	—	—

2. A solution is prepared by dissolving 64.92 grams of $MgCl_2$ in sufficient water to make 600.0 ml of solution. The density of the solution is 1.082 grams per cm^3. Calculate the molarity, molality, and the mole fraction of the solute.

3. Calculate the solubility of hydrogen in water at 25°C in (a) moles per liter and (b) milligrams per liter, when the pressure of the gas is 2 atm.

4. How many grams of oxygen will be absorbed by 4.00 liters of water at 25°C when the partial pressure of the oxygen is 150 mm (approximately the pressure of oxygen in the atmosphere)? How many grams would be absorbed if the pressure of the oxygen were 700 mm?

5. How many milliliters of water would be necessary to absorb 0.10 gram of oxygen at 25°C when the oxygen pressure is (a) 200 mm and (b) 760 mm?

6. A mixture of nitrogen and oxygen containing 30 mole per cent of oxygen is shaken with 5 liters of water at 25°C until the water is saturated with respect to both gases. The total pressure of the gases over the water, excluding the vapor pressure of the water, is 750 mm. How many grams of each gas will be absorbed? What would be the volume of the quantity of each gas absorbed if it were measured under standard conditions? If the water containing the absorbed gases is heated sufficiently to expel all the gas and the resulting gas mixture is dried, what will be the mole fraction of each gas in the mixture?

7. Pure acetone has a vapor pressure of 184.8 mm at a temperature of 20°C. Calculate the vapor pressure of an acetone solution made by dissolving 10 grams of nitrotoluene in 900 grams of acetone at 20°C.

8. How many grams of benzoic acid must be added to 1200 grams of acetone at 20°C to produce a solution whose vapor pressure is 184.2 mm? See Problem I-7 for needed data.

9. Calculate the vapor pressure lowering produced by the addition of 12.8 grams of naphthalene to 500 grams of benzene at 20°C. Pure benzene has a vapor pressure of 74.7 mm at this temperature. What would be the freezing point and the boiling point of this solution?

10. Benzene and toluene form solutions that are almost ideal in behavior. At 30°C pure benzene has a vapor pressure of 118.2 mm of Hg and toluene has a vapor pressure of 36.7 mm. Calculate the partial pressures and the total pressure over a solution composed of 300 grams of benzene and 600 grams of toluene.

11. What would be the composition of a solution of benzene and toluene at 30°C if the vapor in equilibrium with it has a composition such that the mole fraction of the toluene is 0.35? See Problem I-10 for needed data.

12. Calculate the freezing points and boiling points of each of the following solutions: (*a*) 9.00 grams of glucose in 220 grams of water, (*b*) 3.50 grams of benzoic acid in 120 grams of benzene.

13. What is the molecular weight of a substance if a solution of 3.00 grams in 200 grams of benzene freezes at 4.98°C?

14. A solution contains 5.00 grams of glucose and 5.00 grams of urea in 800 grams of water. (*a*) Calculate the freezing point of the solution. (*b*) How much water would have to be evaporated in order that the solution have a freezing point of −0.82°C?

15. How many grams of urea must be added to 4000 grams of water to make the solution boil at 100.32°C?

16. Calculate the number of grams of ethylene glycol that would have to be added to 8.0 kilograms of water in order to lower the freezing point to 10°F. Assume ideal behavior in your calculations.

17. The vapor pressure of benzene at various temperatures is given in Table 3-1. Calculate the vapor pressure of benzene at 20°, 40°, and 60°C for a solution containing 10.00 grams of naphthalene in 800 grams of benzene. What will be the boiling point and the freezing point of this solution? What will be its vapor pressure at the normal boiling point?

II

1. Complete the following table:

Solute	Weight Per Cent	Density	Molality	Molarity	Mole Fraction Solute
(*a*) Potassium hydroxide	—	1.101	—	2.160	—
(*b*) Sucrose	30.00	1.127	—	—	—
(*c*) Sulfuric acid	40.00	1.303	—	—	—

2. A given solution containing 163.2 grams of sodium thiosulfate in 900 ml of solution has a density of 1.138 grams per ml. Calculate the molarity, molality, and mole fraction of the solute.

3. A potassium hydroxide solution is $5.011M$ and has a density of 1.159 grams per ml. Calculate the molality, per cent potassium hydroxide by weight, and the mole fraction of the solute.

4. Calculate the solubility of oxygen in water at 25°C in (a) moles per liter and (b) grams per liter when the pressure of the oxygen over the solution is 1300 mm of Hg.

5. What volume of nitrogen gas will be absorbed by 2.5 liters of water at 25°C when the pressure is 1 atm?

6. A solution of nitrogen in water has a concentration of 0.052 gram per liter at 25°C. What is the partial pressure of nitrogen over this solution?

7. A gaseous mixture consisting of oxygen at 250 mm partial pressure, hydrogen at 300 mm pressure, and nitrogen at 200 mm pressure is shaken with 1100 ml of water at 25°C until the solution is saturated with each gas. How many grams of each will be absorbed? If the gases are expelled and dried, what will be their total volume at 25°C when measured at 1 atm pressure? What will be the mole fraction of each of the gases in the mixture?

8. At 30°C, pure benzene has a vapor pressure of 119.6 mm of Hg. Calculate the vapor pressure of benzene at this temperature over a solution made by dissolving 15.0 grams of naphthalene in 156 grams of benzene.

9. If the vapor pressure of pure toluene is 36.7 mm at 30°C, how much p-dinitrobenzene would have to be dissolved in 100 grams of toluene at this temperature in order to reduce the vapor pressure to 36.0 mm?

10. Benzene and ethylene dichloride form a solution that shows almost ideal behavior. Calculate the partial pressure of these two substances at 50°C over a solution containing 0.30 mole fraction of benzene. At this temperature, benzene has a vapor pressure of 269 mm and ethylene dichloride has a vapor pressure of 236 mm. Calculate the composition of the vapor in equilibrium with the solution.

11. Calculate the total pressure and the composition of the vapor at 50°C in a solution made by mixing 100 grams of benzene with 100 grams of ethylene dichloride. See Problem II-10 for the necessary data.

12. Determine the freezing and boiling points of the following solutions:
   (a) 10.0 grams of sucrose in 32.0 grams of water
   (b) 0.400 gram of urea in 15 grams of acetone
   (c) 6.00 grams of glucose in 150 grams of water

13. The aqueous solution of a certain nonvolatile solute boils at 100.16°C at normal pressure. What is the molality? What is its freezing point? What is its vapor pressure at 100°C?

14. A solution containing 2.80 grams of a substance in 200 grams of acetic acid freezes at 15.95°C. What is the molecular weight of the substance?

15. Calculate the number of grams of ethylene glycol that must be added to 10.0 kg of water in order that the solution shall have a freezing point of 0°F (-17.8°C).

16. A solution of glucose in water freezes at -0.500°C. If the solution contains 300 grams of water, what weight of glucose has been dissolved in the water? How much urea would have to be added to 500 grams of this solution in order that it shall have a freezing point of -1.00°C?

SEVEN

Solutions II:
Osmotic Pressure

The phenomenon of osmosis and the osmotic pressure of solutions are studied in this chapter. The subject matter includes the cause and mechanism of osmotic flow, the measurement and calculation of osmotic pressure, and a consideration of the aspects of osmotic pressure and osmotic flow in biological systems.

THE CAUSE OF OSMOTIC PRESSURE AND THE MECHANISM OF OSMOSIS

7a. The Process of Osmosis. The process of *osmosis* was recognized and studied as early as the latter part of the eighteenth century. When a solution is separated from the pure solvent by a suitable membrane, a diffusion of solvent takes place through the membrane from the pure solvent into the solution. Such a process is illustrated in Figure 7-1. The flared end of the tube is covered by parchment paper or a film of collodian. A sucrose solution is placed in the tube and pure water in the beaker. Sugar molecules are unable to diffuse through the membrane, but water molecules can readily do so. There is a resultant diffusion of water into the sugar solution, and the level of the liquid rises in the tube. The same type of diffusion would take place if the beaker contained sugar solution provided the concentation is less than that in the tube. A membrane, such as that used in the process described, that *permits the flow of water molecules but prevents the passage of the solute molecules, is termed a semipermeable or differentially permeable membrane.*

Osmosis is defined as the diffusion of solvent molecules through a semipermeable membrane from a region of higher solvent concentration to a region of lower solvent concentration (higher solute concentration). If several solutes are present, osmosis will take place if the membrane is impermeable to any one of the various kinds of molecules or ions.

7b. Osmotic Pressure. In the process discussed in 7a it is apparent that there must be some kind of a driving force or potential, which we can term the diffusion pressure, that tends to drive the solvent through the membrane into the solution. As the liquid rises in the tube, a *hydrostatic pressure* develops. This increases the tendency for the solvent molecules to move from the solution back into the pure solvent and operates against the force causing osmosis. As a result, an equilibrium condition is finally reached in which the hydrostatic pressure is sufficient to prevent further diffusion. *That pressure on the solution side of the membrane that is just sufficient to prevent osmosis when pure solvent is present on the opposite side of the membrane is termed the osmotic pressure of the solution.* This statement assumes a membrane permeable only to the solvent. This osmotic pressure is, of course, that of the solution at equilibrium and not the osmotic pressure of the original solution before the passage of the solvent resulted in dilution.

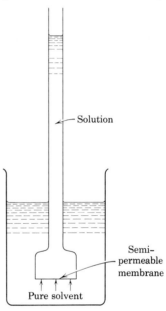

Figure 7-1. The process of osmosis.

7c. The Cause of Osmosis. A rigorous treatment of osmosis involves a thermodynamic treatment and necessitates the use of the calculus. The approach is made through the fact that the free energy of the water in the pure state is greater than that of the water in the solution. The spontaneous flow of the solvent takes place with a loss of free energy. In our treatment we shall discuss the cause of osmosis from the standpoint of vapor pressure, one of the manifestations of the molar free energy of the water. Since a solute lowers the vapor pressure of the solvent, the vapor pressure of the pure solvent is greater than that of the same solvent in any *solution.* Hence, when a semipermeable membrane separates a pure solvent and its solution, a difference in vapor pressure exists on the two sides. Osmosis then takes place because diffusion always occurs from a region of higher vapor pressure to a region of lower vapor pressure. Hence, a transfer of pure solvent takes place through the membrane. In the same manner pure solvent will be transferred from a dilute to a concentrated solution. An explanation of the mechanism by which this transfer takes place is given in the next section.

It can be shown thermodynamically and experimentally that the vapor pressure of a solvent increases with increasing pressure. This is brought about principally by the effect of the pressure in bringing the solvent molecules closer together. For example, in the process taking place in Figure 7-1, the hydrostatic pressure at equilibrium is sufficient to increase the vapor pressure of the solution to a value equal to that of the pure solvent. From this, we can say that osmotic pressure is that pressure that must be applied to a solution in order to increase its vapor pressure enough to equal that of the pure solvent at the temperature of the experiment. This concept involves no assumptions about the nature of the membrane. Furthermore, since the vapor pressure of a solvent in a solution is a function of the concentration of the solute, without regard to its individual nature, all solutions of the same solvent containing an equal number of solute particles (regardless of their kind) per unit volume should have the same osmotic pressure at the same temperature. Experimentation proves this to be the case.

7d. The Mechanism of Osmosis. Since the free energy per mole of the water in its pure state is greater than that of the same quantity in the solution, all that is necessary for a transfer of the water from the pure solvent to the solution is that some process exists that makes the transfer possible. Since we are talking about transfer through the semipermeable membrane, two methods for this can be considered. The water might interact with the membrane to form definite chemical compounds or what may be loosely called a membrane solution. The postulation of such a type of transfer is termed the *membrane solution theory*.

In the simple case the *membrane solution theory* assumes that the solvent is soluble in the membrane or interacts with it in some manner whereas the solute or solutes present do not. Since the solvent differs in concentration on the two sides of the membrane, there will be a continuous solution of the solvent into the membrane from the more dilute side and a subsequent dissolving out of the solvent on the solution side, where the water is less concentrated in the solution. Of course, it may be that the solute could pass through the membrane in the same manner. Further mention will be made of this possibility later in the chapter.

The movement of water through the membrane in most cases, however, can best be explained by the *vapor-pressure theory* of osmosis. It may be assumed that the membrane is made up of many tiny capillaries too small to allow passage of the liquid solvent. Hence, these capillaries act as gas spaces separating the liquid phases. When the spaces are saturated with vapor with respect to the pure solvent, or the solution of lower concentration, they are supersaturated with respect to the other liquid phase, and distillation will take place through the membrane from the more dilute to the more concentrated solution. The effect of the hydrostatic pressure in Figure 7-1 is to increase the vapor pressure of the solution to a value equal to that of the pure solvent and according to our theory flow will stop due to the equalization of the pressures.

The *molecular sieve theory* is the oldest of the theories used to explain membrane permeability. It makes the very simple and naive assumption that the solvent molecules are small enough to pass through pores in the membrane while the solute particles are too large to pass through. This explanation has been discarded except for a very few rather isolated situations. It can apply where the solute particles may be one of the so-called giant molecules or the solute particles are of colloidal size. This theory, however, is inadequate to explain most cases of osmosis.

THE CALCULATION OF OSMOTIC PRESSURE

7e. The Equation for Osmotic Pressure. We may obtain equations for the calculation of osmotic pressure either by means of experimental studies or through a thermodynamic derivation. The thermodynamic derivation involves the use of calculus, and the student is referred to more advanced texts in physical chemistry for the derivation. The equation so obtained has the following form

$$PV_1 = RT \ln \frac{p^{\circ}}{p} \tag{7-1}$$

wherein P is the osmotic pressure. V_1 is the volume of one mole of solvent in the pure state, and p and p° are the vapor pressures, respectively, of the solution and the pure solvent.

Experimental studies of osmotic pressure bring out certain aspects of the relationship of this magnitude to the temperature and the concentration of the solute. In many solutions it is found that the osmotic pressure is directly proportional to the concentration of the solute and the absolute temperature. This proportionality may be expressed mathematically as follows:

$$PV = nRT \qquad P = \left(\frac{n}{V}\right)RT = MRT \tag{7-2}$$

wherein V is the total volume of the solution, n is the number of moles of solute, and M is the molarity. R is the gas constant. The usefulness of this equation may be extended over a wider range of concentration if molality, m, is used in place of molarity. The equation then becomes:

$$P = mRT \tag{7-3}$$

The above equations, established experimentally, follow from Equation

7-1 upon the application of certain assumptions. The ratio of the two vapor pressures may be replaced by the mole fraction of the solvent (Raoult's law). The resulting term, ln N_1 may be expanded into a series and all but the first term of the series dropped out. This is justified if the solution is sufficiently dilute. One further assumption, that the moles of solute are insignificantly small in relation to the moles of solvent in the mole fraction expression, leads to Equation 7-2. Example 7-1 illustrates the use of Equation 7-3 in the calculation of osmotic pressure.

Example 7-1. Calculate the osmotic pressure at 20°C of a solution prepared by dissolving 6.00 grams of urea (molecular weight, 60) in 2.00 liters of water.

$$P = \frac{(6.00/60) \text{ mole} \times 0.082 \text{ liter-atm/mole/degree} \times 293°}{2.00 \text{ liters}}$$

$$= 1.20 \text{ atm}$$

Equation 7-2 illustrates the fact that osmotic pressure is a colligative property of solutions, since its magnitude depends on the concentration of the solute particles and not on their individual natures.

7f. The Magnitude of Osmotic Pressures. In Example 7-1 it was shown that the osmotic pressure of a $0.05M$ solution at 20°C was 1.20 atm. If this solution were placed in an apparatus such as that shown in Figure 7-1 with a membrane impermeable to the solute, the hydrostatic pressure in the column would correspond to 1.20 atm under equilibrium conditions. In other words, this solution under the proper set of conditions would be able to hold up a column of mercury 91.2 cm in height (1.2 × 76 cm). If the column were water instead of mercury, it would be 1240 cm high, since mercury is 13.6 times as dense as water. This height is approximately 41 ft. In a molar solution the height would be 20 times as high. In body and plant fluids, the concentrations are such that osmotic pressures of very large magnitude are found. For example, in certain leaves osmotic pressures of 20 atm are often observed. One must, however, always bear in mind that, for osmosis to take place, there must be a semipermeable membrane with a difference in concentrations of solutes on each side. Biological systems are very complex and osmotic phenomena must be interpreted in the light of a number of complicating factors beyond the scope of this chapter.

THE EXPERIMENTAL DETERMINATION OF OSMOTIC PRESSURE

7g. Indirect Determination. Cryoscopic Method. In Chapter 6 it was shown that the lowering of the freezing point is directly proportional to the molality of the solution. This is expressed mathematically as

$$\Delta T_f = mK_f$$

wherein K_f is the molal freezing point constant.

Since molality and molarity are closely equal in value, as explained in 7e, M can be expressed as

$$M = \frac{\Delta T_f}{K_f} \tag{7-4}$$

If this relationship for M is introduced into Equation 7-2, the following is obtained:

$$P = \frac{\Delta T_f}{K_f} RT \tag{7-5}$$

To use this equation for the calculation of osmotic pressure, it is necessary only to determine the freezing point lowering of the solution. Such a measurement is usually easy to perform, even on very small quantities of solution. The use of this equation is illustrated in Example 7-2.

Example 7-2. A certain biological solution has a freezing point of $-0.200°C$. What is its calculated osmotic pressure at 25°C?

$$P = \frac{0.200°}{1.86°} \text{ moles/liter}$$

$$\times \ 0.082 \text{ liter-atm/mole/degree}$$

$$\times \ 298°$$

$$= 2.63 \text{ atm}$$

7h. Direct Determination. Method of Pfeffer. As has been noted, osmotic pressure can be determined by measuring the maximum height to which a column of water or other liquid is raised by the process of osmosis. This was the method employed by the botanist Pfeffer in 1887. His apparatus is shown in Figure 7-2. Cupric ferrocyanide is used for the semipermeable membrane, but because of its mechanical weakness, it is precipitated in the pores of a porous cup. This is done by filling the cup with a solution of potassium ferrocyanide and then immersing it in a solution of cupric sulfate. The membrane forms as the two solutions meet in the walls of the cup. The solution whose osmotic pressure is to be measured is placed in the cup and connected with the U-tube manometer.

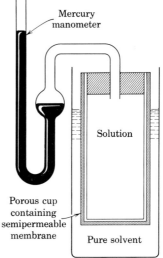

Figure 7-2. Apparatus of Pfeffer.

This is filled with mercury instead of solution to reduce the length of the column. Osmotic flow into the solution causes the mercury column to rise in the manometer until the hydrostatic pressure is sufficient to stop further flow. The osmotic pressure at this point is equal in magnitude to the hydrostatic pressure.

A modification of this method consists in determining the pressure that must be placed on the solution side of the membrane in order to prevent flow through the membrane. This variation of the procedure would give the osmotic pressure of the original solution.

SOME BIOLOGICAL ASPECTS OF OSMOSIS AND OSMOTIC PRESSURE

7i. Osmotic Phenomena in Plant Cells. Plant cells consist of a cell wall lined with a layer of protoplasm, which in turn encloses a vacuole filled with cell sap. The protoplasm is enclosed in the plasma membrane and the vacuolear membrane separates the plasma from the cell sap in the vacuole. The cell walls of most plants appear to be quite freely permeable to water and to most substances dissolved in the water. On the other hand, the cytoplasmic membranes possess the property of differential permeability. Water and certain solutes pass through them much more readily than other solutes. A typical cell in what is termed a state of normal turgor is shown in Figure 7-3(*a*). Here the cytoplasm is held against the cell wall by what is termed the turgor pressure of the cell

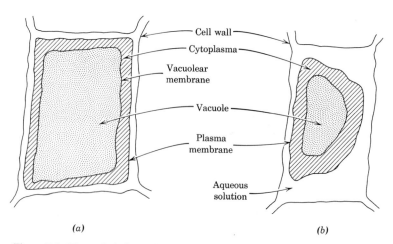

(*a*)   (*b*)

Figure 7-3. Plasmolysis in a plant cell: (*a*) normal turgor; (*b*) condition after plasmolysis.

sap in the vacuole. Now if this cell is immersed in a solution more concentrated than the cell sap in solutes to which the cell membranes are not permeable, water will diffuse from the sap into the surrounding solution. Shrinkage of the vacuole as shown in Figure 7-3(*b*) results. The cell wall remains essentially unchanged. The volume of the plasma undergoes little change, but the contraction of the vacuole results in a contraction of the plasma membranes. The surrounding solution is said to be *hypertonic* with respect to the cell sap. The diffusion of water into a hypertonic solution and the subsequent shrinkage of the cytoplasm from the cell wall is called *plasmolysis*. Now, if the plasmolyzed cell is immersed in a solution of lower concentration of solutes than the cell sap, diffusion of water will take place from the surrounding solution into the cell sap. This will tend to restore the original condition shown in 7-3(*a*). Such a solution is said to be *hypotonic* to the cell sap. If no diffusion takes place, the cell sap and the solution are said to be *isotonic*. It should be carefully noted that even if two solutions are isotonic their osmotic pressures, as they are usually considered, are not necessarily the same. The osmotic pressure of the solution is calculated from the *total* concentration of solute or solutes and exists whether a membrane is present or not. The *tonicity*, on the other hand, is determined by the concentration of those solutes that cannot pass through the membrane. Substances to which the membrane is permeable do not cause osmosis through cell membranes.

Osmotic effects in plant cells vary considerably in different plants and in many cases show wide variation in the same plant under different external conditions. This is particularly true of such low forms of plant life as bacteria and molds. Many can grow in salt solutions over a wide range of concentration because the concentration of the solutes in the cell sap is increased by diffusion of the salts through the cell membranes. The use of salts and sugars in preserving foods, however, is based on the fact that they produce a very hypertonic external solution, which causes plasmolysis of the cells of decay-producing bacteria and fungi. One further complicating factor should be noted. Suppose we have a situation in which we have pure water on one side of a membrane and a solution on the other side. It is possible that this solute may pass through the membrane by a membrane solution process. But if this process is very slow, there may be at first an appreciable flow of solvent in the solution. Thus, osmosis results. In course of time, however, the solute will divide itself between the solutions on the two sides of the membrane and further flow will stop. This situation results in osmotic phenomena in spite of the fact that the membrane is not impermeable to the solute.

As previously stated, osmotic phenomena in biological systems are quite complex and are very important in many phases of plant physiology.

For example, turgor pressure is important in plant cells in supporting nonwoody tissues and in the prevention of wilting. It is important in cell enlargement, which plays a vital role in plant growth.

7j. Osmotic Phenomena in the Blood. The blood consists of a fluid medium known as plasma in which float the white and red corpuscles. The latter are typical cells covered by a semipermeable membrane but lacking the wall characteristic of plant cells. The plasma contains, among other things, various sugars, proteins, and certain salts. Cryoscopic or freezing point measurements show that human plasma has an average osmotic pressure equal to 7.65 atm at 37°C, the normal body temperature. The plasma is usually isotonic or slightly hypotonic with the corpuscles. Should the plasma become sufficiently hypotonic, the corpuscles become distended to such an extent that the cell contents can escape, and the resulting loss of the red hemoglobin is termed *hemolysis*. On the other hand, a hypertonic condition could result in a shrinkage of the corpuscles.

The regulation of the osmotic pressure of the blood is effected largely by the action of the kidneys, which excrete more or less concentrated urine, depending on the composition of the blood, and on the liver, which regulates the concentrations of sugars in the blood. Hence marked variations in the osmotic pressure of the blood may indicate impaired kidney and liver functions.

Proper care must be used in blood transfusions and in intravenous injections to see that the plasma or other solution produces proper tonicity in the blood. For example, in the feeding of patients by glucose injections, a physiological salt solution is used that is adjusted to the tonic requirements of the blood.

REFERENCES

Bull, *Physical Biochemistry*, John Wiley and Sons, New York, 1951, Chapter 12.

Daniels and Alberty, *Physical Chemistry*, John Wiley and Sons, New York, 1961, Chapter 8.

Maron and Prutton, *Principles of Physical Chemistry*, The Macmillan Co., New York, 1958, Chapter 6.

Moore, *Physical Chemistry*, Prentice-Hall, Englewood Cliffs, New Jersey, 1962, Chapter 5.

Sheehan, *Physical Chemistry*, Allyn and Bacon, Boston, 1961, Chapter 5.

Daniels, Williams, Bender, Alberty, and Cornwell, *Experimental Physical Chemistry*, McGraw-Hill Book Co., New York, 1962, Chapters 13 and 21.

REVIEW QUESTIONS

1. Discuss the process of osmotic flow. What conditions are necessary for osmotic flow? What is meant by a *semipermeable membrane*?

2. Give a concise statement of the phenomenon of osmosis.

3. What is meant by *hydrostatic pressure*? How can hydrostatic pressure be used to determine the osmotic pressure of a given solution?

4. Discuss the relationship of the vapor pressures of the solutions on the two sides of a semipermeable membrane to the osmotic pressures in the two solutions.

5. What determines the final level to which a solution rises in a situation such as that shown in Figure 7-1(*a*) when the beaker contains pure solvent, and (*b*) when the beaker contains a solution of the solute of lower concentration than the solution in the thistle tube?

6. Discuss the membrane solution theory and the molecular sieve theory of osmotic flow.

7. Discuss the vapor pressure theory of osmosis. What is the effect of external pressure on vapor pressure? What role does this effect play in osmotic phenomena?

8. Give the mathematical relationship usually used in calculations involving osmotic pressure. Give the more exact expression for osmotic pressure. Using the simpler relationship, show how osmotic pressure changes with (*a*) change in concentration, and (*b*) change in temperature.

9. Discuss the direct determination of osmotic pressure by the method of Pfeffer.

10. Discuss the determination of osmotic pressure by the cryoscopic method.

11. Define the terms *tonicity*, *hypertonic*, *isotonic*, *hypotonic*, and *plasmolysis*.

12. If two solutions have the same osmotic pressure, are they necessarily isotonic? Explain.

PROBLEMS

I

1. What is the osmotic pressure, at 25°C, in a solution containing 30 grams of urea in 1800 ml of water? Assuming no change in volume, what would be the osmotic pressure at 50°C, 75°C, and 90°C? Plot these values against the temperature and note how the osmotic pressure for a given solution changes with change in temperature.

2. Using water as a solvent, calculate the molality of a solution which has an osmotic pressure of 1000 mm of Hg at 27°C. Using the same solution, what would be the osmotic pressure at 50°C?

3. A certain aqueous solution of a nonvolatile solute has an osmotic pressure of 0.80 atm at 27°C. What would be its freezing point, boiling point, and vapor pressure at 20°C?

4. If the solute in Problem I-3 was sucrose, how many molecules would be present in 1 ml of the solution at 27°C? How many molecules would be present in 1 ml if the solute is glucose?

5. How much water must be added to 40 grams of a solute whose molecular weight is 120 if an osmotic pressure of 1.2 atm is to be established at 35°C? How much water must be added if the same osmotic pressure is to be established at 5°C?

6. How many molecules of urea must be added to 10 ml of water at 10°C if an osmotic pressure of 0.8 atm is to be established?

7. A solution consists of 10 grams of glucose, 10 grams of sucrose, and 20 grams of urea in 3000 ml of water. What would be its osmotic pressure at 15°C? How many grams of sucrose would have to be removed in order to reduce the osmotic pressure by 5 per cent?

8. Calculate the freezing point of blood plasma from the fact that its osmotic pressure is 7.65 atm at 37°C.

9. The freezing point of an aqueous solution is −0.750°C. What is its osmotic pressure at 20°C?

10. Given a solution containing 0.50 per cent by weight of cane sugar in water. How many grams of glucose must be added to 200 grams of this solution in order to obtain an osmotic pressure equal to that of blood. See Problem I-8.

II

1. What is the osmotic pressure and vapor pressure, both at 20°C, of an aqueous solution of 20 grams of urea in 900 ml of water? What is the freezing point of the solution?

2. You plan to add glucose to the solution in II-1 until the osmotic pressure is raised to 12 atm at 20°C. How many grams would have to be added?

3. What is the osmotic pressure at 27°C of a solution containing 3×10^{20} molecules of a nonvolatile solute in 10 ml of water?

4. An aqueous solution has an osmotic pressure of 1.2 atm at 27°C. What is its freezing point? What is its vapor pressure at 20°C? What is its molality? If the solute is sucrose, how many grams would have to be added to 1800 ml of water to produce this solution?

5. The freezing point of an aqueous solution is −0.120°C. Calculate its osmotic pressure at the freezing point and at 17°C? How many moles of a solute would have to be added to 200 ml of this solution in order to triple the osmotic pressure?

6. How much water would have to be added to 3.01×10^{22} molecules of sugar in order to obtain a solution whose osmotic pressure is the same as that of a $0.1M$ aqueous solution?

7. How many molecules of solute would have to be added to 1 ml of water in order to produce an osmotic pressure equal to that of blood plasma? See Problem I-6.

8. Given 3 liters of a solution of dextrose in water. Its osmotic pressure is 1.5 atm at 27°C. How much water would have to be removed from this solution for the osmotic pressure to increase to 2 atm at this temperature?

9. What weight of urea would have to be added to 200 ml of a 0.10 per cent by weight of cane sugar in water in order for the resulting solution to have the same osmotic pressure as blood? See Problem I-6.

10. Calculate the osmotic pressure at 25°C of an aqueous solution containing 30 grams of urea, 3.01×10^{22} molecules of sucrose, and 0.01 mole of a non-volatile solute whose molecular weight is 80 in 1800 ml of water.

EIGHT

Solutions III:
Solutions of Electrolytes

The purpose of this chapter is to develop the modern concept of electrolytic solutions. This development includes a historical discussion of the Arrhenius theory. The characteristics of compounds producing ions in solution, the mechanisms by which these ions are produced, the effects of interionic attraction, and the role of the solvent in ionization are discussed and the postulates of the modern ionic theory are summarized. Finally, the Lowry-Brønsted acid-base theory is discussed from a qualitative standpoint.

THE ROLE OF THE ARRHENIUS THEORY IN THE STUDY OF ELECTROLYTIC SOLUTIONS

8a. The Historical Background of the Arrhenius Theory. The general postulates of the *Arrhenius theory of electrolytic dissociation* are so much a part of the modern theory of electrolytic solutions that it is difficult to realize that this theory was not generally accepted until late in the nineteenth century, after it was proposed by the Swedish chemist, Svante Arrhenius, in 1887. The theory was remarkably successful in coordinating seemingly unrelated facts about aqueous solutions of acids, bases, and salts—those compounds classified as *electrolytes* because their aqueous solutions conduct electricity. Before that time, investigators in three independent fields of chemical endeavor had established that aqueous solutions of acids, bases, and salts (1) show anomalous colligative properties, (2) conduct an electric current, and (3) tend to show rapid chemical reactions as compared with solutions of nonelectrolytes. Arrhenius correlated the facts from each of these three fields to form the basis of his electrolytic dissociation theory.

The conclusions reached by Arrhenius may be understood by considering the facts established in three fields of chemical endeavor at the time the theory was developed. *First,* solutions of electrolytes show anomalous colligative properties. It was shown in Chapters 6 and 7 that a given molecular concentration of a nonelectrolyte produces the same effect on the vapor pressure, osmotic pressure, freezing point, and boiling point of a given solvent as the same concentration of any other non-electrolyte. Thus, colligative properties depend solely on the number of solute particles associated with a given quantity of solvent. Solutions of electrolytes, however, have a greater effect on colligative properties than the molecular concentration would indicate. (Sodium or potassium chloride in low concentrations tends to produce twice the effect, and calcium chloride, three times the effect, that their molecular concentration demands.) Hence these solutions must yield two or three particles, respectively, for each "molecule" that is dissolved.

Second, electrolytes in aqueous solutions or in the molten state conduct electric current, whereas nonelectrolytes are virtual nonconductors.) Chemical reaction at the electrodes always accompanies conductance by electrolytic solutions. Nicholson and Carlisle in 1800 demonstrated the decomposition of water by electric current, and Davy prepared sodium and potassium in the pure state in 1807 by the electrolysis of their fused hydroxides. In 1833 Faraday announced his famous laws concerning the amounts of products produced at the *electrodes,* the locations at which current enters and leaves the solution. The concept at this time was that the current split the molecule into charged particles called *ions.* Those carrying a negative charge were termed *anions,* and those carrying a positive charge were called *cations.* The movement of these ions effected the passage of current through the solution. The electrode to which the anions moved was called the *anode,* and that to which the cations moved was termed the *cathode.* The term *electrolyte* was first used at this time to designate any substance whose aqueous solution conducted current. The process of conducting current, together with the resulting reactions that take place at the electrodes, was termed *electrolysis.* These terms had, in fact, acquired their present significance at least thirty years before the work of Arrhenius. The mechanism of conductance in solutions of electrolytes will be discussed in detail in Chapter 12.

Third, chemical reactions between electrolytes take place rapidly, in general, compared with reactions between nonelectrolytes. Furthermore, many electrolytes in solution show reactions that appear to be characteristic of *parts* of the molecule rather than that of the molecule as a whole. Recall that a solution of any silver salt reacts rapidly with a solution of any soluble chloride to produce a precipitate of silver chloride. Also, solutions of acids all have an acid taste and show typical color reactions with indicators. Likewise, all hydroxide bases show typical color reactions with indicators and possess a bitter taste. Solutions of certain salts may be mixed with no evidence of a chemical reaction. On evaporation, however, all the possible salts may be obtained. Thus evaporation of a mixture of sodium chloride and potassium sulfate yields sodium sulfate and potassium chloride along with the two salts originally used. It appears, therefore, that each of the two original substances furnished two parts on solution, and evaporation of the solvent produces salts of all possible combinations of the parts.

Arrhenius saw clearly that he could explain the facts from all these fields of investigation if he assumed that molecules of electrolytes split into charged particles immediately on solution and not, as was previously supposed, only under the influence of the electric current. Thus there would be present in any solution of an electrolyte the particles necessary to explain anomalous colligative properties, to conduct the current, and to explain the typical chemical properties of electrolytes.

8b. The Arrhenius Theory of Electrolytic Dissociation. The main points of the Arrhenius theory follow. Electrolytes, when dissolved in water, partially split up into charged particles called ions. Each ion carries one or more electric charges, and the charge carried by an ion is equal to the valence on the ion. The total number of positive charges on the cations is equal to the total number of negative charges on the anions. The dissociation or ionization of an electrolyte is a reversible chemical reaction, and the equilibrium position is characteristic of a given electrolyte and its concentration in the aqueous solution. Hence an electrolytic solution consists of cations, anions, and undissociated molecules, and the more dilute the solution, the greater is considered to be the degree or extent of dissociation. Dissociation becomes complete only in infinitely dilute solutions. The ions are separate solute particles, each with its own specific chemical and physical properties and each able to effect changes in colligative properties of solutions independently of other ions and molecules present. In certain types of compounds, polyprotic acids, for example, ionization takes place in successive steps.

8c. Facts Explained by the Arrhenius Theory. Among the facts explained in a satisfactory manner by the Arrhenius theory are the following:

1. Why electrolytes conduct electric current and why nonelectrolytes do not. Since *charged* particles are present in electrolytic solutions, they would migrate to the proper electrode under the influence of an electrical potential, there to give up their charge. Thus the circuit is complete and chemical reaction takes place during the discharge process. Nonelectrolytes, however, do not dissociate, and the neutral molecule is not attracted to either electrode.

2. Why an electrolyte causes greater changes in the vapor pressure, boiling point, freezing point, and osmotic pressure of a solvent than an equimolar concentration of a nondissociated solute. In a highly dissociated solute, such as NaCl or $CaCl_2$, the effect would be expected to be nearly two or three times the corresponding effect of a nondissociated solute.

3. Why solutions of electrolytes with a common ion show common chemical properties. For example, all hydroxide bases yield the OH^- ion, and this ion accounts for the bitter taste and the typical color reactions with indicators.

4. Why, when solutions of salts such as NaCl and K_2SO_4 are mixed, all four possible salts are obtained upon evaporation of the water.

8d. Limitations of the Arrhenius Theory. Certain inadequacies in the Arrhenius theory were recognized early. The theory does not in any way explain the role of the solvent in ionization. It does not in any way explain the process of ionization, merely stating that such a process takes place. Since the theory assumes the independent existence and behavior of ions in solution, it does not take into account the possibility that the activity or effective concentration of the particles may be altered by attractive forces between positive and negative ions. Arrhenius did not explain the fact that molten substances such as sodium chloride and sodium hydroxide were excellent conductors and must therefore contain ions. He assumed that ionization took place only when these compounds were in aqueous solution. Other limitations became apparent as a result of the immense amount of work stimulated by the theory. The developments in the field of electrolytic solutions, however, have served to amplify and expand the fundamental ideas of the Arrhenius theory, and the modern ionic theory contains many of its features. Further developments in the field of electrolytic solutions and the modern ionic theory will be discussed later in this chapter.

THE DEVELOPMENT OF THE MODERN IONIC THEORY

8e. Electrovalent and Covalent Compounds. A consideration of compound formation from the standpoint of the electrical structure of the resulting substances is essential to a proper understanding of the development of the modern ionic theory. It will be recalled from general chemistry that many substances exist in the crystalline state solely in the form of ions. That this is true has been demonstrated by X-ray studies on crystal structure. Among such substances are (NaCl, KCl, Na_2SO_4, and KOH.) These substances are examples of compounds that are formed from

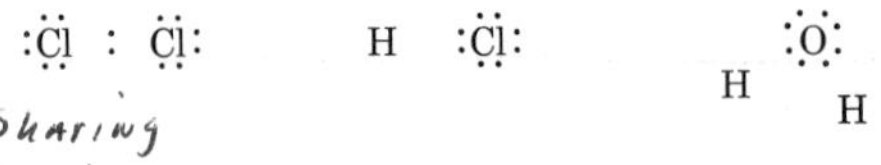

$$:\overset{..}{\underset{..}{Cl}} : \overset{..}{\underset{..}{Cl}}: \qquad H \ :\overset{..}{\underset{..}{Cl}}: \qquad \overset{..}{\underset{}{O}}:$$

Electron Sharing
Covalent Cmpds.

(a) Cl$_2$ (b) HCl   (c) H$_2$O

Figure 8-1.

the original elements by the *transfer* of electrons from one atom to another. Compounds formed in this way are termed *electrovalent compounds*. For example, in the formation of sodium chloride from sodium and chlorine, there is a complete transfer of an electron from the sodium atom to the chlorine atom. Hence, the sodium atom becomes positively charged, and the chlorine atom becomes negatively charged. The crystal of this substance is composed entirely of ions, and no molecule as such exists in the solid state. For example, in solid NaCl a sodium ion is not identified with any particular chloride ion but is shared with the six surrounding chloride ions.

Although many salts and bases are electrovalent, many other compounds, including the acids, are predominantly *covalent*. A *covalent compound* is one formed by a process of electron sharing. Three examples of electron sharing are shown in Figure 8-1. In the chlorine molecule the shared electrons are situated midway between the two chlorine atoms. In the case of HCl the shared pair are located nearer the chlorine atom than the hydrogen atom. In each water molecule we have two pairs of shared electrons, each pair nearer the oxygen atom than the hydrogen atom. The resulting water molecule is nonlinear. This has been established by X-ray studies and the determination of its dipole moment. This also agrees with the atomic orbital theory when applied to water. The sharing of electrons does not result in the formation of ions in the pure state, but it does result in many cases in the formation of *polar* molecules.

In covalent compounds the molecules as a whole are electrically neutral. In the chlorine molecule the shared pair are midway between the two chlorine atoms, and we say that this molecule is *nonpolar*. Placed in an electrical field, it would not be oriented in space. In HCl, however, the two shared electrons are nearer the chlorine atom than the hydrogen atom. This produces a condition of polarity, the chlorine part of the molecule being negative with respect to the hydrogen part. In any electric field the chlorine would be oriented to the positive plate and the hydrogen to the negative plate. In water, as stated above, the two pairs of shared electrons are nearer the oxygen atom than the hydrogen atoms and this, along with the fact that the molecule is nonlinear, causes the water molecule to be quite polar. This polarity plays a major part in the ability of water to support ionization. Polar molecules are termed *dipoles*, and the extent of the polarity is determined by the magnitude of the charges and the distance between the centers of the resultant negative and positive poles. The charge on the electrical centers multiplied by the distance between the centers is termed the *dipole moment* of the substance.

In addition to the strictly electrovalent and covalent compounds, there are others that are *semicovalent*. In these the electrons have shifted their position considerably toward one of the atoms but they are still more or less shared. Many of the compounds of mercury, arsenic, and platinum fall in this group.

8f. The Mechanism of Ionization. As pointed out in 8d, the Arrhenius theory does not offer any explanation for the mechanism of ionization. Modern theories, however, give a satisfactory explanation of this process.

It has been stated that no molecules as such exist in electrovalent compounds even in the crystalline state. The process of ionization in such substances is simply the separation of the ions already present. In sodium chloride and sodium hydroxide the process would take place in accordance with the following equations:

$$\underline{Na^+Cl^-} \rightarrow Na^+ + Cl^-$$

$$\underline{Na^+OH^-} \rightarrow Na^+ + OH^-$$

The underline indicates that these substances are in the solid state, and the charges indicate that in this state they exist completely in the form of ions. Thus solution and "ionization" are one and the same, the substance being completely ionized both in the solid state and in solution. In solution, however, water molecules may be attached more or less firmly to the ions through polar effects as water of hydration.

The ionization of a covalent compound involves a reaction with the solvent. Only acids will be considered in this presentation. The mechanism of the ionization of acids in water involves the transfer of a proton from the covalent acid molecule to a water molecule. This may be represented by the following examples:

$$HCl + H_2O \rightarrow H_3O^+ + Cl^-$$
$$HNO_3 + H_2O \rightarrow H_3O^+ + NO_3^-$$
$$HC_2H_3O_2 + H_2O \rightleftharpoons H_3O^+ + C_2H_3O_2^-$$
$$H_2SO_4 + H_2O \rightarrow H_3O^+ + HSO_4^-$$
$$HSO_4^- + H_2O \rightleftharpoons H_3O^+ + SO_4^{2-}$$

The single arrows indicate that ionization is complete over a wide range of concentrations. The double arrows indicate incomplete ionization, even in dilute solutions. A short arrow pointing towards the ions and a long arrow in the opposite direction indicate very slight ionization. Note that all acids, as shown above, form the characteristic H_3O^+ ion rather than the simple H^+ ion or proton. That H_3O^+ is the formula of the hydrogen ion can be substantiated by a number of independent observations. For example, X-ray analyses of the crystals of certain acids in the solid state have demonstrated the existence of the H_3O^+ group. Phenomena associated with the electrolysis of acid solutions can be explained on the basis of this structure for the hydrogen ion. In spite of the fact that H_3O^+ has been accepted as the formula, many textbooks still indicate this ion with the formula H^+. For the sake of simplicity, the same practice will be followed in this text. The symbol H^+ will generally be used to represent the hydrated ion except in cases where it is desirable to emphasize the role of the solvent.

The discussion of the mechanism of ionization has so far shown that electrovalent compounds exist entirely in the form of ions in solution. Certain of the covalent acids, however, also exist in a highly ionized state in solution. Such electrolytes that exist entirely, or to a very large extent, in the form of ions are termed *strong electrolytes*. On the other hand, electrolytes that are only slightly ionized are termed *weak electrolytes*. Most electrolytes fall into one or the other of these classes, although some are intermediate in their action.

8g. The Effect of Interionic Attraction. Activity. The original Arrhenius theory did not take into account the effect that the various ions would have on one another in solution. Considerations of electrostatics demand that oppositely charged ions attract each other. Yet the Arrhenius theory assumed that each ion acted independently of all the other ions in the solution. This obvious fault in the Arrhenius theory was immediately recognized and stimulated a vast amount of research bearing on the effects of interionic attraction.

Consider a very dilute solution of an electrovalent electrolyte such as sodium chloride. The ions are so far apart in such a solution that the attractive forces between oppositely charged ions are reduced to essentially zero. The ions would act independently of each other in this case, and the colligative and other effects would have values twice those for an undissociated solute of the same concentration. (In a $0.001m$ solution of a nonelectrolyte, the freezing point of the solution would be lowered $0.001 \times 1.86°$.) (But for a strong electrolyte of the same concentration forming two ions the value should be twice this, or $0.00372°$, and this is indeed the case) As the concentration is increased, however, the freezing-point change no longer is twice that of an undissociated solute. In other words, the ions have lost some of their ability to alter this particular colligative property of the solution. As the concentration is further increased, the departure becomes greater. This is due to the fact that with increasing concentration, and hence a lessening of the distances between the ions, the attractive forces become more and more appreciable and the ions lose part of their ability to affect the colligative properties. In other words, they have an *effective concentration* that is less than their *actual concentration*. This effective concentration is termed the *activity* of the ion. The *activity coefficient* is the ratio of the activity to the molality of the ion. It is represented by the Greek letter gamma (γ). The relationship among m, a, and γ is

$$\gamma = \frac{a}{m} \qquad (8\text{-}1)$$

The *activity coefficient* of an ion is the number by which the molality of the ion must be multiplied in order to obtain its activity. The experimentally

Table 8-1. Mean Activity Coefficients of the Ions of Certain Electrolytes at 25°C

m	0.00	0.01	0.05	0.10	0.50	1.00	1.50
NaCl	1.00	0.903	0.823	0.778	0.680	0.656	0.659
KCl	1.00	0.901	0.816	0.770	0.650	0.607	0.585
HCl	1.00	0.905	0.830	0.796	0.758	0.810	0.896

determined mean activity coefficients of the ions of a number of strong univalent electrolytes are given in Table 8-1. The values for the two ions of a given electrolyte at a certain concentration are not necessarily the same, but since the separate values cannot be obtained by any means now available, the mean values are employed. Note that the values pass through a minimum at concentrations around 1m. This is due to the fact that effects in addition to interionic attraction come into play. The presentation of these effects however, is beyond the scope of this discussion.

Example 8-1. Calculate the activity of the ions in a 0.50 m solution of sodium chloride at 25°C. Calculate the osmotic pressure of this solution at 25°C.

$$a_{Na^+} = a_{Cl^-} = 0.50 \times 0.680 = 0.340$$

Therefore, the total effective concentration of solute in such a solution would be 2 × 0.340 = 0.680, and this would be the value used in calculating any colligative property, such as the osmotic pressure.

$P \times 1$ liter $= 0.680$ mole $\times 0.0821$ liter-atm/mole/degree $\times 298$ degrees

$P = 16.63$ atm

The situation is more complex for electrolytes in which dissociation is not complete. Assume, for example, that a certain electrolyte that dissociates into two ions is 20 per cent ionized in 0.10m solution. The actual concentration of each ion would therefore be 0.02m, and the total ionic concentration would be 0.04m. But again interionic attraction forces usually come into play and result in an effective concentration, or activity, of the ions differing from the actual ionic concentration. Instead of employing an actual degree of dissociation in combination with an activity coefficient, the two are often combined into what is termed the *apparent degree of ionization*, and this is used in the calculation of colligative magnitudes. Because this apparent degree of dissociation has no theoretical significance and little practical application, it will not be discussed further.

The concepts of activity and activity coefficient were developed by G. N. Lewis of the University of California. It was not, however, until Debye and Hückel proposed their *interionic attraction theory* in 1923 that a satisfactory explanation of the significance of the activity coefficient was obtained. This theory is so highly mathematical that it cannot be treated in this discussion. Some of its qualitative aspects, however, and the final mathematical relation for very dilute solutions are discussed.

Debye and Hückel obtained a relationship that enabled them to calculate the activity coefficient of an ion from fundamental considerations without resort to experimental data. To do this, they assumed that each ion in a solution of finite concentration is surrounded by an ion atmosphere which, on the average, contains more ions of the opposite charge than ions of the charge in question. This condition is brought about because of the attraction existing between ions of unlike charge and the repulsion between ions of like charge. This results in an ionic distribution in the solution that is not a random one. Now, if the solution is diluted, the ions have greater distances between them, the attractive forces are decreased, and there is at least a partial breakdown of the ion atmosphere. [With sufficient dilution, attractive forces become nil and the ion distribution becomes completely random] In order to effect this breakdown of the ion atmosphere with dilution, work must be done to overcome the attractive forces. Debye and Hückel termed this work *the energy of dilution*, and they computed its magnitude by a series of complicated mathematical operations. For the simplest type of solution at low concentrations the final mathematical relationship obtained is

$$\log \gamma = -KZ^2\sqrt{\mu} \tag{8-2}$$

In this formula γ is the activity coefficient of the ion under consideration, Z is the valence of the ion without regard to sign. K is a constant which, besides the temperature and the dielectric constant of the solution, contains several other universal constants, and the Greek letter mu (μ) is the ionic strength of the solution. The latter is defined as follows:

$$\left(\mu = \Sigma\tfrac{1}{2}cZ^2 \right) \tag{8-3}$$

in which Σ indicates a summation of the term, $\tfrac{1}{2}cZ^2$, for each kind of ion present in the solution, c being the molarity of the ion and Z its valence. An example will best illustrate its application.

Example 8-2. (a) Calculate the ionic strength of a solution that is $0.001\,M$ in sodium chloride and $0.002M$ in barium chloride. (b) Calculate the activities of the sodium and barium ions in this solution at $25°C$. At this temperature K in Equation 8-2 has a value of 0.509.

(a) The value of $\tfrac{1}{2}cZ^2$ must be computed for each ion in the solution.

Sodium ion	$\tfrac{1}{2} \times 0.001 \times 1^2 = 0.0005$
Chloride ion from NaCl	$\tfrac{1}{2} \times 0.001 \times 1^2 = 0.0005$
Chloride ion from BaCl$_2$	$\tfrac{1}{2} \times 0.004 \times 1^2 = 0.002$
Barium ion	$\tfrac{1}{2} \times 0.002 \times 2^2 = 0.004$
	Ionic strength $= 0.007$

(b) For the sodium ion

$$\log \gamma_{Na^+} = -0.509 \times 1^2 \times \sqrt{0.007}$$
$$\gamma_{Na^+} = 0.91$$

and

$$a_{Na^+} = 0.91 \times 0.001 = 0.0009\,M$$

For the barium ion

$$\log \gamma_{Ba^{2+}} = -0.509 \times 2^2 \times \sqrt{0.007}$$
$$\gamma_{Ba^{2+}} = 0.68$$

and

$$a_{Ba^{2+}} = 0.68 \times 0.002 = 0.0014M$$

In the above, molality and molarity were considered as being equal. Equation 8-2 contains no term having to do with the individual nature of the ion except its valence. It therefore enables us to calculate the value of γ for any ion solely in terms of the number and valences for all ions present in the solution. As a result, the activity coefficient of an ion is constant as long as the ionic strength is constant. In other words, the concentration of an ion can be altered, but the activity coefficient can be kept constant by regulating the ionic strength. Of course, constancy of the activity coefficient does not result in constancy of activity, since activity is the product of the concentration of the ion and its activity coefficient. A check of Equation 8-2 can be obtained by comparing the experimentally determined activity coefficients of Table 8-1 with the calculated values. Agreement is very good at the lower concentrations.

→ **8h. The Role of the Solvent in Ionization.** Although not accounted for in the Arrhenius theory, the solvent plays a very important part in the process of ionization. One important role was discussed in connection with the ionization of acids. It will be recalled that the ionization process was one involving direct reaction of the acid with water molecules and the resulting formation of the hydrogen ion. Also, in the case of semicovalent salts, the ionization process is usually one in which reaction with water takes place with the subsequent formation of hydrated ions.

Another important role of the solvent is to weaken the electrostatic forces existing between the ions and hence to reduce the effect of interionic attraction. Without this effect it would be expected that the ions of opposite charge would attract each other enough to produce undissociated molecules. The solvent plays a vital role in diminishing the magnitude of the attraction. This is done in several ways. Water, being a polar compound, is attracted to the ions, forming thereby an atmosphere of oriented water molecules around the ions. This tends to keep the centers of the ions apart and helps keep interionic attraction forces from coming into full play. Again, the polar nature of the water diminishes the effect of attraction through the operation of that property of the solvent known as the dielectric constant. This is illustrated in Equation 8-4, which gives the expression for the force existing between two charged bodies. In this equation, F is the force operating, q and q' are the charges on the bodies, r is the distance between their centers, and D is a constant characteristic of the medium between the bodies. This is the dielectric constant referred to above.

$$F = \frac{q \times q'}{D \times r^2} \tag{8-4}$$

The formula shows that the greater the value of the dielectric constant, the smaller will be the force acting between the two bodies. Hence solvents with high dielectric constants should be better supporters of ionization than those with low dielectric constants, and this proves to be the case. Table 8-2 gives the values for certain solvents with a statement of the ionizing powers of each.

8i. The Postulates of the Modern Ionic Theory. The postulates of the original electrolytic dissociation theory of Arrhenius, when incorporated with and modified by the modern developments in the field of electrolytic solutions, are known as the *modern ionic theory*. Its postulates are as follows:

1. Certain compounds, known as electrolytes, in an ionizing solvent,

yield charged particles called ions, one carrying a negative charge and one a positive charge. The number of charges on the ion, representing the number of electrons lost or gained by the atom or group of atoms, is identical with the valence of the ions. The sum of the negative charges equals the sum of the positive charges.

2. The ions are produced mainly in one of two ways: (*a*) in electrovalent compounds by a simple separation of the ions already existing as such in the crystalline state, or (*b*) by interaction of the compound with water or any ionizing solvent. In most strong electrolytes, except in the more concentrated solutions, the ionization is complete. In weak electrolytes, the ionization is incomplete in all but the most dilute of solutions.

Table 8-2. The Dielectric Constant and Ionizing Power of Certain Solvents at 25°C

Solvent	Dielectric Constant	Ionizing Power
Dioxane	2	Extremely small
Ethanol	24	Moderately strong
Formic acid	62	Strong
Water	79	Very strong

3. When an electric current is passed through a solution of an electrolyte, the positively charged cations move toward the cathode and the negatively charged anions move toward the anode. The movement of these ions constitutes the electric current in the solution. By ionic reactions at the two electrodes, electrons are given up to the external circuit at the anode and received from the external circuit at the cathode.

4. The ions act like uncharged solute molecules in depressing the freezing point, raising the boiling point, lowering the vapor pressure, and establishing osmotic pressure in solutions. Thus, an electrolyte yielding two ions from each molecule will have about twice the effect of an unionized molecule, and one yielding three ions will have about three times the effect. Ions, however, do not act independently except in very dilute solution, and their effect on the colligative properties is reduced in most solutions by the operation of interionic forces.

5. The properties of solutions of electrolytes are essentially the properties of the individual ions. Chlorides are characterized by the properties of the chloride ion, and acids, by the properties of the hydrogen ion. The reactions of electrolytes are essentially reactions between ions.

The original Arrhenius theory is applicable in most respects to weak electrolytes. Weak electrolytes are partially ionized and exist mostly in molecular form. Of course, in strong electrolytes a degree of ionization does not exist, since the molecules are completely ionized. In solutions of strong electrolytes, however, we do have the formation of ion pairs if the concentration becomes sufficiently great.

THE PROTON-TRANSFER THEORY OF ACIDS AND BASES

8j. The Lowry-Brønsted Theory. Until recent years chemists used the original concept of Arrhenius by defining those substances that produced hydrogen ions in solutions as acids and those substances that produced hydroxyl ions as bases. This has proved to be rather restricted and does not explain satisfactorily many of the phenomena of electrolytic solutions.

In 1923 T. M. Lowry and J. N. Brønsted proposed independently a concept of acids and bases that applies to nonaqueous solvents as well as water, and it has proved most useful in interpreting many phenomena associated with ionic equilibria. This is known as the *Lowry-Brønsted acid-base theory and states that an acid is any substance, molecular or ionic, capable of giving up a proton, whereas a base is any substance, molecular or ionic, capable of accepting a proton.* An acid and a base may be defined by the following equation:

$$Acid = base + proton (H^+)$$

Consider the process of the ionization of HCl.

$$HCl + H_2O \rightarrow H_3O^+ + Cl^-$$

The hydrogen chloride molecule donates a proton to the water. In this reaction, HCl is acting as an acid and water is acting as a base. In the reverse reaction, H_3O^+ can donate a proton and therefore is an acid, whereas the chloride ion can accept a proton and is, therefore, a base. Typical reactions illustrating proton transfers are given in Table 8-3. Note that each reaction involves two pairs of acids and bases. These are known as *conjugate pairs.* For example, HCl and H_2O are the conjugate pair to H_3O^+ and Cl^-. The strength of an acid or base depends upon how readily it gives up or accepts a proton. In Table 8-3 strong acids are located at the upper part of the first column, and strong bases are located at the bottom of the last column. Note that many of the acids and bases are ions, hence the inclusion in the definition of the theory that acids and bases can be either molecular or ionic. The strongest base is the OH^-, and sodium hydroxide, potassium hydroxide, etc., are bases only because they yield the base OH^-. They are therefore termed hydroxide bases to distinguish them from other bases, such as the S^{2-} ion, the CO_3^{2-} ion, and

NH_3, which are all examples of strong bases. Notice also that water can act as both an acid and a base.

In consulting Table 8-3 it should be remembered that the term *acid strength* is a relative one, depending on the substance that acts as a base. In the table given, the base is water, so these relative strengths apply to water only. If another solvent is used, the relative position of each acid or base may be completely altered.

Table 8-3. Relative Strengths of Acids and Bases

	Acid$_1$	+	Base$_1$	=	Acid$_2$	+	Base$_2$
	(Strong acids at top of column)				(Strong bases at bottom of column)		
	HCl	+	H_2O	=	H_3O^+	+	Cl^-
	HNO_3	+	H_2O	=	H_3O^+	+	NO_3^-
	H_2SO_4	+	H_2O	=	H_3O^+	+	HSO_4^-
	H_3PO_4	+	H_2O	=	H_3O^+	+	$H_2PO_4^-$
	HSO_4^-	+	H_2O	=	H_3O^+	+	SO_4^{2-}
	CH_3COOH	+	H_2O	=	H_3O^+	+	CH_3COO^-
	HSO_3^-	+	H_2O	=	H_3O^+	+	SO_3^{2-}
	H_2CO_3	+	H_2O	=	H_3O^+	+	HCO_3^-
	HCN	+	H_2O	=	H_3O^+	+	CN^-
	NH_4^+	+	H_2O	=	H_3O^+	+	NH_3
	HCO_3^-	+	H_2O	=	H_3O^+	+	CO_3^{2-}
	HPO_4^{2-}	+	H_2O	=	H_3O^+	+	PO_4^{3-}
	HS^-	+	H_2O	=	H_3O^+	+	S^{2-}
	H_2O	+	H_2O	=	H_3O^+	+	OH^-

The Lowry-Brønsted theory is actually a special case of a more general acid-base theory proposed by G.N. Lewis. In the *Lewis theory*, a base is defined as a substance that can furnish an electron pair, while an acid is considered to be a substance that can react with an electron pair. In the more restricted Lowry-Brønsted theory, the proton is always the substance attaching itself to an electron pair. Thus Lewis had extended the definition of an acid to many substances other than proton-donating ones. The Lewis theory is most helpful in interpreting many reactions and in explaining a large number of chemical phenomena.

REFERENCES

Bull, *Physical Chemistry*, John Wiley and Sons, New York, 1951, Chapter 4.

Daniels and Alberty, *Physical Chemistry*, John Wiley and Sons, New York, 1961, Chapter 15.

Maron and Prutton, *Principles of Physical Chemistry*, The Macmillan Co., New York, 1958, Chapters 6 and 16.

Moore, *Physical Chemistry*, Prentice-Hall, Englewood Cliffs, New Jersey, 1962, Chapter 9.
Sheehan, *Physical Chemistry*, Allyn and Bacon, Boston, 1961, Chapter 5.

REVIEW QUESTIONS

1. What three major fields of study led Arrhenius to propose his theory of ionization? Discuss these three fields.

2. Define each of the following terms: *ion, anion, cation, anode, cathode, electrode, electrolyte, electrolysis*.

3. Distinguish between *electrovalent, covalent*, and *semicovalent compounds*.

4. Give the postulates of the Arrhenius theory. What facts can be explained by the theory? What are the major defects of the theory?

5. Discuss the mechanism of ionization in (*a*) electrovalent substances and (*b*) covalent substances. Give some equations showing how several covalent substances form ions in aqueous solution.

6. Distinguish between strong and weak electrolytes. Compare two strong acids with two weak acids from the standpoint of the hydrogen-ion concentration in solutions of the same concentration.

7. Discuss the concept of activity. What is meant by the term *activity coefficient*? Discuss why the activity of an ion may be different from its concentration.

8. Compare the concept of the activity coefficient with the *apparent degree of dissociation*.

9. What general procedure did Debye and Hückel use in deriving the D-H equation?

10. What is the significance of the various terms in the Debye-Hückel equation? Show how the activity coefficient is independent of the concentration of the electrolyte except insofar as its concentration affects the ionic strength.

11. Discuss the significance of the ionic strength of a solution. Using various types of electrolytes, calculate the ionic strength of a number of solutions.

12. What is the role of the solvent in ionization? What is meant by the dielectric constant of a substance? What role does it play in the ionizing properties of a solvent?

13. What are polar molecules? What is meant by the dipole moment of a substance? Discuss the role that the polarity of the water molecule plays in the ionizing power of this substance.

14. Give the postulates of the modern ionic theory. Carefully point out how it differs from the Arrhenius theory and in what respects it is like the Arrhenius theory.

15. Discuss the Lowry-Brønsted theory of acids and bases. What is meant by a conjugate pair? In accordance with the Lowry-Brønsted theory, list a number of acids and bases in the order of their comparative strengths when water is the solvent.

16. Discuss the Lewis theory of acids and bases. Compare this theory with the Lowry-Brønsted theory.

PROBLEMS

I

1. Calculate the ionic strength of each of the following solutions:
   (a) $0.05M$ LiCl
   (b) $0.02M$ KNO$_3$ and $0.02M$ Ca(NO$_3$)$_2$
   (c) $0.128M$ Al(NO$_3$)$_3$
   (d) $0.122M$ K$_2$SO$_4$ and $0.122M$ MgSO$_4$

2. Using the Debye-Hückel equation, calculate the activity coefficients and the activities of the various ions in the various solutions given in Problem I-1.

3. Using Table 8-1, calculate the activity of the ions in each of the solutions listed for KCl and NaCl. Calculate the osmotic pressures of the solutions for $0.1M$ and $0.05M$ NaCl and KCl. $t = 25°C$.

4. Given a solution that is $0.012M$ in KCl. How many grams of sodium nitrate would have to be added to 800 ml of solution to increase the ionic strength to 0.040? If sodium sulfate were added to effect the change, how many grams of this salt would have to be added?

5. Calculate the activity of Na$^+$, SO$_4^{2-}$, and Cl$^-$ in a solution that is $0.04M$ in sodium sulfate and $0.02M$ in sodium chloride.

6. What is the ionic strength of 2 liters of solution containing 2 grams each of NaCl, MgCl$_2$, MgSO$_4$, and Mg(NO$_3$)$_2$?

II

1. From the values given in Table 8-1, calculate the activity of each of the ions in the various solutions of HCl. What would be the osmotic pressure of each of these solutions at 25°C?

2. Given a solution that is $0.12M$ in sodium sulfate and $0.08M$ in sodium chloride. Calculate the ionic strength of the solution and the activity coefficients and activities of the various ions present in the solution at 25°C. Calculate the osmotic pressure of the solution at this temperature.

3. A solution is $0.10M$ in potassium sulfate, $0.05M$ in hydrochloric acid, and $0.03M$ in magnesium nitrate. Calculate the activity coefficients and the activities of each of the ions present in the solution for a temperature of 25°C.

4. A solution is prepared by adding 1200 ml of a $0.006M$ sodium chloride solution to 1500 ml of a $0.005M$ calcium chloride solution. What is the resulting ionic strength?

5. Calculate the activity of each of the ions present at 25°C in a solution that is $0.075M$ in potassium sulfate and $0.06M$ in potassium chloride.

6. How many grams of (a) NaNO$_3$ and (b) CaCl$_2$ would have to be added to the solution in Problem II-5 in order to double the ionic strength?

NINE

Chemical Equilibrium

The purpose of this chapter is to discuss in a general way the significance and use of the equilibrium constant. A simplified derivation of the equilibrium constant expression from kinetic considerations is included. The ideas developed in this chapter furnish the foundation for the study of ionic equilibrium in Chapter 11.

DERIVATION OF THE EXPRESSION FOR THE EQUILIBRIUM CONSTANT

9a. The Concept of the Reversible Reaction. Detailed experimental studies show that most chemical reactions as usually carried out do not go to completion. That is, measurable quantities of all reactants are still present at the time when all apparent reaction has ceased. For example, if ethanol and acetic acid are mixed together, they react to yield ethyl acetate and water in accordance with the equation

$$CH_3COOH + C_2H_5OH \rightleftharpoons CH_3COOC_2H_5 + H_2O$$

No matter what relative quantities of acetic acid and ethanol are mixed, at the time all reaction has apparently ceased, some of each remains in the reaction mixture along with the products of the reaction. Experimental studies show further that, if ethyl acetate and water are mixed together, they react to form acetic acid and ethanol, but after reaction has apparently stopped, there still remain appreciable quantities of unreacted ester and water. Note that this reaction is the exact reverse of the ethanol-acetic acid reaction.

Experiments show that, if a gram-molecular weight of ethanol is mixed at about 100°C in a sealed glass tube with 1 mole of acetic acid, changes in concentrations cease when two thirds of a gram-molecular weight each of alcohol and acid have reacted to form a corresponding quantity of

150

ester and water, leaving one third of a mole each of unreacted acid and alcohol. This may be represented as follows:

Initial amounts:

$$1 \text{ mole} \qquad 1 \text{ mole} \qquad 0 \text{ mole} \qquad 0 \text{ mole}$$
$$CH_3COOH + C_2H_5OH \rightleftharpoons CH_3COOC_2H_5 + H_2O$$

Final amounts:

$$\tfrac{1}{3} \text{ mole} \qquad \tfrac{1}{3} \text{ mole} \qquad \tfrac{2}{3} \text{ mole} \qquad \tfrac{2}{3} \text{ mole}$$

When the above amounts are obtained, no further changes in the quantities of either reactants or products take place.

If the above procedure is reversed so that 1 mole each of ethyl acetate and water are mixed, reaction apparently ceases when one third of each reactant is transformed. This may be represented as follows:

Initial amounts:

$$1 \text{ mole} \qquad 1 \text{ mole} \qquad 0 \text{ mole} \qquad 0 \text{ mole}$$
$$CH_3COOC_2H_5 + H_2O \rightleftharpoons C_2H_5OH + CH_3COOH$$

Final amounts:

$$\tfrac{2}{3} \text{ mole} \qquad \tfrac{2}{3} \text{ mole} \qquad \tfrac{1}{3} \text{ mole} \qquad \tfrac{1}{3} \text{ mole}$$

Thus the reverse reaction proceeds until the composition of the mixture is *identical* with that obtained in the forward reaction, using, of course, the same amounts of reactants in each case. This type of reaction is termed a *reversible reaction.* Reversible reactions are characterized by the fact that, while reactants will form products through the operation of the forward reaction, the products can reform the reactants through the operation of the reverse reaction. In summarizing, it may be stated that *reversible reactions are reactions in which both the forward and the reverse reactions take place to a considerable extent.*

Instead of starting with acid and alcohol or with ester and water, if any three of these substances, or even all four, are mixed together in any proportion whatever, experimentation shows that a final definite set of equilibrium amounts will be obtained whose values depend solely on the relative starting amounts. In most reactions, the relative amounts at equilibrium will depend on the temperature as well as the starting concentrations. This condition in which all substances have reached a final value of concentration is spoken of as a *state of equilibrium.* No consideration is given here to the time necessary to establish this state of equilibrium.

The question may be raised as to whether or not all reaction has ceased when equilibrium is established. In the ester formation discussed above, reaction begins as soon as the acid and the alcohol are mixed. A study of the rate of formation of the ester shows that it is formed more rapidly at the start of the experiment when the acid and alcohol concentrations are highest. The rate then decreases with time and becomes zero at equilibrium. Although there is no further change in ester concentration at equilibrium, it does not follow that its formation has stopped because there is still an appreciable concentration of acid and alcohol capable of reacting with each other. Furthermore, ester and water molecules both being present, the reverse reaction will also be taking place. As a matter of fact, ester and water molecules would be expected to begin reacting as soon as an appreciable concentration of each is formed early in the experiment. (Therefore, the rate of the reverse reaction would be expected to increase with time, whereas the rate of the forward reaction decreases with time.) At equilibrium the two rates become equal. Reaction at that point does not stop; it simply takes place at the same rate in the forward and reverse directions. Hence the equilibrium condition is *dynamic* rather than *static*.

While the ester formation reaction has been used to develop the concept of the reversible reaction, similar reasoning may be used on any reaction. All chemical reactions are reversible in varying degrees, although some go so nearly to completion that they are regarded as complete.

9b. The Mathematical Derivation of the Expression for the Equilibrium Constant. Experimentation is one of the best means to demonstrate that there is a definite relationship between the concentrations of reactants and products at equilibrium. In such experiments various concentrations of reactants and products are allowed to come to equilibrium, and the various equilibrium mixtures are then analyzed. The analyses yield data from which the *equilibrium constant* can be calculated.

The equilibrium expression can also be derived by thermodynamic considerations using the concept of free energy. This procedure is by far the more rigorous method and involves no assumptions. It will be used in Chapter 10 to derive a general expression for free energy change in a chemical reaction, from which expression the equilibrium constant expression can be obtained.

A simpler but less rigorous derivation based on kinetic considerations follows. It is exact only if the mechanism of the reaction is exactly that ascribed to it by the chemical equation as written. If the equation is a summary of a number of steps, the constant so derived embraces the constants of all the steps. Whether or not the intermediate steps are correctly described, the final expression is correct and may be used with complete assurance.

The kinetic derivation makes use of the *mass action law*, first proposed by

Guldberg and Waage in 1854. According to this law, as originally stated, the speed of a chemical reaction is proportional to the product of the active masses of the reacting substances. A modern statement of this law is that *the speed of a chemical reaction is proportional to the product of the activities* *of each reacting substance raised to a power equal to the number of times the particular substance appears in the equation.*

In our treatment at this time we shall assume that the activities in a homogeneous system—wholly gaseous or liquid—are essentially equal to the molar concentrations.

The equilibrium constant expression for a reversible reaction is derived by applying the mass action law to a reaction at equilibrium. The ester formation reaction could be used for this purpose but, in order to make the derivation general for any reversible reaction, the following hypothetical reaction will be considered:

$$aA + bB + \cdots \leftrightharpoons lL + mM + \cdots$$

A and B represent molecules (or ions) of the reactants, and L and M represent molecules of the products. The small letters a, b, l, and m are the coefficients that show the number of times each molecule appears in the equation. For example, in the ester reaction a, b, l, and m are all equal to 1. According to the mass action law, the speed of the forward reaction is given by the following expression in which the brackets, [ ], stand for molar concentrations:

$$S_f \propto [A]^a[B]^b \cdots$$

Mathematically, a proportionality sign may be replaced by an equality if a constant is introduced. Thus

$$S_f = k[A]^a[B]^b \cdots \tag{9-1}$$

Likewise, the speed of the reverse reaction is

$$S_r \propto [L]^l[M]^m \cdots$$

and

$$S_r = k'[L]^l[M]^m \cdots \tag{9-2}$$

The two constants above, k and k', are termed *velocity constants* and are specific for each reaction. Their values depend upon the individual natures of the reacting substances (hence k does not equal k') and upon the temperature.

When the reversible reaction is at equilibrium, the speed of the forward reaction equals the speed of the reverse reaction. Hence

$$S_f = S_r$$

and

$$k[A]^a[B]^b \cdots = k'[L]^l[M]^m \cdots \tag{9-3}$$

By rearranging terms, Equation 9-3 becomes

$$K = \frac{k}{k'} = \frac{[L]^l[M]^m \cdots}{[A]^a[B]^b \cdots} \qquad (9\text{-}4)$$

In Equation 9-4 the ratio of the two velocity constants is replaced by a single constant K, known as the *equilibrium constant*. It is characteristic of a given reaction and changes value only with a change in temperature. Mathematically, the equilibrium constant expression demands that reaction take place until the concentrations of all reactants and products reach values which, when substituted in Equation 9-4, satisfy the value of K for the particular reaction. This is true whether a reaction is started by mixing pure A and B, or pure L and M, or any three, or all four of the reactants.

Since Equation 9-4 was obtained by the use of concentrations rather than activities, the expression is not a general one. Using activities in place of concentrations the equation becomes

$$\left(K = \frac{a_L{}^l a_M{}^m \cdots}{a_A{}^a a_B{}^b \cdots} \right) \qquad (9\text{-}5)$$

The method for expressing activity will vary with the physical state of the substance. In addition, we may look on activity as an "effective concentration." The activity concept is particularly important when dealing with ionic species, for in these instances interionic attraction can result in the activity having quite a different value from the actual concentration. The concept of activities will be discussed in further detail later in the chapter.

APPLICATIONS OF THE EQUILIBRIUM EXPRESSION

9c. Application to Equilibria in Liquid Systems. The most important applications of the equilibrium constant in biological phenomena are in connection with ionic equilibria. These applications are discussed in detail in Chapter 11. The discussion is confined at this time to several examples of nonionic equilibria.

The alcohol-acid-ester-water equilibrium, discussed in 9a, furnishes an excellent example of a reaction taking place entirely in one liquid phase. The technique consists of allowing various quantities of alcohol, acid, ester, and water to come to equilibrium in sealed tubes so that they may be heated to speed the time for equilibrium without loss of reactants or products. If the starting mixture is 3 moles each of acid and alcohol, it is found that 2 moles each of ester and water are formed at a temperature of about 100°C. In this particular reaction the concentrations found at equilibrium are essentially independent of temperature so that the conclusions drawn apply to a rather wide temperature range. According to the equation for the reaction, 1 mole each of alcohol and acid are needed to form a mole each of ester and water. Hence the concentrations of unreacted alcohol and acid must be $3 - 2 = 1$ mole of each. This is better shown by the equation:

Starting amounts:

$$3 \text{ moles} \quad 3 \text{ moles} \quad 0 \text{ mole} \quad 0 \text{ mole}$$
$$CH_3COOH + C_2H_5OH \leftrightharpoons CH_3COOC_2H_5 + H_2O$$

Equilibrium amounts (in moles):

$$3 - 2 = 1 \quad 3 - 2 = 1 \quad 2 \quad 2$$

The molar concentrations of each will be $1/V$, $1/V$, $2/V$, and $2/V$, respectively, for the acid, alcohol, ester, and water. V is the total volume of the solution in liters. The equilibrium constant at the temperature of the experiment is, therefore,

$$K = \frac{[\text{ester}][\text{water}]}{[\text{acid}][\text{alcohol}]} = \frac{2/V \times 2/V}{1/V \times 1/V} = 4$$

The volume terms cancel in this case because the number of molecules of reactants equals the number of molecules of products. Whenever this is true, the concentrations can be replaced by the number of moles.

It was stated earlier that, if the starting mixture consisted of 1 mole each of acid and alcohol, two thirds of a mole each of ester and water were formed, leaving in the final mixture a third of a mole each of acid and alcohol. Again, substituting in Equation 9-4,

$$K = \frac{2/3 \times 2/3}{1/3 \times 1/3} = 4$$

In the examples cited for this reaction, the starting materials were in the same proportion. If the starting proportions were different, however, or if one or more of the products were present in the starting mixture, it would be found that, by substituting the equilibrium concentrations in Equation 9-4, a value of 4 is still obtained for the equilibrium constant. The use of the equilibrium constant is illustrated by the following examples.

Example 9-1. If 5 moles each of acetic acid and ethanol are allowed to react in a sealed tube at 100°C until equilibrium is established, how many moles of ester and water are formed, and how many moles of acid and alcohol remain?

Let x = number of moles of ester formed = number of moles of water formed.

Then $5 - x$ = number of moles of acid at equilibrium = number of moles of alcohol at equilibrium.

Substituting in Equation 9-4 and remembering that the constant for this reaction has a value of 4,

$$\frac{x^2}{(5 - x)(5 - x)} = 4$$

$x = 3.33$ = number of moles of ester and water at equilibrium

and

$5 - x = 1.67$ = number of moles of acid and alcohol present at equilibrium

That these answers are correct can be seen by substituting in the original expression

$$\frac{(3.33)^2}{(1.67)^2} = 4$$

Example 9-2. A mixture consisting of 1 mole each of acid and alcohol and 3 moles each of ester and water is heated in a sealed tube at 100°C. (*a*) Determine in which direction the reaction proceeds, and (*b*) calculate the moles of each substance present at equilibrium.

(*a*) Reaction must proceed until the value of K is reached. Substituting the original number of moles in the expression yields

$$\frac{3 \times 3}{1 \times 1} = 9$$

Since the value of K is 4, ester and water must react to form acid and alcohol, thereby decreasing the numerator terms and increasing the denominator terms until K is satisfied.

(*b*) Let x = number of moles each of acid and alcohol formed. Then, total moles each of acid and alcohol = $1 + x$, and moles each of ester and water remaining = $3 - x$. Substituting,

$$\frac{(3 - x)(3 - x)}{(1 + x)(1 + x)} = 4$$

Solving,

$x = 0.33$ mole of alcohol and ester formed

Therefore, the final values are:

$1 + 0.33 = 1.33$ moles each of acid and alcohol

and

$3 - 0.33 = 2.67$ moles each of ester and water

Example 9-3. The dissociation constant for N_2O_4 at $8°C$ in chloroform solutions has been found by Cundall [*J. Chem. Soc.* **59**, 1076 (1891) **67**, 794 (1895)] to be 1.10×10^{-5}. If 0.40 mole of N_2O_4 is dissolved in 600 ml of chloroform solution, calculate (*a*) the concentration of NO_2 in the solution at equilibrium, and (*b*) the per cent dissociation of N_2O_4.

(*a*) Since N_2O_4 dissociates according to the equation

$$N_2O_4 \leftrightharpoons 2NO_2$$

the equilibrium constant expression is

$$\frac{[NO_2]^2}{[N_2O_4]} = 1.10 \times 10^{-5}$$

The original molar concentration of $N_2O_4 = 0.40 \times 1000/600 = 0.67M$

Let x = number of moles of N_2O_4 dissociating per liter;

then $2x$ = number of moles of NO_2 formed per liter, since each mole of N_2O_4 yields 2 moles of NO_2;

$2x$ = equilibrium concentration of NO_2;

and $0.67 - x$ = molar concentration of N_2O_4 at equilibrium. Substituting and solving,

$$\frac{[2x]^2}{[0.67 - x]} = 1.10 \times 10^{-5}$$

Therefore x = number of moles of N_2O_4 dissociating per liter = 1.36×10^{-3}, and the molar concentration of $NO_2 = 2 \times 1.36 \times 10^{-3} = 2.72 \times 10^{-3}$ mole/liter.

(*b*) Per cent dissociation $= \dfrac{\text{moles } N_2O_4 \text{ dissoc. per liter}}{\text{orig. conc. of } N_2O_4} \times 100$

$$= \frac{1.36 \times 10^{-3}}{0.67} \times 100 = 0.20\%$$

9d. Application to Gaseous Equilibria. In the Haber process for the formation of ammonia, the reactants and products are gases. The equation for the reaction is

$$N_2 + 3H_2 \leftrightharpoons 2NH_3$$

and the equilibrium constant expression may be written

$$K_c = \frac{[NH_3]^2}{[N_2][H_2]^3}$$

Note that the concentration of hydrogen must be cubed and the concentration of ammonia must be squared because 3 and 2 molecules, respectively, appear in the equation. The equilibrium constant is designated as

K_c because the quantities of reactants and products are expressed in concentration units. Since it follows from the general gas law equation that the concentration of a gas is directly proportional to its partial pressure through the relationship $P = (n/v)RT = cRT$, the equilibrium constant expression for a gaseous reaction may be written using pressures instead of concentrations. The equilibrium expression then becomes

$$K_p = \frac{P_{NH_3}^2}{P_{H_2}^3 P_{N_2}}$$

Since it is convenient to specify pressures when dealing with gases, K_p is used more often than K_c. Note, however, that K_p is not identical to K_c in the above reaction because gas pressures are *directly proportional to* but *not equal to* gas concentrations.

K_p is equal to K_c, however, in a gaseous reaction such as the dissociation of hydrogen iodide because the *same number of gas molecules* appears on both sides of the equation.

$$2HI \leftrightharpoons H_2 + I_2$$

Since

$$K_c = \frac{[H_2][I_2]}{[HI]^2}$$

and

$$c = \frac{P}{RT}$$

Then

$$K_c = \frac{\left[\dfrac{P_{H_2}}{RT}\right]\left[\dfrac{P_{I_2}}{RT}\right]}{\left[\dfrac{P_{HI}}{RT}\right]^2} = \frac{P_{H_2}P_{I_2}}{P_{HI}^2} = K_p$$

Example 9-4. [Verhoek and Daniels, *J. Am. Chem. Soc.* **53,** 1250 (1931)]. Nitrogen tetroxide in the gas phase dissociates into nitrogen dioxide according to the equation $N_2O_4 \leftrightharpoons 2NO_2$. (a) If the equilibrium pressures at 25°C are $P_{N_2O_4} = 0.69$ atm and $P_{NO_2} = 0.31$ atm, what is K_p for the reaction? (b) Calculate the partial pressures of each substance if N_2O_4 at 10.0 atm is allowed to stand until equilibrium is established at 25°C.

(a)
$$K_p = \frac{(0.31)^2}{0.69} = 0.14$$

(b) N_2O_4 must react to give NO_2 until the value of K_p as calculated in part (a) is satisfied.

Let x = loss in partial pressure of N_2O_4 due to the reaction. Then $2x$ = partial pressure of NO_2 formed. Substituting in the expression,

$$K_p = \frac{P_{NO_2}^2}{P_{N_2O_4}} = \frac{(2x)^2}{10 - x} = 0.14$$

Therefore,

$$x = 0.57 \text{ atm}$$

and

$$P_{N_2O_4} = 10.0 - 0.57 = 9.43 \text{ atm}$$

and

$$P_{NO_2} = 2 \times 0.57 = 1.14 \text{ atm}$$

The number of moles of both NO_2 and N_2O_4 at equilibrium could be calculated from their partial pressures by using the general gas equation if V, the volume of the reaction vessel, is known. Then $n = PV/RT$.

In solving Example 9-4 the following equation was written for the equilibrium involved:

$$N_2O_4 \leftrightharpoons 2NO_2$$

and K was calculated as having a value of 0.14. The reaction could equally as well be represented by the following equation:

$$\tfrac{1}{2}N_2O_4 \leftrightharpoons NO_2$$

In this case the equilibrium constant would be

$$K_p = \frac{0.31}{\sqrt{0.69}} = 0.37$$

The solution to part (b) would then be

$$\frac{2x}{\sqrt{10 - x}} = 0.37$$

and

$$x = 0.57 \text{ atm}$$

Thus the same set of answers is obtained with either equation. It is well to write an equation for the equilibrium in question so that there will be no confusion as to what is meant by the value of K.

9e. Application to Heterogeneous Equilibria. When solids are present in a reaction, as for example, in the decomposition of calcium carbonate,

$$CaCO_3 \text{ (solid)} \leftrightharpoons CaO \text{ (solid)} + CO_2 \text{ (gas)}$$

if the equilibrium constant is written in its most accurate form it becomes

$$K = \frac{a_{CaO} \times a_{CO_2}}{a_{CaCO_3}}$$

It, however, has been determined experimentally that, as long as the solids are present, their effect on the equilibrium is constant. Hence the equilibrium constant expression for a reaction involving solids is simplified by assigning a value of *unity* to the activity of each solid so that the solid terms do not appear in the final equilibrium expression. Since CO_2 is a gas, its concentration can be expressed in terms of pressure. The expression for the reaction constant is usually written

$$K_p = P_{CO_2}$$

The value of the equilibrium constant at any temperature is therefore determined solely by the equilibrium pressure of CO_2.

Similarly, the precise equilibrium constant expression for the reaction, $Cu^{2+} + Zn \text{ (solid)} \leftrightharpoons Cu \text{ (solid)} + Zn^{2+}$, would be written

$$K = \frac{a_{Cu} \times a_{Zn^{2+}}}{a_{Cu^{2+}} \times a_{Zn}}$$

So long as both solid copper and zinc are present, their activities are constant, and if these activities are assigned a value of unity, the expression reduces to

$$K = \frac{a_{Zn^{2+}}}{a_{Cu^{2+}}}$$

9f. The Concept of Standard States. As has been pointed out, the expression for the equilibrium constant is exact only if activities are used. For substances in solution, especially nonionic solutes, the activities are not very different in most cases from the molar or molal concentrations, and the usual practice is to use concentration terms for equilibrium calculations. Even if activities are used, they are still expressed either in molarity or molality units.

In a gas, it has been pointed out that concentration can be expressed in terms of partial pressure. If the gas is ideal in behavior, the partial pressure can be substituted for the activity.

(As long as the solid exists in the pure state its activity is fixed and can be assigned a value of one.) This is justified if the concentration of the solid is expressed in terms of the mole fraction because the mole fraction of a pure substance is one. In amalgams or other forms of solid solutions, the activity of the solid in question is different from its activity in the pure state. Then the procedure is to let the mole fraction equal the activity.

For a substance present in solution in a highly concentrated form, as for example water in a dilute solution of hydrogen chloride, it is again convenient to express its concentration, and in the ideal case its activity, in terms of its mole fraction. Since, at a given temperature, pressures are related to concentrations, and mole fractions to molality and molarity by constant terms, the various activity terms appearing in the equilibrium constant expression may be expressed in a number of different ways without disturbing the accuracy of the mass law relationship. Such substitutions may, however, alter the actual value of the constant.

Summarizing, then, it is convenient to express activities in the following ways:

Gas	partial pressure
Substance in solution	molarity or molality
Solvent or substance in a	mole fraction
solution at high concentrations	
Solid	mole fraction

The activities then all become equal to 1 when a gas is at a partial pressure of 1 atm, substances in solutions are present at unit molarity, solids are present in their pure form, and solvents are present at very high concentrations (dilute solutions). Substances present at an *activity value of one* are said to be present in their *standard states.* Thus the zinc in the following reaction:

$$Zn + 2H_3O^+ \rightleftharpoons Zn^{2+} + H_2 + 2H_2O$$

would be in its standard state in the pure metallic form, the hydrogen ions and the zinc ions would be in their standard states when their activities have molarities equal to one, the water would be present in its standard state when the solution is quite dilute, and the hydrogen gas would be in its standard state when its pressure over the reaction mixture is 1 atm.

FACTORS INFLUENCING EQUILIBRIUM CONCENTRATIONS

9g. Le Châtelier's Principle. A reversible reaction at equilibrium will maintain this condition indefinitely unless disturbed by changes from the outside. Among such changes would be the addition or removal of heat, addition or removal of a reactant or product (change of concentration), and change of pressure. The effect of changing the various factors listed above is included in a far-reaching principle applicable to any physical or chemical equilibrium. This principle, termed *Le Châtelier's principle,* states that, *when a system is in equilibrium, a change in any one of the factors upon which the equilibrium depends will cause the equilibrium to shift in such*

a way as to diminish the effect of the change. The application of this
principle to the factors given above will be discussed in the following
paragraphs.

At this point it should be stated that the presence of a catalyst in no
way affects the final state of equilibrium. Catalysis affects only the *speed*
with which equilibrium is attained. This subject will be discussed in detail
in the chapter on reaction kinetics.

9h. Influence of Temperature Change. As stated in Chapter 5, chemical
reactions are classed as *exothermic* or *endothermic*, depending upon
whether heat is evolved or absorbed as the reaction proceeds. For example,
in the Haber reaction for the preparation of ammonia the complete equation for the reaction is

$$N_2 + 3H_2 \leftrightarrows 2NH_3 + \text{heat} \qquad \Delta H = -21.9 \text{ Kcal}$$

Since this reaction evolves heat, it is exothermic. The symbol ΔH, or as
it is termed, the enthalpy change, is used to represent the heat change when
the reaction takes place at constant pressure. By convention, when heat
is evolved, ΔH is negative, and when heat is absorbed, ΔH is positive.
The reverse of the Haber reaction is therefore endothermic, that is, 21.9
Kcal of heat must be absorbed to change 2 moles of ammonia into nitrogen
and hydrogen. At equilibrium forward and reverse reactions are pro-
ceeding at the same rate, so that the heat liberated by the forward reaction
is absorbed in the reverse reaction and no heat effect can be observed.

If a reaction is *endothermic*, heating a system at equilibrium causes
a shift in the equilibrium to the right with the formation of more products
and hence an increase in the value of the equilibrium constant. On the
other hand, if the reaction is *exothermic*, the application of heat will cause
the reaction equilibrium to shift to the left. These effects can be explained
by Le Châtelier's principle. The reaction resists the heating by shifting
in that direction that absorbs heat. On the other hand, if a reaction mixture at equilibrium is cooled, it will shift in such a way as to evolve heat.
For example, in the Haber reaction heating will cause a decomposition of
ammonia with a decreased yield whereas cooling will produce an increased
yield of ammonia.

The change of the equilibrium constant with temperature change can
also be approached from a quantitative standpoint. It is found that a
straight line is obtained in many cases if the logarithm of the equilibrium
constant is plotted against the reciprocal of the absolute temperature.
This is particularly true if a comparatively short temperature range is used.
Moreover, from the slope of the line we can calculate a heat of reaction
very close to the average heat of reaction for the temperature range being

studied. The mathematical expressions for the relationship follow:

$$\left(\log K_p = \frac{-\Delta H}{2.303RT} + I\right) \tag{9-6}$$

$$\log\frac{(K_p)_2}{(K_p)_1} = \frac{\Delta H}{2.303R}\left(\frac{1}{T_1} - \frac{1}{T_2}\right) = \frac{\Delta H}{2.303R}\left(\frac{T_2 - T_1}{T_2 T_1}\right) \tag{9-7}$$

In these equations ΔH is the average heat of reaction over the range studied and $(K_p)_2$ and $(K_p)_1$ are the equilibrium constants at the temperatures T_2 and T_1. Note that the heat of reaction may be either a minus or plus sign depending on whether the reaction is exothermic or endothermic. Hence, for an exothermic reaction K_p decreases in value with an increase in temperature and for an endothermic reaction it increases in value with a rise in temperature. This is in accordance with the conclusions arrived at earlier from a consideration of Le Châtelier's principle. In the acetic acid-ethanol-ethyl acetate-water equilibrium, the heat of reaction is essentially zero, and hence the value of the equilibrium constant is essentially independent of temperature as noted in 9c.

Equations 9-6 and 9-7 are similar in form to the equations relating the vapor pressure of a liquid to the absolute temperature, and like these equations may be derived from thermodynamic considerations. If K_c is used in Equations 9-6 and 9-7 instead of K_p, ΔH is replaced by ΔE, the heat of reaction at constant volume.

The use of Equation 9-7 is illustrated in Example 9-5.

Example 9-5. For the reaction

$$N_2O_4 (g) = 2NO_2 (g)$$

the values of K_p at 25° and 65°C are 0.141 and 2.80 respectively. Calculate the average heat of reaction for this temperature range.

$$\log\frac{2.80}{0.141} = \frac{\Delta H}{2.303 \times 1.99}\left(\frac{338 - 298}{338 \times 298}\right)$$

$$\Delta H = 16,200 \text{ cal}$$

9i. Influence of Concentration Change. If the hypothetical reaction, $A + B \rightleftharpoons C + D$, is considered at constant temperature, definite sets of concentrations of A, B, C, and D will be present at equilibrium. Now, if in one of the sets the concentration of either A or B is increased, the equilibrium will shift to the right because in that way the added A or B tends to be used up. In other words, in accordance with Le Châtelier's principle, the increase in the concentration of A or B is counteracted, in part at least, by the reaction shift. From another point of view the addition of either A or B, or both causes the speed of the forward reaction to be greater than the speed of the reverse reaction. Equilibrium can be reached again only by having the concentrations of A and B lowered while those of C and D increase. In this way the opposing reaction rates again become equal at a new equilibrium position. By similar reasoning the addition of either C or D to the system at equilibrium causes a shift to the left with the production of more A and B. If the equilibrium constant and the various concentrations present at equilibrium are known for a given reaction, the extent of the shift on adding an additional known quantity of a reactant or product can easily be calculated from the equilibrium constant expression. In this connection it will be recalled from general chemistry that reactions are made to go to completion by *removing* one of the products as it is formed. This produces a negative stress, and the system tries to compensate for it in accordance with Le Châtelier's principle by producing more of the substance.

9j. Influence of Pressure Change. According to the principle of Le Châtelier, an *increase in pressure* on a reaction involving a gas or gases should cause the equilibrium to shift in the direction that will cause a decrease in volume. In accordance with the gas law, this would cause a decrease in pressure, the result of the attempt of the system to relieve the imposed increase. In the Haber reaction

$$N_2 + 3H_2 \leftrightharpoons 2NH_3$$

four volumes of reactants yield two volumes of products. As the reaction proceeds to the right, at constant pressure, the volume of the system decreases. Thus, if pressure is applied to the system at equilibrium, more ammonia is formed at the expense of nitrogen and hydrogen. The effect of the externally applied pressure is thereby diminished by the volume decrease. A similar line of reasoning would lead to the conclusion that a decrease in the pressure in the Haber process should favor the decomposition of ammonia into hydrogen and nitrogen. This is in accordance with experimental fact.

If the same number of gas molecules appears on both sides of an equation, a change in pressure has no effect on the equilibrium position. According to Avogadro's law, (equal numbers of gas molecules occupy the same volume at the same pressure and temperature) Hence if an equal number of gas molecules appear on both sides of the equation, an increase in pressure affects both sides equally. Thus the volume of the system cannot decrease by having the reaction shift to either the right or left, and the original equilibrium condition will persist.

The effect of pressure change is in reality a special case of concentration change. Suppose that in a nitrogen-hydrogen-ammonia system at equilibrium an external pressure is imposed. Temperature remaining constant, the volume will decrease, thereby increasing the concentration of all three gases. This will alter the speeds of the forward and reverse reactions in a different manner, since there are four gas molecules of nitrogen and hydrogen and only two of ammonia. The two speeds will again be brought to the same value by a diminution of the nitrogen and hydrogen concentrations and an increase in the ammonia concentration. In a reaction such as the formation of HI from hydrogen and iodine, the speeds of both the forward and reverse reactions would be affected to the same extent, since there are two gas molecules on both sides of the equation for the reaction.

REFERENCES

Bull, *Physical Biochemistry*, John Wiley and Sons, New York, 1951, Chapter 7.

Daniels and Alberty, *Physical Chemistry*, John Wiley and Sons, New York, 1961, Chapter 9.

Maron and Prutton, *Principles of Physical Chemistry*, The Macmillan Co., New York, 1958, Chapter 12.

Moore, *Physical Chemistry*, Prentice-Hall, Englewood Cliffs, New Jersey, 1962, Chapter 6.

Sheehan, *Physical Chemistry*, Allyn and Bacon, Boston, 1961, Chapter 6.

Daniels, Williams, Bender, Alberty, and Cornwell, *Experimental Physical Chemistry*, McGraw-Hill Book Co., New York, 1962, Chapter 5.

Crockford and Nowell, *Laboratory Manual of Physical Chemistry*, John Wiley and Sons, New York, 1956, Experiments 16 and 17.

REVIEW QUESTIONS

1. Explain the difference between reversible reactions and those reactions that seem to go to completion. Give examples of each.

2. Describe the equilibrium that exists in a reversible reaction when all interaction has apparently ceased. Why is it a dynamic rather than a static equilibrium?

3. Derive from kinetic considerations the expression for the equilibrium constant for the general hypothetical reaction

$$a\text{A} + b\text{B} + \cdots \rightleftharpoons l\text{L} + m\text{M} + \cdots$$

4. Using kinetic considerations, derive the equilibrium constant expression for each of the following reactions:

(a) $2\text{A} + 3\text{B} \rightleftharpoons \text{C} + 2\text{D}$

(b) $2\text{NO} + \text{O}_2 \rightleftharpoons 2\text{NO}_2$

(c) $3\text{H}_2 + \text{N}_2 \rightleftharpoons 2\text{NH}_3$

(d) $4\text{NH}_3 + 5\text{O}_2 \rightleftharpoons 4\text{NO} + 6\text{H}_2\text{O}$

5. What is meant by the term, *velocity constant*, when applied to a chemical reaction? What factors enter into its value?

6. What relationship exists between the equilibrium constant and the velocity constants for a given reaction?

7. What is the significance of an equilibrium constant whose value is 1000 as compared to one whose value is 0.001?

8. In the general reaction, $A + B \rightarrow C + D$, what would the value of the equilibrium constant have to be in order that the two velocity constants have the same value?

9. Explain why partial pressures can be used instead of concentrations in equilibria involving gases.

10. When can the number of moles of reactants and products be used in the equilibrium expression in place of concentrations? Explain carefully.

11. Why must activities be used in order to obtain exact equilibrium constant expressions?

12. When is a substance said to be in its standard state? Illustrate with a gas, a liquid, a solid, and a solute.

13. Given a reaction involving a gas, a low concentration of a dissolved substance, a solvent, and a pure solid. The value of the equilibrium constant has been calculated from activity data. In order to use this value of K in equilibrium calculations, what units must be used for expressing the activities of the various substances?

14. Derive the general expression for the relation of K_c to K_p for a gaseous reaction. Under what circumstances is the value of each identical?

15. Give a statement and an explanation of Le Châtelier's principle.

16. Knowing that water expands when it freezes, use Le Châtelier's principle to predict and explain the effect of pressure change on the freezing point of water.

17. Using Le Châtelier's principle, explain the effect of temperature change on the equilibria in exothermic and endothermic reactions.

18. How does the value of the equilibrium constant change with (*a*) an increase in temperature and (*b*) a decrease in temperature, in an exothermic reaction? Apply the same changes to an endothermic reaction. Under what circumstance would the equilibrium constant value remain unchanged with a change in temperature?

19. Discuss the mathematical equations that show the variation of the equilibrium constant with temperature. How may equilibrium constant data be used to calculate heat of reaction?

20. Explain the effect of pressure change on the equilibrium position of gaseous reactions. Illustrate with some typical reactions.

21. In a reversible reaction at equilibrium, what happens if the concentration of a reactant or product is changed? Explain carefully both from the mathematical point of view using the equilibrium constant expression and from the point of view of Le Châtelier's principle.

22. Given the following exothermic gaseous reactions:

(*a*) $2SO_2 + O_2 \rightleftharpoons 2SO_3$

(*b*) $N_2 + 3H_2 \rightleftharpoons 2NH_3$

Explain the effect of simultaneously increasing the temperature and the pressure on equilibrium mixtures in the above systems.

23. Given the following endothermic gaseous reactions:

(a) $N_2 + O_2 \rightleftharpoons 2NO$

(b) $2HI \rightleftharpoons H_2 + I_2$

(c) $N_2O_4 \rightleftharpoons 2NO_2$

Explain the effect of simultaneously increasing the temperature and decreasing the pressure on equilibrium mixtures in each of the above systems.

PROBLEMS

Note: All reactions concerned with the formation of ethyl acetate from acetic acid and ethanol are carried out in a sealed tube.

I

1. The equilibrium constant is 4.00 for the reaction

$$CH_3COOH + C_2H_5OH \rightleftharpoons CH_3COOC_2H_5 + H_2O$$

at 100°C. Calculate the number of moles of each substance present at equilibrium if the starting number of moles is

	Acid	Alcohol	Ester	Water
(a)	4	4	0	0
(b)	2	1	1	2
(c)	0	0	2	2
(d)	1	3	1	2

2. Using the reaction in Problem I-1, calculate the number of grams of each substance at equilibrium if 11.5 grams of ethanol are allowed to react with 30 grams of acetic acid.

3. If 20 grams of ethanol, 10 grams of ethyl acetate, 10 grams of acetic acid, and 9 grams of water are allowed to react, in which direction will the reaction proceed and how many grams of each substance will be present at equilibrium?

4. At equilibrium 400 ml of chloroform contains 0.28 mole of N_2O_4 and 1.12×10^{-3} mole of NO_2 when the temperature is 8°C. Calculate the equilibrium constant at this temperature for the reaction:

$$N_2O_4 \rightleftharpoons 2NO_2$$

5. From the equilibrium constant value obtained in I-4, calculate the number of moles of NO_2 and N_2O_4 in 1500 ml of chloroform in which 0.75 mole of N_2O_4 have been dissolved. Calculate the concentration of each of the oxides present at equilibrium.

6. The equilibrium mixture in Problem I-5 is diluted with an additional 1000 ml of chloroform. In which direction will the equilibrium shift? What will be the final concentrations of nitrogen dioxide and nitrogen tetroxide?

7. According to the data of Larson and Dodge [*J. Am. Chem. Soc.* **45,** 2918 (1923), **46,** 367 (1924)], at 400°C in an equilibrium mixture of nitrogen, hydrogen, and ammonia the partial pressures are

$$P_{N_2} = 6.74 \text{ atm} \qquad P_{H_2} = 20.23 \text{ atm} \qquad P_{NH_3} = 3.03 \text{ atm}$$

Calculate K_p for each of the following reactions at this temperature:

$$N_2 + 3H_2 \rightleftharpoons 2NH_3$$
$$\tfrac{1}{2}N_2 + \tfrac{3}{2}H_2 \rightleftharpoons NH_3$$

8. In an equilibrium mixture of nitrogen, hydrogen, and ammonia at 400°C, the partial pressures of the ammonia and the nitrogen are 4.00 and 3.50 atm, respectively. What is the partial pressure of the hydrogen? What is the mole fraction of each component in the equilibrium mixture?

9. Given 10 liters of the equilibrium mixture in Problem I-8 at 400°C. What will be the total number of moles in this system? How many moles of each gas will be present? What is the total weight of the system?

10. Nernst and Hohmann [*Z. Physik. Chem.* **11,** 352 (1893)] determined that the equilibrium constant for the reaction:

$$CHCl_2COOC_5H_{11} \rightleftharpoons CHCl_2COOH + C_5H_{10}$$

in the liquid state at 100°C has a value of 3.40 when the concentrations are expressed in moles per liter. If 1.0 mole of the acid is mixed with 5.90 moles of the hydrocarbon, it is found that at equilibrium the total volume is 790 ml. Calculate the number of moles of each substance present in this mixture and the mole fraction of each.

11. At 250°C, K_p for the gaseous reaction

$$PCl_5 \rightleftharpoons PCl_3 + Cl_2$$

is 1.80. Calculate the partial pressures and the concentrations of all substances present at equilibrium if 0.20 mole of PCl_5 is placed in a 4-liter vessel at 250°C.

12. Using the data of Problem I-11, calculate how many grams of PCl_5 must be added to a 2-liter container at 250°C in order to obtain a concentration of 0.1 mole per liter of chlorine at equilibrium.

II

1. The constant for the reaction between acetic acid and ethanol to form water and ethyl acetate has a value of 4.00 at 100°C. What will be the number of moles of each substance present at equilibrium when the starting mixture is 2 moles of alcohol, 2 moles of acid, and 2 moles of ester?

2. How many grams of acetic acid will have to be added to 30 grams of ethanol to produce an equilibrium mixture containing 0.30 mole of ester?

3. Calculate the mole fraction of each substance present at equilibrium in the reaction given in Problem II-1 when the starting mixture consists of 3 moles of ester and 2 moles of water.

4. Given an initial mixture consisting of 18 grams each of ester, acid, water, and ethanol. In which direction will the reaction proceed in order to produce equilibrium conditions? Calculate the number of grams of each substance present at equilibrium. See Problem II-1 for needed data.

5. Using the data of Problem I-4, calculate the concentration of N_2O_4 at equilibrium when 0.05 mole of NO_2 is added to 800 ml of chloroform at 8°C. How many moles of NO_2 will be present in the 800 ml of reaction mixture?

6. From the data of Problem I-4 calculate the degree of dissociation and the concentration of nitrogen tetroxide at equilibrium when 0.60 mole of N_2O_4 is dissolved in 1200 ml of chloroform at 8°C. What would be the degree of dissociation if the same amount were dissolved in 800 ml of chloroform?

7. When pressure is expressed in atmospheres, K_p at 25°C for the gaseous equilibrium between nitrogen dioxide and nitrogen tetroxide has a value of 0.14 when the reaction is written

$$N_2O_4 \rightleftharpoons 2NO_2$$

In a 500-ml bulb containing an equilibrium mixture of these two substances, it is found that the partial pressure of the NO_2 is 500 mm. What is the partial pressure of the N_2O_4? If the equilibrium mixture was produced by introducing NO_2 into the flask, what would be the quantity of this substance initially present?

8. Consider the reaction of Problem II-7 at 25°C. In a bulb of 500-ml capacity the equilibrium partial pressure of the nitrogen dioxide is 400 mm. If the gas in the bulb is allowed to flow into another bulb until the total volume of the gas becomes 2 liters, what will be the partial pressure of each gas?

9. According to the data of Taylor and Crist [*J. Am. Chem. Soc.* **63**, 1381 (1941)], the value of K_c for the reaction

$$2HI \rightleftharpoons H_2 + I_2$$

is 3.3×10^{-2} at 300°C. Calculate the number of grams of HI formed when 1 mole each of hydrogen and iodine vapor and 0.001 mole of HI are allowed to come to equilibrium at this temperature in a 4-liter flask.

10. If K_p for the reaction
$$2HI \rightleftharpoons H_2 + I_2$$

is 1.83 at 698.6°C, what is the partial pressure of each gas present at equilibrium when 10 grams each of hydrogen and iodine are allowed to come to equilibrium in a 12-liter flask at this temperature? How many grams of each gas are present at equilibrium?

11. Using the data of Problem II-10, calculate the partial pressures at equilibrium when HI is introduced into a 4-liter flask at 698.6°C until the total initial pressure of the HI is 2 atm.

12. Using the data of Problem II-10, calculate the partial pressures at equilibrium of each substance resulting from the mixing of 2 grams each of hydrogen, iodine, and hydrogen iodide in a 3-liter flask at 698.6°C. Calculate the number of grams of each substance present in the equilibrium mixture.

13. Using the data of Problem I-10, calculate the number of moles of each substance present at equilibrium at 100°C when 2 moles of dichloroacetic acid are added to 8.90 moles of amylene. The final equilibrium volume is 1.28 liters.

TEN

Entropy and Free Energy

The purpose of this chapter is to discuss the concept and use of the thermodynamic functions: entropy and free energy. The third law of thermodynamics is introduced in the study of entropy, and special emphasis is placed on the relation between the free energy change in a reaction and the equilibrium constant for that reaction.

ENTROPY

10a. The Concept of Entropy. In Chapter 4 it was stated in the discussion of the second law of thermodynamics that one procedure for studying the implications of that law involved *entropy*. We shall now consider this thermodynamic concept in further detail. Entropy developed from the search for a thermodynamic function that would serve as a general criterion of spontaneity for physical and chemical changes. A further consideration of entropy showed that it could be identified with the randomness of a system. It is from the standpoint of randomness that the function is discussed in this chapter.

As a system goes from a more orderly to a less orderly state, there is an increase in its randomness, and hence by definition an increase in its entropy. Conversely, if the change is one in which there is an increase in the orderliness, there is a decrease in entropy. For example, when a solid changes to a liquid, there is an increase in entropy because the orderly arrangement of the molecules in the crystal breaks down to the randomness of the liquid state. Conversely, the process of solidification is accompanied by a decrease in entropy. The process of vaporization produces an increase in randomness in the distribution of the molecules with a resulting increase in entropy. If two gases diffuse into each other, there is an increase in entropy. A heating process, with the accompanying increase in kinetic energy, rotational effects, and vibrational effects, is accompanied by an increase in the entropy of the system. And, again, conversely, cooling results in a decrease in entropy. Entropy as a measure of randomness or orderliness leads to the conclusion that a substance in its normal crystalline state at the absolute zero of temperature would be in a condition in which orderliness would be at a maximum because all motion has essentially ceased. (Hence entropy is at a minimum.) This idea is the basis of the third law of thermodynamics.

The use of entropy change as a criterion of spontaneity, involving as it does the need to consider all entropy changes in all systems involved, is beyond the scope of this presentation. The treatment in this chapter will be limited to the calculation of the entropy change for physical changes and chemical reactions. As with enthalpy, entropy, noted by the symbol S, is a function of the state of the system and is not affected by prior changes. Unlike enthalpy, however, it is possible to determine the absolute value of S for a given system instead of a value relative to some arbitrarily selected standard state or reference state. As with enthalpy, it is the delta magnitude, ΔS, that is usually of most interest.

10b. The Calculation of ΔS. It has been established that for an infinitely small change in entropy, dS, the following relation is applicable:

$$\left(\; dS = \frac{dQ_{rev}}{T} \; \right) \tag{10-1}$$

wherein dQ_{rev} is the heat change accompanying the change in the system, provided the change takes place in a reversible manner. It is necessary to emphasize that no matter how the change takes place, even if in a completely irreversible manner, the entropy change is the same and is calculated from the numerical value of Q associated with the reversible process. Equation 10-1 is now applied to certain physical changes.

ISOTHERMAL CHANGE OF STATE. In such a process Q_{rev} is the heat of transition, and since the temperature remains constant, Equation 10-1 reduces to

$$\Delta S = \frac{\Delta H_{transition}}{T} \tag{10-2}$$

Depending upon whether or not heat is evolved or absorbed in the process, $\Delta H_{transition}$ can be positive or negative. In fusion, evaporation, or sublimation it is positive, and there would be an increase in entropy. (In solidification or condensation it is negative, and there would be a decrease in entropy. Examples 10-1 and 10-2 illustrate the use of Equation 10-2.

Example 10-1. Calculate the entropy change when 9 grams of water change from the liquid state to the vapor state at 100°C and at a pressure of 1 atm. The heat of vaporization of water is 540 cal per gram.

Here the heat of vaporization of water is the reversible heat of transition and substitution in Equation 10-2 gives

$$\Delta S = \frac{540 \text{ cal/gram} \times 9 \text{ grams}}{373°\text{A}} = 13.03 \text{ cal/degree} = 13.03 \text{ E.U.}$$

Note that entropy is expressed in calories per degree. The unit involved is termed the entropy unit (E.U.). If the process in the example had been one of condensation, the sign of the heat of transition would have been negative, since heat would be evolved, and the sign of the entropy change would have been negative.

Example 10-2. Calculate the entropy change when 9 grams of water in the solid state are changed to liquid at 0°C. The heat of fusion is 79.7 cal per gram.

$$\Delta S = \frac{79.7 \text{ cal/gram} \times 9 \text{ grams}}{273°\text{C}} = 2.63 \text{ E.U.}$$

Note that the entropy change is approximately six times as great for vaporization as for fusion. This is in accordance with the concept of entropy as a measure of randomness, since the vaporization process with the formation of gas molecules involves a much greater change in the orderliness of the system.

THE ISOTHERMAL EXPANSION OF A GAS. In Chapter 4 it was shown that the work done in the reversible isothermal expansion of a perfect gas is given by Equation 4-7. The work performed is also equal to the heat absorbed in the process, which in the following equations is represented by $Q_{\text{expansion}}$. The entropy change for such a process is therefore

$$\left\{ \Delta S = \frac{Q_{\text{expansion}}}{T} = \frac{W_{\text{max}}}{T} = \frac{nRT}{T} \ln \frac{V_2}{V_1} \right\} \qquad (10\text{-}3)$$

The process of isothermal expansion takes place with an increase in entropy. Note that the temperature does not enter into the calculation. Note that the example that follows *does not* state that the expansion is a reversible one. It could have taken place into an evacuated space or against a low pressure. In these cases the process would have been irreversible. Nevertheless, the calculation of the entropy change would be the same in all cases and would involve a change calculated for a reversible process. The use of Equation 10-3 is illustrated in Example 10-3.

Example 10-3. Calculate the entropy change when 14 grams of nitrogen expand from a volume of 10 liters at 10°C to a volume of 30 liters at the same temperature. Assume ideal behavior for the gas.

$$\Delta S = 14 \text{ grams/28 grams/mole} \times 1.99 \text{ cal/mole/degree}$$
$$\times 2.303 \times \log (30 \text{ liters/10 liters})$$
$$= 1.09 \text{ E.U.}$$

CHANGE IN TEMPERATURE. For processes involving changes in temperature, Q_{rev} in Equation 10-1 would be replaced by $nC_v \, dT$ or $nC_p \, dT$, depending on whether the change in temperature takes place at constant volume or constant pressure. In these expressions n is the number of moles, and C_v and C_p are the molar heat capacities at constant volume and pressure, respectively. For a temperature change at constant volume, the following expression is obtained through the use of Equation 10-1:

$$\int_{S_1}^{S_2} dS = \int_{T_1}^{T_2} nC_v \, dT/T = \Delta S = nC_v \ln T_2/T_1 \qquad (10\text{-}4)$$

In this integration C_v is considered as being constant or independent of temperature. The corresponding expression for a change in temperature at constant pressure would be

$$\left(\Delta S = nC_p \ln \frac{T_2}{T_1} \right) \qquad (10\text{-}5)$$

The use of these last two equations is illustrated in Example 10-4.

Example 10-4. Calculate the entropy change when 14 grams of nitrogen are heated from 27° to 127°C (a) at constant volume, and (b) at constant pressure. Assume that in this temperature range C_v has the value of 4.94 cal/mole.

(a) $\Delta S = 14 \text{ grams/28 grams/mole} \times 4.94 \text{ cal/mole}$
$$\times 2.303 \log 400°/300°C$$
$$= 0.70 \text{ E.U.}$$

(b) Since it was shown in Equation 4-5 that the difference between C_v and C_p is 1.99 cal/mole for an ideal gas, it follows that for nitrogen C_p is 6.94 cal/mole. Therefore

$$\Delta S = (14 \text{ grams/28 grams/mole}) \times 6.94 \text{ cal/mole}$$
$$\times 2.303 \log 400°/300°C$$
$$= 0.99 \text{ E.U.}$$

For more complicated processes various combinations of these procedures could be used. For example, if we wished to calculate the entropy change when 18 grams of ice at −10°C is changed to steam at 120°C and at 1 atm pressure, the calculations can be carried out readily by the following steps:

1. The solid is heated to 0°C and ΔS is calculated for this process. It is necessary to know the heat capacity of solid H_2O. Equation 10-4 is used.

2. The solid is melted isothermally and reversibly at 0°C. It is necessary to know the heat of fusion. Equation 10-2 is used.

3. The liquid is heated to 100°C. It is necessary to know the heat capacity of liquid water. Equation 10-4 is used.

4. The liquid is isothermally and reversibly evaporated at 100°C. The necessary datum is the heat of vaporization.

5. The resulting vapor is heated to 120°C at constant pressure. It is necessary to know the value of C_p. Equation 10-5 is used.

10c. The Third Law of Thermodynamics. *The third law of thermodynamics states that the entropy of a substance in its normal crystalline state at the absolute zero of temperature is zero.* This law does not account for the entropy effect associated with the presence of two or more isotopic species or with the existence of nuclear spin. These factors do not invalidate the use of this law in thermodynamic calculations associated with chemical reaction provided isotopic separation does not take place and no nuclear changes take place.

This law is based on the assumption that at the absolute zero of temperature all motion has ceased and maximum orderliness has been achieved. The conclusion is based on theoretical considerations. Assuming that the entropy of a given atomic or molecular species is zero at 0°A, it is then possible to calculate the absolute entropy of that substance at any other temperature, provided its heat capacity is known from 0°A to the temperature in question and that all heats of transition, with the corresponding temperatures of transition, are known. The calculations would be similar to the calculations given at the end of 10b.

In this manner the absolute entropy of many substances have been calculated for a temperature of 25°C. By combining these data with other thermodynamic data, a comprehensive list of entropies has been compiled. Not only does this list contain the entropies of molecular and atomic substances but also the entropies of individual ions. In the case of ions, however, the value relative to the H^+ ion is usually given. The hydrogen ion is assumed to have a value of zero E.U. at 25°C for a solution in which the activity of the ion is unity. Table 10-1 gives the standard entropies for a number of substances at 25°C. It will be recalled that the standard state of a gas is 1 atm pressure, that of a solid, its normal crystalline form at the given temperature, for a liquid, the pure substance, and for a solute, a concentration or, more precisely, an activity of $1m$.

Table 10-1. Standard Entropies at 25°C
($S°$ in cal per degree per mole)

H_2O (l)	16.72	$H_2(g)$	31.21	$C_2H_6(g)$	54.85
$H_2O(g)$	45.11	$O_2(g)$	49.00	S (rhombic)	7.62
$NO_2(g)$	57.47	C (s)	1.36	$SO_2(g)$	59.40
$N_2O_4(g)$	72.73	CO (g)	47.30	$Cl_2(g)$	53.29
NO (g)	50.34	$CO_2(g)$	51.06	AgCl (s)	22.97
$N_2(g)$	45.77	$CH_4(g)$	44.50	Ag (s)	10.21
HCl (g)	44.62	Cu^{2+}	−23.6	Cl^-	13.17
Ag^+	17.67	Zn^{2+}	−25.45	Br^-	19.29

See footnote, Table 5-1.

10d. The Calculation of $\Delta S°$ for a Chemical Reaction. The calculation of $\Delta S°$ for a chemical reaction is carried out in exactly the same manner as the calculation of ΔH. For the hypothetical reaction,

$$aA + bB \rightleftharpoons lL + mM$$

$$\Delta S° = \Sigma S° \text{ (products)} - \Sigma S° \text{ (reactants)}$$
$$= lS_L° + mS_M° - aS_A° - bS_B° \quad (10\text{-}6)$$

The use of Equation 10-6 is illustrated in Examples 10-5 and 10-6.

Example 10-5. Calculate $\Delta S°$ for the following reaction at 25°C:

$$Ag (s) + \tfrac{1}{2}Cl_2 (g) = AgCl (s)$$
$$\Delta S° = S_{AgCl}° - S_{Ag}° - \tfrac{1}{2}S_{Cl_2}° = 22.97 - 10.21 - \tfrac{1}{2} \times 53.29$$
$$= -13.88 \text{ E.U.}$$

In this reaction there is a decrease in entropy. This is to be expected, since one mole of a solid is reacting with a gas to form a solid, a situation that results in an increase in the orderliness of the system. The value of −13.88 E.U. is termed the standard entropy of formation of silver chloride.

Example 10-6. Calculate the entropy change for the following reaction

$$AgCl (s) = Ag^+ + Cl^-$$
$$\Delta S° = S_{Cl^-}° + S_{Ag^+}° - S_{AgCl(s)}° = 13.17 + 17.67 - 22.97$$
$$= 7.87 \text{ E.U.}$$

FREE ENERGY

10e. The Significance of Free Energy. Earlier in this chapter it was stated that the concept of entropy was developed for the purpose of obtaining a function that could be used to determine whether or not a given process would take place spontaneously. It was found that in an actual or spontaneous process there would be an increase in the entropy of the universe. This is the most general criterion of equilibrium that thermodynamics has to offer, but to employ this concept we must take into account every conceivable process that accompanies the change under consideration. As a result, entropy is entirely too general a criterion and one which is difficult to apply. Therefore, attempts were made to invent a less fundamental and less general thermodynamic function that would be of more practical convenience and use in the study of particular processes. Such a function is termed the *Gibbs free energy function.* It may be defined in the following way:

$$G = H - TS \tag{10-7}$$

In this expression H is the enthalpy and S is entropy. The letter, capital G, is used for the free energy. The use of the letter G is in recognition of the contributions of Professor J. Willard Gibbs of Yale University to the development and application of thermodynamics to chemistry. It should be added that another form of free energy is sometimes used. This is the *Helmholtz free energy* defined as follows:

$$A = E - TS$$

In this chapter we shall consider only the Gibbsian free energy and will term it simply free energy.

Now if we limit the application of Equation 10-7 to an isothermal change, we will obtain the following expression for the *free energy change* for a given process.

$$\Delta G = \Delta H - T\,\Delta S \tag{10-8}$$

If Equation 10-8 is considered for a typical chemical reaction or other process, it is found that the free energy change, ΔG, is equal to the maximum useful work that can be done in excess of the pressure-volume work, provided the change is carried out reversibly *and at constant temperature and pressure.*

Consider the following reaction

$$Zn + 2H^+ = Zn^{2+} + H_2$$

This is a spontaneous reaction and therefore has the possibility of furnishing free energy for useful work. The reaction can be carried out in an irreversible manner by simply adding the zinc to a solution of an acid in a beaker. In this process the free energy appears entirely in the form of heat. On the other hand, we could construct a chemical cell as shown in Figure 13-2a. If this cell could be discharged reversibly, all the free energy could be obtained in the form of electrical energy and could be used for useful work. Whether carried out irreversibly in the beaker or reversibly through the use of a cell, there would still be the pressure-volume work resulting from the evolution of the hydrogen gas. (This work cannot be employed for a useful purpose and therefore is not part of the free energy change.)

10f. Free Energy as a Criterion of Spontaneity. Experimentation shows that in every spontaneous process carried out at constant temperature and pressure there is an evolution of free energy. In other words, the free energy of the system after the change is less than the free energy of the original system. The same convention used to designate heat evolved or absorbed will be used. Free energy evolved will be given a negative sign and if free energy must be added, as in the charging of a lead-acid storage battery, the sign will be positive. Therefore, we may write for a spontaneous process

$$\left(\Delta G = -\text{useful work} \right)$$

and for a galvanic cell

$$\left(\Delta G = -EnF \right) \tag{10-9}$$

wherein EnF is the electrical energy produced. E is the electromotive force of the cell, n the number of equivalents change, and F is the faraday, 96,500 coulombs. This relationship will be discussed in further detail in Chapter 12 (Conductivity). The application of free energy considerations to galvanic cells will be deferred until Chapter 13 (Electromotive Force). We can therefore say that if the free energy change as calculated has a negative sign, the process is spontaneous. If it has a positive sign, the process is not spontaneous and will not take place without outside energy being added. (If the free energy change is zero, the system must be in equilibrium) In applying these criteria, it must be kept in mind that *free energy can be used as a criterion of spontaneity only if the process is carried out at constant temperature and pressure*. In order to apply these concepts to chemical reactions, it is first necessary to consider the *standard free energies of formation*.

10g. Standard Free Energies of Formation. While it is not possible to obtain the absolute values of the free energies of formation of compounds and ions, it is possible to compile a table of free energies based on the assumption that the free energies of elements in their normal standard states and that of the hydrogen ion at unit molality are all equal to zero. It will be recalled that this was the procedure used in compiling the table of the enthalpies of formation. A selected list of standard free energies of formation is given in Table 10-2. All values are for 25°C.

Table 10-2. Free Energies of Formation at 25°C
($\Delta G°$ in kcal per mole)

$H_2O(g)$	-54.636	Benzene, C_6H_6 (l)	29.756
H_2O (l)	-56.690	Methanol, CH_3OH (l)	-39.73
$HCl(g)$	-22.770	Ethanol, C_2H_5OH (l)	-41.77
$SO_2(g)$	-71.79	Acetic acid, $C_2H_4O_2$ (l)	-93.8
$NO(g)$	20.720	Zn^{2+}	-35.18
$NO_2(g)$	12.390	Cu^{2+}	16.0
$CO_2(g)$	-94.260	Ag^+	18.43
$CO(g)$	-32.808	Cl^-	-31.35
$AgCl$ (s)	-26.224	Br^-	-24.57
Methane, CH_4 (g)	-12.140	OH^-	-37.60
Ethane, C_2H_6 (g)	-7.860	$C_2H_3O_2^-$	-89.72

See footnote Table 5-1.

10h. Standard Free Energy Change in a Chemical Reaction. The standard free energy change in a chemical reaction is calculated in the same manner as the entropy change and the enthalpy change. The procedure is represented by the equation

$$\Delta G° = \Sigma \Delta G° \text{(products)} - \Sigma \Delta G° \text{(reactants)} \quad (10\text{-}10)$$

Illustrations of the use of this expression are given in Examples 10-7 and 10-8.

Example 10-7. Calculate $\Delta G°$ for the combustion of ethane at 25°C.

$$C_2H_6(g) + 3\tfrac{1}{2}O_2(g) = 2CO_2(g) + 3H_2O(l)$$
$$\Delta G° = 2\,\Delta G°(CO_2) + 3\,\Delta G°(H_2O, l) - 3\tfrac{1}{2}\,\Delta G°(O_2) - \Delta G°(C_2H_6)$$
$$= 2 \times (-94,260) + 3 \times (-56,690) - 0 - (-7860)$$
$$= -350,730 \text{ cal}$$

Example 10-8. Calculate $\Delta G°$ at 25°C for the reaction

$$Zn + 2H^+ = Zn^{2+} + H_2$$

This reaction is somewhat unusual, as 3 of the substances, H^+, Zn, and H_2, all have a standard free energy of zero. Hence

$$\Delta G° = \Delta G°(Zn^{2+}) + \Delta G°(H_2) - \Delta G°(Zn) - 2\,\Delta G°(H^+)$$
$$= -35,180 + 0 - 0 - 0 = -35,180 \text{ cal}$$

It should be noted that in both of these examples the sign of the free energy change is minus. Consider Example 10-7. If we place ethane, oxygen, and carbon dioxide, all at 1 atm pressure, in the presence of liquid water, the result will be the further formation of carbon dioxide and water. In Example 10-8, if metallic zinc is placed in a solution of hydrogen ions *and* zinc ions, each at unit molality and with a pressure of hydrogen gas equal to 1 atm over the solution, further formation of hydrogen and zinc ions will result. Example 10-9 illustrates a reaction in which the free energy change is positive.

Example 10-9. Calculate ΔG for the following reaction

$$AgCl\,(s) = Ag^+ + Cl^-$$

in aqueous solution.

$$\Delta G^\circ = \Delta G^\circ(Ag^+) + \Delta G^\circ(Cl^-) - \Delta G^\circ(AgCl)$$
$$= 18{,}430 - 31{,}350 + 26{,}224 = +13{,}304 \text{ cal/mole}$$

The fact that the free energy change has a positive value shows that if we place solid AgCl in a solution in which both the silver ion and the chloride ion have an activity of $1m$ precipitation of AgCl will result. It does not say that such a solution could exist. It simply states that if we should by some chance prepare such a solution the precipitation of silver chloride will result. This example will be further discussed in 10k.

10i. The General Expression for Free Energy Change in a Chemical Reaction. Having considered the free energy change in a chemical reaction when all reactants and products are in their standard states, we shall now consider the free energy change when these are *not* in their standard states. In order to do this, we must use an expression for the free energy of a substance as a function of its activity. Without justifying it or giving its derivation, we will simply state the expression and proceed with its use.

$$G = G^\circ + RT \ln a \qquad (10\text{-}11)$$

In this expression G° is the standard free energy at the particular temperature and G is the free energy when the activity of the substance is a. For example, if the substance is a gas, the expression would be

$$G = G^\circ + RT \ln p$$

and if a substance in solution

$$G = G^\circ + RT \ln m$$

wherein m is the activity expressed in molality units. The molal free energy of a substance is sometimes referred to as its *chemical potential*. Equation 10-11 will now be applied to the perfectly general equation:

$$aA + bB + \cdots = lL + mM + \cdots$$

The free energy change for this reaction will be the sums of the free energies of the products less the sum of the free energy of the reactants. The only difference between this derivation and that used in Equation 10-10 is that here we have the reactants and products in states different from the standard ones.

$$\Delta G = l(G_L^\circ + RT\ln a_L) + m(G_M^\circ + RT\ln a_M)$$
$$- a(G_A^\circ + RT\ln a_A) - b(G_B^\circ + RT\ln a_B)$$
$$= (lG_L^\circ + mG_M^\circ - aG_A^\circ - bG_B^\circ) + RT\ln \frac{a_L{}^l a_M{}^m \ldots}{a_A{}^a a_B{}^b \ldots}$$

The terms in the parentheses are the standard free energies of the reactants and their products. Their absolute values are not obtainable. We, however, may substitute for them the standard free energies of formation as given in Table 10-2. When this is done, the term in the parenthesis becomes equal to the standard free energy change for the reaction and

$$\left(\Delta G = \Delta G^\circ + RT\ln \frac{a_L{}^l a_M{}^m}{a_B{}^b a_A{}^a} = \Delta G^\circ + RT\ln \frac{\text{products}}{\text{reactants}} \right) \quad (10\text{-}12)$$

The use of this equation will be demonstrated in Example 10-10.

10j. Free Energy Change and the Equilibrium Constant. If a system is in equilibrium, the value of the free energy change, ΔG, will be zero. Therefore, if the activities of the various substances are such that no further reaction takes place in a system, Equation 10-12 may be written

$$0 = \Delta G^\circ + RT\ln \left(\frac{a_L{}^l a_M{}^m}{a_A{}^a a_B{}^b} \right)_{eq} \quad (10\text{-}13)$$

The subscript, eq, indicates that the expression in the parenthesis must represent a set of equilibrium activity values. Since free energy is a function solely of the state of a system, ΔG° must be a constant. If such is the case, the expression in the parenthesis must also be a constant at a given temperature. Therefore, we may write

$$\Delta G^\circ = a \text{ constant} = -RT\ln \left(\frac{a_L{}^l a_M{}^m}{a_A{}^a a_B{}^b} \right)_{eq} = -RT\ln K \quad (10\text{-}14)$$

and

$$\left(\frac{a_L{}^l a_M{}^m}{a_B{}^b a_A{}^a} \right)_{eq} = K \quad (10\text{-}15)$$

This is the derivation of the mass law expression referred to in Chapter 9 (Chemical Equilibrium).

10k. Some Applications of the Free Energy Change to Reactions. The following examples show some typical calculations involved with the calculation of the equilibrium constant and the free energy change when activities have values other than one.

Example 10-10. Given the reaction

$$AgCl\ (s) = Ag^+ + Cl^-$$

at 25°C.

(a) Calculate the solubility product for this reaction.

(b) Calculate the free energy change when each ion activity is 1×10^{-3} m.

(c) Calculate the free energy change when each ion activity is 1×10^{-6} m.

(a) The equilibrium constant for this reaction is given by the following expression:

$$K = \frac{a_{Ag^+} a_{Cl^-}}{a_{AgCl}}$$

Since the silver chloride is in its normal crystalline state, its activity (that of a pure substance) is unity. Therefore, this expression reduces to

$$\left(K = a_{Ag^+} a_{Cl^-} \right)$$

This type of equilibrium constant is termed a *solubility product* and the equilibrium constant is written as K_{sp}. From Equation 10-14 and from the value of $\Delta G°$ calculated in Example 10-9

(a) $\Delta G° = 13{,}304 \text{ cal/mole} = -RT \ln K_{sp} = -1.99 \text{ cal/mole/degree}$
$$\times 298° \times 2.303 \log K_{sp}$$

$$K_{sp} = 1.8 \times 10^{-10}$$

(b) $\Delta G = 13{,}304 + 1.99 \times 298 \times 2.303 \log (1 \times 10^{-3})^2$
$$= 5110 \text{ cal}$$

(c) $\Delta G = 13{,}304 + 1.99 \times 298 \times 2.303 \log (1 \times 10^{-6})^2$
$$= -3084 \text{ cal}$$

An examination of the answers to parts (a) and (b) shows that in (a) the free energy change is plus. Therefore, if we could obtain a solution in which the activities of the silver ion and the chloride ion were both 1×10^{-3} m, more silver chloride would precipitate. In other words, the solution would be more than saturated. In (c) the free energy change is minus. Therefore, the reaction would go to the right with further solution of AgCl. Here the starting solution with the two ions each at 1×10^{-6} m was not saturated.

Example 10-11. (*a*) Calculate the value of the equilibrium constant for the following reaction at 25°C. The value of ΔG° at this temperature is 1160 cal.

$$N_2O_4\,(g) = 2NO_2\,(g)$$

$$1160\ \text{cal} = -RT \ln K = -1.99 \times 298 \times 2.303 \log K$$

$$K = 0.142 = \left(\frac{P^2_{NO_2}}{P_{N_2O_4}}\right)_{eq}$$

(*b*) Calculate ΔG at 25°C for the reaction:

$$N_2O_4\,(1\ \text{atm}) = 2NO_2\,(0.1\ \text{atm})$$

$$\Delta G = 1160 + 2 \times 2.303 \times 298 \log \frac{0.1^2}{1}$$

$$\Delta G = -1582\ \text{cal}$$

(*c*) Calculate ΔG at 25°C for the reaction

$$N_2O_4\,(0.1\ \text{atm}) = 2NO_2\,(1\ \text{atm})$$

$$\Delta G = 1160 + 2 \times 2.303 \times 298 \log \frac{1}{0.1}$$

$$\Delta G = +2533\ \text{cal}$$

Example 10-11 shows that in a system in which the nitrogen tetroxide and nitrogen dioxide are both at 1 atm pressure the reaction will result in the formation of the tetroxide. This is shown by the fact that ΔG° is equal to $+1160$ cal. In (*b*), in which the pressure of the nitrogen dioxide is 0.1 atm and that of the nitrogen tetroxide is 1 atm, the reaction will result in the formation of more of the dioxide since the value of ΔG is -1582 cal. However, in (*c*) where the dioxide is at 1 atm pressure and the tetroxide at 0.1 atm pressure, more of the latter will be formed since the value of ΔG is $+2533$ cal.

Example 10-12. Calculate the ion-product constant of water at 25°C. The equation for the ionization of water is:

$$H_2O\,(l) = H^+ + OH^-$$

$$\Delta G^\circ = \Delta G^\circ_{H^+} + \Delta G^\circ_{OH^-} - \Delta G^\circ_{H_2O} = 0 - 37{,}600\ \text{cal} + 56{,}690\ \text{cal}$$

$$\Delta G^\circ = -RT \ln K_w = 19{,}090\ \text{cal}$$

$$-\log K_w = \frac{19{,}090}{1.99 \times 298.2 \times 2.303} = 13.94$$

$$K_w = 1.1 \times 10^{-14}$$

10l. Relationship of Free Energy Change to Changes in Enthalpy and Entropy. In an earlier section of this chapter it was pointed out that the change in free energy in a given process was related to the change in enthalpy and the change in entropy by the following expression at constant temperature:

$$\Delta G = \Delta H - T \Delta S \qquad (10\text{-}8)$$

This is an extremely useful equation for calculating the value of the free energy change for a reaction when this magnitude and the equilibrium constant cannot be determined by direct measurements. If the necessary calorimetric data for the evaluation of ΔS and ΔH are available, then ΔG can be calculated. The use of this procedure is shown in Example 10-13.

Example 10-13. Calculate $\Delta G°$ at 25°C for the reaction

$$CO\,(g) + \tfrac{1}{2}O_2\,(g) = CO_2\,(g)$$

from the standard enthalpies of formation and the standard entropies. The enthalpies of $CO_2\,(g)$ and $CO\,(g)$ at 25°C are respectively, -94.05 and -26.42 kcal. The entropies can be found in Table 10-1.

$\Delta H° = -94{,}050$ cal $+ 26{,}420$ cal $= -67{,}630$ cal

$\Delta S° = 51.06$ cal/degree $- 47.3$ cal/degree $- 24.5$ cal/degree
   $= -20.7$ E.U.

$\Delta G° = -67{,}630$ cal $+ (298 \times 20.7)$ cal $= -61{,}461$ cal

The calculated value of $\Delta G°$ from the free energy data of Table 10-2 is $-61{,}452$ cal at 25°C.

REFERENCES

Bull, *Physical Biochemistry*, John Wiley and Sons, New York, 1951, Chapter 2.
Daniels and Alberty, *Physical Chemistry*, John Wiley and Sons, New York, 1961, Chapters 5 and 9.
Maron and Prutton, *Principles of Physical Chemistry*, The Macmillan Co., New York, 1958, Chapters 10 and 11.
Moore, *Physical Chemistry*, Prentice-Hall, Englewood Cliffs, New Jersey, 1962, Chapters 3 and 6.
Sheehan, *Physical Chemistry*, Allyn and Bacon, Boston, 1961, Chapter 4.
Daniels, Williams, Bender, Alberty, and Cornwell, *Experimental Physical Chemistry*, McGraw-Hill Book Co., New York, 1962, Chapter 9.

Crockford and Nowell, *Laboratory Manual of Physical Chemistry*, John Wiley and Sons, New York, 1956, Experiments 17 and 30.

REVIEW QUESTIONS

1. Discuss the concept of randomness as it applies to chemical systems. How is the randomness of a system related to its entropy? Discuss some processes, both chemical and physical, that are accompanied with a change in entropy.

2. Give the general mathematical expression for an infinitesimal change in entropy, dS. What is meant by the term, Q_{rev}?

3. Discuss the calculation of the entropy change in isothermal reversible changes in state.

4. Apply the general equation for entropy change to the isothermal change in volume of an ideal gas. What mathematical relationship is used in the calculation of the entropy change in such a process? Would the same equation be used for a reversible process as well as for an expansion into a vacuum?

5. Apply the general equation for entropy change to a change in temperature. What mathematical relations are used when the process takes place at (*a*) constant pressure and (*b*) constant volume?

6. You have the problem of calculating the entropy change when a solid below its melting point is changed to a gas above the boiling point. What data would be needed? What mathematical relationships would you use? How would you carry out the calculations?

7. What is the third law of thermodynamics? Show how the third law could be used to calculate the absolute entropy of a substance at a selected temperature.

8. Show how standard entropy values are used in the calculation of $\Delta S°$ for a given chemical reaction.

9. Discuss free energy change as a measure of useful work. Show how the free energy evolved in certain spontaneous chemical reactions can be obtained in the form of electrical energy.

10. Compare free energy change and entropy change in a process as measures of the spontaneity of the process. What limitations are imposed on the use of free energy change as a measure of spontaneity?

11. What sign conventions are employed in free energy calculations? How is the free energy change in a process at constant temperature related to the change in entropy and the change in enthalpy?

12. What are standard free energies of formation? What types of substances are assumed to have a standard free energy of zero? How are the standard free energies of formation used in evaluating $\Delta G°$ for a chemical reaction?

13. How can equilibrium constants be calculated from free energy data?

14. Derive the general expression for ΔG for a chemical reaction. Discuss the effect of changes in the activities of the reactants and products on the magnitude and sign of ΔG.

15. Discuss the use of the relationship among $\Delta H°$, $\Delta S°$, and $\Delta G°$ for a chemical reaction.

PROBLEMS

Note: See Tables 4-2, 4-3, 10-1, and 10-2 for needed data. Additional data needed: $S_{Cu}^{\circ} = 7.96$, $S_{OH^-}^{\circ} = -2.52$, $S_{Zn}^{\circ} = 99.5$, $S_{H_2}^{\circ} = 31.21$.

I

1. Calculate ΔS for the following changes in state:
   (*a*) The evaporation of 25 grams of benzene at its normal boiling point;
   (*b*) The condensation of 27 grams of water at its normal boiling point;
   (*c*) The solidification of 20 grams of acetone at its normal freezing point;
   (*d*) The fusion of 10 grams of benzene at its normal freezing point.

2. A system consisting of 8 grams of helium in a volume of 40 liters and at a pressure of 0.8 atm expands into a vacuum until the final total volume is 60 liters. Calculate the entropy change. Assume ideal behavior.

3. A system consisting of 8 grams of helium in a volume of 40 liters and at a pressure of 0.8 atm expands reversibly and isothermally until the final volume is 60 liters. Calculate the entropy change in the process.

4. A system containing 48 grams of oxygen is compressed isothermally and reversibly until the volume is reduced to one third the original value. The process takes place at 27°C. Calculate the entropy change in the process.

5. Fourteen grams of nitrogen gas at 10°C and at a pressure of 1 atm are heated to 140°C. Calculate the entropy change when (*a*) the process takes place at constant volume and (*b*) when the process takes place at constant pressure.

6. Given 36 grams of H_2O at 125°C and at a pressure of 1 atm. This system is cooled until the temperature is −10°C. The heat capacity of solid H_2O is 0.5 cal per gram per degree. Calculate the entropy change in each step in the process and the over-all entropy change.

7. Calculate the values of ΔS°, ΔH°, and ΔG° for the following reactions at 25°C.

   (*a*) $2C_2H_6(g) + 7O_2(g) \rightarrow 4CO_2(g) + 6H_2O(l)$
   (*b*) $2Ag(s) + Cl_2(g) \rightarrow 2AgCl(s)$
   (*c*) $Ag^+ + Cl^- \rightarrow AgCl(s)$
   (*d*) $H_2O(l) \rightarrow H^+ + OH^-$

8. Calculate the equilibrium constant for the five reactions given in I-7 for a temperature of 25°C. Will the value of the equilibrium constant increase with an increase in temperature?

9. Calculate the solubility product of silver bromide at 25°C. The standard free energy of AgBr is −22.39 kcal at this temperature.

10. Calculate the free energy change for the following reactions at 25°C:

(a) $Ag^+ (a = 1 \times 10^{-6}) + Cl^- (a = 1 \times 10^{-6}) \rightarrow AgCl\,(s)$

(b) $Ag^+ (a = 1 \times 10^{-3}) + Cl^- (a = 1 \times 10^{-3}) \rightarrow AgCl\,(s)$

(c) $Zn\,(s) + 2Ag^+ (a = 0.2) \rightarrow Zn^{2+} (a = 0.1) + 2Ag\,(s)$

(d) $NO\,(P = 0.8\ atm) + \frac{1}{2}O_2\,(P = 1\ atm) \rightarrow NO_2\,(P = 0.1\ atm)$

(e) $Zn\,(s) + 2Ag^+ (a = 0.6) \rightarrow Zn^{2+} (a = 0.14) + 2Ag\,(s)$

(f) $AgCl\,(s) + \frac{1}{2}H_2\,(780\ mm) \rightarrow Ag\,(s) + H^+ (a = 0.5) + Cl^- (a = 0.3)$

II

1. Calculate ΔS for the following changes in state:

(a) The evaporation of 20 grams of acetic acid at its normal boiling point;

(b) The condensation of 10 grams of benzene at its normal boiling point;

(c) The solidification of 10 grams of benzene at its normal freezing point.

2. A system consisting of 20 grams of nitrogen at 27°C and in a volume of 20 liters expands until its volume becomes 80 liters. The process is an isothermal one. Calculate the entropy change in this process (a) when the expansion takes place reversibly and (b) when it takes place into a vacuum.

3. A system containing 64 grams of oxygen in 80 liters at 25°C is compressed reversibly and isothermally. The entropy change in the process is 2.76 E.U. What is the final volume?

4. Thirty-two grams of oxygen at 27°C and in a volume of 24 liters is heated (a) at constant volume and (b) at constant pressure until the temperature becomes 86°C. Calculate the entropy change in both processes.

5. Given 36 grams of solid H_2O at -10°C. The system is heated until the water is in the form of vapor at 27°C. Calculate the entropy change for the various steps in this process and the over-all entropy change. The heat capacity of ice is 0.5 cal per gram per degree.

6. Calculate the value of $\Delta S°$, $\Delta H°$, and $\Delta G°$ for the following reactions at 25°C:

(a) $Zn\,(s) + 2H^+ \rightarrow Zn^{2+} + H_2\,(g)$

(b) $S\,(s) + O_2\,(g) \rightarrow SO_2\,(g)$

(c) $C_6H_6\,(l) + 7\frac{1}{2}O_2\,(g) \rightarrow 6CO_2\,(g) + 3H_2O\,(l)$

(d) $2NO\,(g) + O_2\,(g) \rightarrow 2NO_2\,(g)$

(e) $C_2H_5OH\,(l) + 3O_2\,(g) \rightarrow 2CO_2\,(g) + 3H_2O\,(l)$

(f) $Cu\,(s) + 2Ag^+ \rightarrow Cu^{2+} + 2Ag$

7. Calculate the equilibrium constant for the six reactions given in Problem II-7 for a temperature of 25°C. Will the value of the equilibrium constant increase or decrease with an increase in temperature?

8. Calculate the free energy change for the following reactions at 25°C:

(a) $Zn\,(s) + 2H^+ (a = 1 \times 10^{-3}) \rightarrow Zn^{2+} (a = 0.80) + H_2\,(g)\,(1\ atm)$

(b) $2NO\,(P = 0.8\ atm) + O_2\,(P = 0.1\ atm) \rightarrow 2NO_2\,(P = 0.2\ atm)$

(c) $Cu\,(s) + 2Ag^+ (a = 0.2) \rightarrow Cu^{2+} (a = 0.01) + 2Ag\,(s)$

(d) $Cu\,(s) + 2Ag^+ (a = 0.02) \rightarrow Cu^{2+} (a = 0.2) + 2Ag\,(s)$

(e) $H^+ (a = 0.002) + OH^- (a = 0.01) \rightarrow H_2O\,(l)$

ELEVEN

Ionic Equilibrium
and Buffer Action

The purpose of this chapter is to study equilibrium phenomena in aqueous solutions of electrolytes. Since all aqueous solutions contain both hydrogen and hydroxyl ions, the first topic will be the ion-product constant of water. Next the pH unit as a means of expressing hydrogen-ion concentration will be developed. Equilibrium conditions will be studied in solutions of acids, bases, and hydrolyzed salts with emphasis on the calculation of the hydrogen-ion concentration and pH in such solutions. Other topics to be treated will be the solubility product, common ion action, ampholytes and solutions of acid salts.

Buffer phenomena will be discussed in a separate section because of its extreme importance in chemical and biological processes.

THE ION-PRODUCT CONSTANT OF WATER AND THE pH SCALE

11a. The Ion-Product Constant of Water. Since water is by far the most useful solvent and since aqueous media constitute those in biological processes, we shall start this chapter by considering the ionization phenomena resulting from the presence of the water. Water may be classed both as an acid and as a base (see Chapter 8) because water molecules can donate protons on reaction with a base (such as ammonia) and accept protons on reaction with an acid (such as acetic and hydrochloric acid). Therefore, it is not surprising to find that there are a few ions even in absolutely pure water. Some few water molecules transfer protons to an equal number of water molecules, giving rise to the equilibrium

$$H_2O + H_2O \rightleftharpoons H_3O^+ + OH^-$$

That ions are actually present even in the purest water is evidenced by the fact that pure water is a slight conductor of electricity. But, since H_3O^+ and OH^- are so powerful as acid and base, respectively, they could never exist together in large concentrations. The equilibrium constant for the ionization of water is represented by the expression

$$\left(K = \frac{a_{H_3O^+} \times a_{OH^-}}{a_{H_2O}^2} \right) \tag{11-1}$$

Since the extent of the ionization is very slight under all circumstances, the activity of un-ionized water may be considered constant. It may therefore be replaced by a constant k. Equation 11-1 then becomes

$$K \times k^2 = a_{H_3O^+} \times a_{OH^-} = K_w \tag{11-?}$$

The product of the two constants gives a constant K_w, called the *ion-product constant* of water. In dilute solutions activities may be replaced by

Table 11-1. Ion Product of Water*

Temperature (°C)	0	10	25	30	40	50
K_w	0.113	0.292	1.008	1.468	2.917	5.474×10^{-14}

* Harned and Hamer, *J. Am. Chem. Soc.*, **55**, 2194 (1933).

concentrations and, using H^+ in place of H_3O^+, give

$$[H^+][OH^-] = K_w \tag{11-3}$$

K_w has been determined by several independent methods. Its numerical value, like that of most equilibrium constants, varies with temperature. At 25°C it is approximately 1×10^{-14}. In pure water the H^+ ion concentration must equal the OH^- ion concentration. Each must, therefore, have a value of 1×10^{-7} mole per liter in order to satisfy the value of K_w. Equation 11-3, however, demands only that the product of the concentrations of H^+ and OH^-, regardless of their source and the acidity of the solution, shall satisfy the value of K_w. If HCl were added to water, the H^+ concentration would be made large and the OH^- concentration correspondingly small. (Their product would still satisfy the value of K_w.) If a base were added to water, $[OH^-]$ would be large and $[H^+]$ correspondingly small. Thus, if either $[H^+]$ or $[OH^-]$ is known in any aqueous solution, the other may be calculated by using Equation 11-3.

As stated above, the value of K_w is a function of temperature. Table 11-1 gives a series of these values. It should be remembered that the hydrogen-ion and hydroxyl-ion concentrations are equal only at the neutral point. If any substance is added that alters this equality, the product of the two will satisfy the value of K_w at that temperature.

While the values of K_w given in Table 11-1 were determined by experimental means, it is quite simple to calculate the values from thermodynamic data. One such procedure was illustrated in Example 10-12 wherein the value of K_w was calculated at 25°C from free energy data. Calculations using the ion-product constant of water will be included in several of the examples to be used later in this chapter.

11b. The pH Scale for Expressing Hydrogen-Ion Concentration. It was shown in the preceding section that every aqueous solution contains both OH^- and H_3O^+ ions. The latter is written in the simplified form, H^+. Whether the solution is acidic or basic is simply a question of which ion is present in the greater concentration. If one is known, the other may be calculated by means of the ion-product constant of water. Usually the acidity or basicity of a solution is described by listing the hydrogen-ion concentration although the solution may be basic. The H^+ concentration may be expressed in moles per liter or in pH units. The pH is used extensively in biological and industrial work and is a much more convenient unit than molarity.

The pH scale for expressing hydrogen-ion concentration was developed by Sørensen in 1909. As defined by him, *the pH of a solution is the negative value of the logarithm of the hydrogen-ion concentration.* With the introduction of the activity concept, pH may be defined as the negative of the logarithm of the hydrogen-ion activity. Since the activity and the concentration of the hydrogen ion are usually not far different in a given solution, the pH as calculated from either is almost identical.

To obtain the pH of a solution, the H^+ concentration expressed in moles per liter is determined and the pH is calculated by the relationship

$$pH = -\log [H^+] = \log \frac{1}{[H^+]}$$

The change from hydrogen-ion concentration to pH and from pH to hydrogen-ion concentration may be illustrated by the following examples.

Example 11-1. Calculate the pH of a solution if the hydrogen-ion concentration is 1.92×10^{-5} mole per liter.

$$pH = -\log [H^+] = -\log 1.92 \times 10^{-5} = 5 - \log 1.92$$
$$= 5 - 0.28 = 4.72$$

Example 11-2. If the pH of a solution is 7.36, what is the hydrogen-ion concentration of the solution?

If pH $= 7.36$, then the value of $[H^+] = $ antilog $- 7.36 = $ antilog $\overset{-}{8}.\overset{+}{64} = 4.37 \times 10^{-8}$ mole per liter.

It should be noted that the minus sign in front of the number 7.63 above applies to both the characteristic and the mantissa. Since logarithm tables are constructed for positive mantissas only, it is necessary to add 1 to the negative mantissa in order to get a positive value. The addition of +1 necessitates the addition of −1. So the characteristic becomes −8, although the over-all value remains unchanged for the logarithmic term as a whole.

Table 11-2. Hydrogen-Ion-pH-pOH Relations

H$^+$ Concentration (moles per liter)		pH	pOH	
1	1	0	14	acid solutions
0.1	1×10^{-1}	1	13	
0.01	1×10^{-2}	2	12	
0.001	1×10^{-3}	3	11	
0.0001	1×10^{-4}	4	10	
0.000001	1×10^{-6}	6	8	
0.0000001	1×10^{-7}	7	7	neutral point
$0.0_7 1$	1×10^{-8}	8	6	basic solutions
$0.0_8 1$	1×10^{-9}	9	5	
$0.0_{10} 1$	1×10^{-11}	11	3	
$0.0_{13} 1$	1×10^{-14}	14	0	

It has been shown in 11a that in any aqueous solution the ion-product constant of water must be achieved.

$$[H^+][OH^-] = K_w$$

Taking logs of both sides of the above equation and changing signs yields

$$-\log [H^+] - \log [OH^-] = -\log K_w \qquad (11\text{-}4)$$

From the definition of pH and by defining pOH as the negative value of the logarithm of the hydroxyl-ion concentration and pK_w as the negative logarithm of the ion product of water, Equation 11-4 becomes

$$pH + pOH = pK_w \qquad (11\text{-}5)$$

At 25°C, since $K_w = 1 \times 10^{-14}$, pK_w equals 14 and

$$pH + pOH = 14 \qquad (11\text{-}6)$$

The relation between hydrogen-ion concentration, pH, and pOH at 25°C is given in Table 11-2. This table illustrates the fact that a tenfold change in the hydrogen-ion concentration results in a change of one pH unit.

EQUILIBRIA IN SOLUTIONS OF ACIDS, BASES, AND SALTS

11c. The Ionization Constant of a Weak Acid. In a solution of a weak electrolyte an equilibrium exists between the molecular and ionic forms of the substance. With a weak acid this equilibrium is represented by the equation (see Chapter 8)

$$HA + H_2O \rightleftharpoons H_3O^+ + A^-$$

in which A^- represents the anion produced from the acid. The general expression for the equilibrium constant is

weak acid
$$K = \frac{a_{H_3O^+} \times a_{A^-}}{a_{HA} \times a_{H_2O}} \tag{11-7}$$

The activity of water in dilute solutions is almost constant, and it may be replaced by k. Then equation 11-7 becomes

$$K = \frac{a_{H_3O^+} \times a_{A^-}}{k \times a_{HA}} \tag{11-8}$$

Since the product of the two constants, K and k, is equal to another constant, now called K_a, it follows that

$$K_a = \frac{a_{H_3O^+} \times a_{A^-}}{a_{HA}} \tag{11-9}$$

$\left(K_a \text{ is known as the ionization constant of a weak acid.} \right)$

The numerical values for the activities of the various components for dilute solutions of weak acids differ only slightly from their concentrations. Equation 11-9 may therefore be written

$$\left(K_a = \frac{[H_3O^+][A^-]}{[HA]} \right) \tag{11-10}$$

in which the concentration of each substance is expressed in moles per liter (molarity).

In deriving and justifying Equation 11-10 from the mathematically true equilibrium constant expression shown in Equation 11-7, the activity of water was included as part of the constant, and molarity was substituted for activity in expressing the concentrations of the other components in the expression. Again, for the sake of simplicity, *the symbol for the hydronium ion*, H_3O^+, *is replaced by* H^+, and Equation 11-10 is written

$$K_a = \frac{[H^+][A^-]}{[HA]} \tag{11-11}$$

It must be emphasized again that the hydrogen ion, H^+, is in reality attached to a water molecule, but, *unless it is desirable to emphasize the role of the solvent in the mechanism of ionization, the use of the symbol* H^+ *simplifies the handling of equations and the writing of the mathematical expressions concerned with ionic equilibria.*

The implication in such a mathematical representation, as given in Equation 11-11, is that a weak acid will ionize, regardless of its concentration, to such an extent that K_a will always be satisfied. That is, the product of the concentrations of the hydrogen ion and the anion, regardless of their source, divided by the concentration of the un-ionized acid will equal a constant that is characteristic of the acid. Experimental evidence shows this representation to be essentially correct. It must be remembered that K_a, like all equilibrium constants, varies with temperature. Most tables of ionization constants are for 25°C so that their relative values may be easily compared.

The expression for the ionization constant may be represented in terms of α, the *degree of ionization* (fraction ionized), and *c*, the total concentration of the acid. Since $[H^+]$ and $[A^-]$ are equal to the concentration of the acid multiplied by the fraction ionized the stepwise derivation becomes

$$[H^+] = \alpha c$$

$$[Ac^-] = \alpha c$$

$$[HAc] = c - \alpha c$$

Substituting these values in Equation 11-11

$$K_a = \frac{\alpha c \times \alpha c}{c - \alpha c} = \frac{\alpha^2 c^2}{(1 - \alpha)c} = \frac{\alpha^2 c}{1 - \alpha} \qquad (11\text{-}12)$$

Since the ionization constant expression is valid only for weak electrolytes, α, the degree of ionization, is always small except in extremely dilute solutions. Therefore it may usually be neglected in the denominator of Equation 11-12, since its value is small compared to unity. The expression then reduces to

$$\left(K_a = \alpha^2 c \right) \qquad (11\text{-}13)$$

11d. The Ionization of a Weak Base. It is the usual practice to use BOH to represent the general formula of a weak base. Hydroxide bases, however (see Chapter 8), are strong electrolytes, and ammonia and its organic derivatives constitute the majority of weak bases. It therefore seems logical to use RNH_2 to represent the general formula of a weak base. R may be the hydrogen atom, as in ammonia, or an organic radical. The ionization of a weak base, then, is represented by the equation

$$RNH_2 + H_2O \rightleftharpoons RNH_3^+ + OH^-$$

In the special case of ammonia the equation would be

$$NH_3 + H_2O \rightleftharpoons NH_4^+ + OH^-$$

Starting with the general equation above and using a line of reasoning exactly similar to that used in obtaining the expression for K_a, it may be shown that the ionization constant expression for a weak base is

$$\left(K_b = \frac{a_{RNH_3^+} \times a_{OH^-}}{a_{RNH_2}} \right) \tag{11-14}$$

In terms of concentrations the expression becomes

$$K_b = \frac{[RNH_3^+][OH^-]}{[RNH_2]} \tag{11-15}$$

and in terms of α, the degree of ionization, and c, the total concentration of base,

$$K_b = \frac{\alpha c \times \alpha c}{c - \alpha c} = \frac{\alpha^2 c^2}{(1 - \alpha)c} = \frac{\alpha^2 c}{1 - \alpha} \tag{11-16}$$

Since α is usually small compared with unity, it may be neglected in the denominator, and Equation 11-16 reduces to

WEAK
BASE >
$$\left(K_b = \alpha^2 c \right) \tag{11-17}$$

11e. Calculation of the Ionization Constant. If the extent of the ionization expressed in per cent or in degree of ionization is known for a given acid or base, its ionization constant may be calculated by using the expressions developed in 11c or 11d.

Example 11-3. In a solution of 0.100M acetic acid 1.34 per cent of the acid is ionized at 25°C. Calculate the ionization constant at this temperature.

SOLUTION 1. Neglecting the role of the solvent in the ionization, we may represent the ionization of the acid by the equation

$$HAc \rightleftharpoons H^+ + Ac^-$$

According to Equation 11-11, the equilibrium constant expression is

$$K_a = \frac{[H^+][Ac^-]}{[HAc]}$$

If HAc is 1.34 per cent ionized at this concentration, the [H$^+$] and [Ac$^-$] concentrations must be 1.34 per cent of the total HAc concentration, or

$$[H^+] = 0.0134 \times 0.100 = 0.00134 \text{ mole per liter}$$
$$[Ac^-] = 0.0134 \times 0.100 = 0.00134 \text{ mole per liter}$$

The concentration of un-ionized HAc must then be 100 per cent − 1.34 per cent of its total concentration, or 98.66 per cent. This results in a molar concentration of un-ionized acetic acid equal to 0.9866 × 0.100. A different way to consider this is

$$[HAc] = 0.1 \text{ (total conc.)} - 0.0134 \times 0.100 \text{ (moles ionized)}$$
$$= 0.0987 \text{ mole per liter}$$

Substituting the values for $[H^+]$, $[Ac^-]$, and $[HAc]$ in the expression gives

$$K_a = \frac{0.00134 \times 0.00134}{0.0987} = 1.82 \times 10^{-5} \text{ at } 25°C$$

SOLUTION 2. According to Equation 11-12, K_a may be calculated by the expression

$$K_a = \frac{\alpha^2 c}{1 - \alpha}$$

If HAc is 1.34 per cent ionized, then α is 0.0134. Thus

$$K_a = \frac{0.0134^2 \times 0.100}{(1 - 0.0134)} = 1.82 \times 10^{-5}$$

Notice that the value for α is small compared with unity in the denominator, so that Equation 11-13 might have been used instead of Equation 11-12 with little loss of accuracy.

11f. Calculation Using the Ionization Constant. Common Ion Effect. Once the ionization constant of a given acid or base is known, it may be used to calculate ionic concentrations and degree of ionization.

Example 11-4. Calculate the hydrogen-ion concentration and the degree of ionization in a $0.20M$ solution of acetic acid at $25°C$. Assume a value of 1.8×10^{-5} for the ionization constant.

SOLUTION 1. Acetic acid ionizes as follows:

$$HAc \rightleftharpoons H^+ + Ac^-$$

until the ionization constant is established, or

$$K_a = \frac{[H^+][Ac^-]}{[HAc]} = 1.8 \times 10^{-5}$$

The only source of ions is from the acid itself, and for each molecule of HAc ionizing one H^+ and one Ac^- ion are formed. Therefore, if x represents the concentration of HAc that ionizes, then

$$[H^+] = [Ac^-] = x$$

and
$$[HAc] = 0.20 - x$$
Substituting,
$$\frac{x \cdot x}{0.20 - x} = 1.8 \times 10^{-5}$$

As can be seen from Example 11-3, x is small compared to the total concentration of HAc. Therefore, the term $0.20 - x$ is changed but little if x is neglected. Solving the equation

$$\frac{x^2}{0.20} = 1.8 \times 10^{-5}$$

$$x = 1.9 \times 10^{-3} \text{ mole per liter} = [H^+]$$

The calculation of the degree of ionization is made as follows:

$$\alpha = \frac{\text{concentration of HAc ionizing}}{\text{total concentration of HAc}} = \frac{1.9 \times 10^{-3}}{0.20} = 0.0095$$

SOLUTION 2. The degree of ionization might first be calculated by using Equation 11-13:
$$K_a = \alpha^2 c \quad \text{or} \quad \alpha = \sqrt{K_a/c}$$
Substituting,
$$\alpha = \sqrt{\frac{1.8 \times 10^{-5}}{0.2}} = 0.0095$$

Finally,
$$[H^+] = \alpha c = 0.0095 \times 0.20 = 1.9 \times 10^{-3} \text{ mole per liter}$$

If a very accurate calculation of ionic concentrations is desired and if the data are accurate enough to warrant such a procedure, the x and α terms neglected in Example 11-4 are retained. This necessitates the solution of a quadratic equation. Such calculations, although not difficult, are rarely resorted to, for it will be remembered that equilibrium constants are exact only if activities are employed instead of concentrations. Since activity data are not generally available for calculations of this type, the final values are sufficiently reliable when the shorter method of calculation is used.

If acetate ions are added to a solution of acetic acid, the ionization of the acid is repressed; the result is a greatly decreased hydrogen-ion concentration. The acetate ions may be supplied from a strong electrolyte such as sodium or potassium acetate. The repression of the ionization of a weak electrolyte by adding one of its ions is called the *common-ion effect*, and the added ion is the *common ion*. The ionization constant is not altered by the addition of this common ion. The repression of the ionization is explained by the necessity of maintaining a constant value of K_a.

Example 11-5. Calculate the hydrogen-ion concentration at 25°C in a solution made by mixing 500 ml of 0.20M acetic acid and 500 ml of 0.30M sodium acetate. Assume complete ionization of the sodium acetate.

In a solution containing only acetic acid, $[H^+] = [Ac^-]$. In the presence of the completely ionized sodium acetate, however, Ac^- ions greatly outnumber H^+ ions. In order that K_a be unchanged on the addition of Na^+Ac^-, it follows that hydrogen ions must combine with acetate ions until the ionic concentrations satisfy the value of K_a. The mathematical solution follows. It should be noted that the volume after mixing the two solutions is 1000 ml.

Let
$$x = [H^+]$$

Total $[Ac^-]$ = concentration of acetate ion from the Na^+Ac^-
+ concentration of acetate ion from the HAc
$$= \left(\frac{500}{1000} \times 0.30\right) + x$$
$$= 0.15 + x$$

$[HAc]$ = total HAc concentration
− amount ionizing into $[H^+]$ and $[Ac^-]$
$$= \left(\frac{500}{1000} \times 0.20\right) - x$$
$$= 0.10 - x$$

Substituting these values in the ionization constant expression for acetic acid,
$$\frac{(x)(0.15 + x)}{(0.10 - x)} = 1.8 \times 10^{-5}$$

Since x is small compared with 0.15 and 0.10, it may be neglected in the two terms shown, and the equation reduces to
$$\frac{(x)(0.15)}{0.10} = 1.8 \times 10^{-5}$$

and
$$x = 1.2 \times 10^{-5} \text{ mole per liter} = [H^+]$$

The tremendous effect of the common ion, as calculated in Example 11-5, may be seen by determining the hydrogen-ion concentration that results when 500 ml of water is added instead of the 500 ml of 0.3M

Na^+Ac^-. The hydrogen-ion concentration would be 1.34×10^{-3} mole per liter instead of 1.2×10^{-5} mole per liter. Thus the hydrogen-ion concentration is reduced approximately 110-fold by the addition of the common ion. The student should calculate these values for himself.

Example 11-6. Calculate the hydrogen-ion concentration in a solution made by mixing 3.70 grams of propionic acid (C_2H_5COOH) and 4.8 grams of sodium propionate (C_2H_5COONa) with sufficient water to make 200 ml of solution. K_a for propionic acid is 1.4×10^{-5} at 25°C.

The first step is the determination of the concentrations in moles per liter. Since the molecular weight of propionic acid is 74, the total concentration of propionic acid is

$$\frac{3.70}{74.0} \times \frac{1000}{200} = 0.25 \text{ mole per liter}$$

Total concentration of sodium propionate is

$$\frac{4.80}{96.0} \times \frac{1000}{200} = 0.25 \text{ mole per liter}$$

Let

$$x = [H^+]$$

Then

$$0.25 + x = [C_2H_5COO^-] \text{ (complete ionization of the salt assumed)}$$

and

$$0.25 - x = [C_2H_5COOH]$$

Substituting these values in the ionization constant expression for propionic acid,

$$\left(K_a = \frac{[H^+][C_2H_5COO^-]}{[C_2H_5COOH]} = 1.4 \times 10^{-5} = \frac{(x)(0.25 + \cancel{x})}{(0.25 - \cancel{x})} \right)$$

The crossed-out x terms are so small compared with 0.25 that they are neglected. Then
$$x = 1.4 \times 10^{-5} \text{ mole per liter} = [H^+]$$

11g. The Ionization of Polyprotic Acids. Acids containing two or more ionizable hydrogens are termed *polyprotic acids*. Such acids always ionize stepwise; that is, the first or *primary* ionization possesses its own characteristic equilibrium equation and ionization constant, and each succeeding ionization has a different equation and constant. This may be illustrated by considering the equilibria involved in the ionization of carbonic acid, a typical diprotic acid.

$$H_2CO_3 + H_2O \rightleftharpoons H_3O^+ + HCO_3^- \quad \text{(primary ionization)}$$
$$HCO_3^- + H_2O \rightleftharpoons H_3O^+ + CO_3^{2-} \quad \text{(secondary ionization)}$$

The corresponding equilibrium constant for each equation is derived as for a monoprotic acid, again using H^+ to symbolize the H_3O^+ ion. The resulting expressions are

$$\frac{[H^+][HCO_3^-]}{[H_2CO_3]} = K_1 = 4.3 \times 10^{-7} \qquad \text{at } 25°C \qquad (11\text{-}18)$$

$$\frac{[H^+][CO_3^{2-}]}{[HCO_3^-]} = K_2 = 5.6 \times 10^{-11} \qquad \text{at } 25°C \qquad (11\text{-}19)$$

Both of these ionizations are taking place simultaneously, but the secondary ionization is much smaller than the primary. The explanation lies in the fact that a neutral H_2CO_3 molecule can transfer an H^+ or proton to water more readily than a negative HCO_3^-. This negative charge on the latter hinders the release of the proton. Notice that K_1, the primary ionization constant, is approximately 10,000 times larger than K_2.

It is often useful to combine the two ionization equations to obtain

$$H_2CO_3 \rightleftharpoons 2H^+ + CO_3^{2-}$$

Then the ionization expression becomes

$$\frac{[H^+]^2[CO_3^{2-}]}{[H_2CO_3]} = K \qquad (11\text{-}20)$$

K is known as the over-all or complete ionization constant, and its numerical value may be obtained by multiplying the K_1 expression by the K_2 expression.

$$\frac{[H^+][HCO_3^-]}{[H_2CO_3]} \times \frac{[H^+][CO_3^{2-}]}{[HCO_3^-]} = K_1 \times K_2 = K \qquad (11\text{-}21)$$

Since HCO_3^- cancels in the numerator and denominator, Equation 11-21 is identical with Equation 11-20. The complete constant, K, is numerically equal to the product of K_1 and K_2 or 2.4×10^{-17}.

Phosphoric acid is the commonest of the triprotic acids and one of the most important acids in medical and biological phenomena. Its stepwise ionization may be shown as follows:

$$H_3PO_4 \rightleftharpoons H^+ + H_2PO_4^- \quad \text{(primary ionization)}$$

$$H_2PO_4^- \rightleftharpoons H^+ + HPO_4^{2-} \quad \text{(secondary ionization)}$$

$$HPO_4^{2-} \rightleftharpoons H^+ + PO_4^{3-} \quad \text{(tertiary ionization)}$$

The expressions for the ionization constants are

$$\frac{[H^+][H_2PO_4^-]}{[H_3PO_4]} = K_1 = 7.5 \times 10^{-3} \quad \text{at } 25°C \quad (11\text{-}22)$$

$$\frac{[H^+][HPO_4^{2-}]}{[H_2PO_4^-]} = K_2 = 6.2 \times 10^{-8} \quad \text{at } 25°C \quad (11\text{-}23)$$

$$\frac{[H^+][PO_4^{3-}]}{[HPO_4^{2-}]} = K_3 = 4.8 \times 10^{-13} \quad \text{at } 25°C \quad (11\text{-}24)$$

Finally the complete ionization constant expression becomes

$$\frac{[H^+]^3[PO_4^{3-}]}{[H_3PO_4]} = K_1 \times K_2 \times K_3 = K$$
$$= 2.23 \times 10^{-22} \quad \text{at } 25°C \quad (11\text{-}25)$$

In the solution of problems involving polyprotic acids, the student often finds it difficult to decide which ionization constant expression, or which combination of expressions, to use. The following examples should help clear up this difficulty.

Example 11-7. Calculate the hydrogen-ion concentration at 25°C in a 0.050M solution of carbonic acid.

As stated previously, K_1 is approximately 10,000 times larger than K_2. Therefore, for all practical purposes, all the H^+ ions come from the first ionization of the carbonic acid and the K_1 expression can therefore be used. Since the $[H^+]$ is equal to $[HCO_3^-]$ in the first ionization, sub-solution in the K_1 expression (11-18) gives

$$\frac{[H^+]^2}{0.05} = 4.3 \times 10^{-7}$$

Then

$$[H^+]^2 = 2.15 \times 10^{-8}$$

and

$$[H^+] = 1.5 \times 10^{-4} \text{ mole per liter}$$

Note that Example 11-7 cannot be solved by using the complete ionization constant expression (Equation 11-20). Since most of the H^+ ions come from the first ionization and all the CO_3^{2-} come from the second ionization, there is no simple relationship between the two. Since there are two unknowns, the equation cannot be solved by substituting in the expression for the over-all constant.

Example 11-8. Calculate the carbonate-ion concentration in a 0.050M solution of carbonic acid that is also 0.10M in hydrochloric acid. (Assume

Table 11-3. Ionization Constants of Some Acids at 25°C*

Monoprotic Acids

Acid	K_a	Acid	K_a
Formic	1.77×10^{-4}	Lactic	1.40×10^{-4}
Acetic	1.75×10^{-5}	Glycolic	1.52×10^{-4}
Benzoic	6.30×10^{-5}	Hydrocyanic	7.2×10^{-10}
Chloroacetic	1.40×10^{-3}	Boric	5.8×10^{-10}

Polyprotic Acids

Acid	K_1	K_2	K_3
Oxalic	6.5×10^{-2}	6.1×10^{-5}	—
Carbonic	4.3×10^{-7}	5.6×10^{-11}	—
Hydrogen sulfide	5.7×10^{-8}	1.2×10^{-15}	—
Citric	8.7×10^{-4}	1.8×10^{-5}	4.0×10^{-6}
Phosphoric	7.5×10^{-3}	6.2×10^{-8}	4.8×10^{-13}

* Most of the values in this table are taken from Lange's *Handbook of Chemistry*, 10th Edition, Handbook Publishers, Inc., Sandusky, Ohio.

the HCl to be completely ionized at this concentration.) The over-all constant $= 2.4 \times 10^{-17}$.

$$\frac{(0.10)^2[CO_3^{2-}]}{0.050} = K = 2.4 \times 10^{-17}$$

$$[CO_3^{2-}] = 1.2 \times 10^{-16} \text{ mole per liter}$$

Tables 11-3 and 11-4 give the accepted values of the ionization constants for a number of acids and bases.

11h. The Calculation of pH in Solutions of Acids and Bases. If pH is to be calculated in a solution containing a strong acid, such as HCl, ionization may be assumed to be complete unless otherwise specified. Hence the H^+ concentration is taken to be that of the acid, and the pH is the negative of the logarithm of the acid concentration. The same

Table 11-4. Ionization Constants of Some Bases at 25°C*

Base	K_b	Base	K_b
Ammonia	1.8×10^{-5}	Aniline	3.8×10^{-10}
Methylamine	4.4×10^{-4}	Pyridine	1.4×10^{-9}
Trimethylamine	5.3×10^{-5}	Quinoline	6.3×10^{-10}

* Most of the values in this table are taken from Lange's *Handbook of Chemistry*, 10th Edition, Handbook Publishers, Inc., Sandusky, Ohio.

consideration applies to the OH^- concentration of a strong hydroxide base, such as Na^+OH^-.

If the acid is weak, the H^+ concentration will, of course, depend not only on the acid concentration but also on the value of K_a. As shown in 11c, the ionization constant expression for a weak monoprotic acid is

$$K_a = \frac{[H^+][A^-]}{[HA]}$$

If the solution contains no common ion, $[H^+]$ equals $[A^-]$, and one may therefore be substituted for the other. The ionization constant expression is then written

$$[H^+]^2 = K_a[HA] \tag{11-26}$$

and

$$(\quad [H^+] = \sqrt{K_a[HA]} \quad) \tag{11-27}$$

If the acid is only slightly ionized, the total concentration of acid may be substituted for $[HA]$. This gives

$$[H^+] = \sqrt{K_a c} \tag{11-28}$$

Taking logarithms of both sides and changing signs yields

$$-\log [H^+] = \tfrac{1}{2}(-\log K_a - \log c) = pH \tag{11-29}$$

If pK_a is defined as the negative logarithm of K_a, Equation 11-29 gives

$$pH = \tfrac{1}{2}(pK_a - \log c) = \tfrac{1}{2}pK_a - \tfrac{1}{2}\log c \tag{11-30}$$

$\left(\text{The ionization constant of a weak base is given by the expression }\right)$

$$\Rightarrow K_b = \frac{[RNH_3^+][OH^-]}{[RNH_2]}$$

If the base is weak, c, its total concentration, may be substituted for $[RNH_2]$. Also, if the solution does not contain a common ion, $[RNH_3^+]$ equals $[OH^-]$. Making these substitutions and solving for $[OH^-]$ give

$$[OH^-]^2 = K_b \cdot c \tag{11-31}$$

Since $[OH^-]$ is equal to $K_w/[H^+]$ in any aqueous solution, Equation 11-31 becomes

$$\frac{K_w}{[H^+]} = \sqrt{K_b \cdot c} \tag{11-32}$$

and

$$[H^+] = \frac{K_w}{\sqrt{K_b \cdot c}} \tag{11-33}$$

Taking logs of both sides and changing signs give

$$pH = -\log [H^+] = -\log K_w + \tfrac{1}{2} \log K_b + \tfrac{1}{2} \log c \quad (11\text{-}34)$$

By defining pK_b as the negative of the logarithm of the ionization constant of the base, Equation 11-34 becomes

$$\left\{ pH = pK_w - \tfrac{1}{2}pK_b + \tfrac{1}{2} \log c \right\} \quad (11\text{-}35)$$

Thus, by means of Equations 11-30 and 11-35, the pH of a solution of a weak acid or base may be calculated directly, provided the solution does not contain a common ion.

Example 11-9. Calculate the pH at 25°C of a 1.0M solution of the weak base trimethylamine. $K_b = 5.3 \times 10^{-5}$.

$$pK_b = -\log K_b = -(\log 5.3 \times 10^{-5}) = (5 - \log 5.3) = 4.28$$

Substituting in Equation 11-35 gives

$$pH = pK_w - \tfrac{1}{2}pK_b + \tfrac{1}{2} \log c = 14 - 2.14 = 11.86 \quad \cdot$$

The above solution serves as a convenient and rapid method for solving such problems. The same results could be obtained, however, by calculating the OH$^-$ concentration from the usual ionization constant expression and then solving for the hydrogen-ion concentration and pH. The latter method, although longer, is recommended until the student becomes thoroughly familiar with the use and significance of the various expressions involved.

11i. The Solubility Product. The equilibrium between a slightly soluble salt, such as silver chloride, and its ions in solution may be represented by the following

$$Ag^+Cl^- \text{ (solid)} \rightleftharpoons Ag^+ + Cl^-$$

Here Ag^+Cl^- represents the solid salt and the presence of the charges on the two elements shows that the salt is ionized in the solid state. The equilibrium constant for the reaction is

$$K = \frac{a_{Ag^+} \times a_{Cl^-}}{a_{Ag^+Cl^-}} \quad (11\text{-}36)$$

Since the activity of the solid is unity (see Chapter 9), Equation 11-36 becomes

$$K = a_{Ag^+} \times a_{Cl^-} \quad (11\text{-}37)$$

In dilute solutions activities may be replaced by concentrations, giving

$$[Ag^+][Cl^-] = K_{sp} \quad (11\text{-}38)$$

where K_{sp} is known as the *solubility product constant* of silver chloride.

The same type of mathematical treatment can be applied to any slightly soluble electrolyte. For silver sulfate the reaction will be

$$Ag_2^+SO_4^{2-} \text{ (solid)} \rightleftharpoons 2Ag^+ + SO_4^{2-}$$

and the expression for the solubility product constant will be

$$K_{sp} = [Ag^+]^2[SO_4^{2-}]$$

The *solubility product principle* may therefore be stated: *In a saturated solution of any slightly soluble electrolyte, the product of the concentrations of the ions, raised to a power equal to the number of times the ion occurs in the equation representing the solution of the electrolyte, is a constant at a fixed temperature.*

In accordance with the solubility product principle, the product of the concentrations of the silver and the chloride ions is a constant in a saturated solution of silver chloride. The source of the ions is immaterial. If Cl^- ions are added to a solution of silver chloride, the Ag^+ concentration will decrease, through interaction with Cl^- ions, until the value of K_{sp} is satisfied. This, of course, results in the precipitation of silver chloride and is an example of common ion action. The principle is useful in qualitative and quantitative analysis in predicting completeness of precipitation. The following examples illustrate the use of the solubility product principle.

Example 11-10. A liter of water at 25°C dissolves 1.31×10^{-4} mole of silver chromate. Calculate K_{sp} for this salt at 25°C. The resulting equilibrium when silver chromate dissolves may be represented by the equation

$$Ag_2^+CrO_4^{2-} \text{ (solid)} \rightleftharpoons 2Ag^+ + CrO_4^{2-}$$

and

$$K_{sp} = [Ag^+]^2[CrO_4^{2-}]$$

When each mole of silver chromate dissolves, 2 moles of silver ion and 1 mole of chromate ion are formed; therefore, the ion concentrations in the saturated solution are

$$Ag^+ = 2 \times 1.31 \times 10^{-4} = 2.62 \times 10^{-4} \text{ mole per liter}$$

$$CrO_4^{2-} = 1 \times 1.31 \times 10^{-4} = 1.31 \times 10^{-4} \text{ mole per liter}$$

Substituting in the K_{sp} expression,

$$(2.62 \times 10^{-4})^2 \times (1.31 \times 10^{-4}) = K_{sp} = 9.00 \times 10^{-12}$$

Example 11-11. How many grams of Mg^{2+} are present in 200 ml of a saturated solution of $Mg^{2+}(OH)_2^-$ at 18°C if the K_{sp} at this temperature is 1.4×10^{-11}?

The equilibrium equation is

$$Mg^{2+}(OH)_2^- \text{ (solid)} \rightleftharpoons Mg^{2+} + 2OH^-$$

and

$$K_{sp} = (Mg^{2+}][OH^-]^2$$

If the molar concentration of Mg^{2+} is represented by x, then the molar concentration of OH^- is $2x$, for two hydroxyl ions are produced for each magnesium ion. Substituting in the K_{sp} expression gives

$$(x)(2x)^2 = 1.4 \times 10^{-11}$$
$$4x^3 = 1.4 \times 10^{-11}$$
$$x = 1.5 \times 10^{-4} = \text{concentration of } Mg^{2+} \text{ in moles per liter}$$

To convert the magnesium-ion concentration from moles per liter to grams per liter, the molar concentration must be multiplied by the atomic weight.

$$1.5 \times 10^{-4} \times 24.3 = 36.5 \times 10^{-4} \text{ gram per liter}$$

$$36.5 \times 10^{-4} \times \frac{200}{1000} = 7.3 \times 10^{-4} \text{ gram per 200 ml}$$

Example 11-12. If Na^+Cl^- is added to a liter of $0.010M$ solution of $Ag^+NO_3^-$ until the Cl^--ion concentration is 1.0×10^{-3} mole per liter, how many grams of Ag^+ ion will precipitate and how many grams of Ag^+ ion will remain unprecipitated? Assume no change in volume on the addition of the sodium chloride. K_{sp} for $Ag^+Cl^- = 1.56 \times 10^{-10}$ at 25°C, the temperature of the experiment.

Silver chloride will precipitate until the value of K_{sp} is satisfied. If the final chloride-ion concentration is 1.0×10^{-3} mole per liter, then

$$[Ag^+](1 \times 10^{-3}) = K_{sp} = 1.56 \times 10^{-10}$$

and the silver-ion concentration is $[Ag^+] = 1.56 \times 10^{-10}/1 \times 10^{-3} = 1.56 \times 10^{-7}$ mole per liter. This is the number of moles of silver ion remaining in the solution after the addition of the sodium chloride. The atomic weight of silver being 108, the weight of silver remaining in solution is

$$108 \times 1.56 \times 10^{-7} = 1.68 \times 10^{-5} \text{ gram}$$

The original quantity of silver in the solution was

$$108 \times 0.01 = 1.08 \text{ grams}$$

and the amount precipitating is the difference between 1.08 grams and 1.68×10^{-5} gram. Therefore, for all practical purposes the precipitation is complete.

11j. Salt Effect. If neutral salts, such as sodium chloride and potassium chloride, are added to water solutions of weak acids and bases or to saturated solutions of slightly soluble electrolytes, the calculated values of the ionic concentrations are not strictly accurate, indicating an *apparent* change in the equilibrium constant of the electrolyte. This effect on the ionization constant of a weak electrolyte or on the solubility product constant of a slightly soluble electrolyte by the addition of a foreign electrolyte is called the *salt effect*. The magnitude of the effect is not pronounced in solutions of weak acids and bases in ordinary concentrations. Solubility product calculations, however, may give results that vary significantly from experimental values in solutions made concentrated by the presence of foreign electrolytes.

This discrepancy does not mean that the equilibrium laws are in error. If activities are used instead of concentrations, the equilibrium laws hold and the constants maintain a fixed value even if other electrolytes are present. For example, K_a for acetic acid is about 1.8×10^{-5} at $25°C$, regardless of added electrolytes, if K_a is calculated from activity data. But K_a does vary somewhat from this value upon the addition of neutral salts if concentrations are used.

The Debye-Hückel theory (see Chapter 8) explains this apparent discrepancy and gives a mathematical treatment of the effect of ionic concentration on activities. This treatment is involved and unnecessary at this point, since concentration calculations are more frequently encountered and are accurate enough for most practical purposes.

11k. The Ionization of Ampholytes. In addition to water, a number of other substances are capable of acting both as proton donors and proton acceptors. In other words, under one set of conditions a substance may act as a base and under another set of conditions it may act as an acid. Many metal hydroxides, for example, $Zn(OH)_2$, $Pb(OH)_2$, and $Al(OH)_3$, act in this manner. This type of substance is known as an *amphoteric electrolyte*, a name usually shortened to *ampholyte*. The most important ampholites in medical and biological work are the amino acids and proteins. These contain basic amino groups and acidic carboxyl groups. The simplest amino acid is glycine, and this compound will be used to illustrate the dual nature of such substances. Glycine, NH_2—CH_2—$COOH$, exists as a *hybrid ion* both in the solid state and in solution. The formation of this hybrid ion is effected by the transfer of a proton from the acid carboxyl group to the basic amino group. Thus, one part of the molecule acquires a positive charge while another part acquires a negative charge. The molecule as a whole is electrically neutral. The conversion to the hybrid, or *zwitterion*, as it is often called, is almost complete.

It may be represented by the following equation:

$$NH_2-CH_2-COOH \rightleftharpoons NH_3^+-CH_2-COO^-$$

If an acid is added to an aqueous solution of glycine, the proton adds to the $-COO^-$ group to form an undissociated carboxyl group. On the other hand, the addition of a base results in the removal of a proton from the NH_3^+-group by the added OH^-, thus forming a neutral amino group. The equations for these reactions are

$$NH_3^+-CH_2-COO^- + H_3O^+ \rightleftharpoons NH_3^|-CH_2-COOH + H_2O$$
$$NH_3^+-CH_2-COO^- + OH^- \rightleftharpoons NH_2-CH_2-COO^- + H_2O$$

The acid and base equilibrium of the hybrid ion may be represented as

$$H_3O^+ + NH_2-CH_2-COO^- \rightleftharpoons H_2O + NH_3^+-CH_2-COO^-$$
Acid ionization

$$\rightleftharpoons NH_3^+-CH_2-COOH + OH^-$$
Basic ionization

The ionization constants for these two reactions are given by the expressions

$$K_a = \frac{[H_3O^+][NH_2CH_2COO^-]}{[NH_3^+CH_2COO^-]} = 1.67 \times 10^{-10} \qquad \text{at } 25°C$$

$$K_b = \frac{[NH_3^+CH_2COOH][OH^-]}{[NH_3^+CH_2COO^-]} = 2.22 \times 10^{-12} \qquad \text{at } 25°C$$

Similar expressions may be formulated for other ampholytes.

There is one value of pH, called the *isoelectric point*, at which the $NH_2CH_2COO^-$ ion and the $NH_3^+CH_2COOH$ ion have equal concentrations. Experimentation shows that with glycine the isoelectric point is 6.0. This value can be checked by the two ionization expressions given above. The concentrations of the two ions are equal at this point and simultaneous solution of the two equations gives the hydrogen-ion concentration at the isoelectric point.

The isoelectric point is important in the study of proteins by *electrophoresis* as discussed in Chapter 18. At this characteristic pH there is no net migration of the protein in an electric field.

THE HYDROLYSIS OF SALTS

111. Aqueous Salt Solutions. When a salt is added to water, the solution may remain neutral or it may become acidic or basic, depending upon the type of salt. In pure water the hydrogen and hydroxyl ions are equal in number. If one or more of the added salt ions react with either of the ions of the water, their equality may be destroyed and the solution may become acidic or basic. If such a reaction occurs, the salt is said to be hydrolyzed. *Hydrolysis* is, therefore, the interaction of the ions of salts with the ions of water.

Salts are usually classified into four types in order to study their reaction in water. These classes are (1) salts of strong acids and strong bases, such as sodium chloride and potassium nitrate; (2) salts of weak acids and strong bases, such as sodium acetate and potassium cyanide; (3) salts of strong acids and weak bases, such as ammonium chloride; and (4) salts of weak acids and weak bases, such as ammonium acetate. The last three classes become hydrolyzed in water and therefore merit separate and detailed consideration (11m, 11n, 11o). The first class, salts of strong acids and strong bases, does not hydrolyze because neither of the salt ions is capable of reacting with either the hydrogen or the hydroxyl ion of the water. If Na^+Cl^- is added to water, there is no tendency for Na^+ ions to react with OH^- ions because Na^+OH^- is completely ionized. Similarly, there is no tendency for Cl^- ions to react with H_3O^+ ions to form un-ionized HCl. Therefore, the relation of H_3O^+ ions and OH^- ions remains unchanged and the solution continues to show a neutral reaction.

11m. Hydrolysis of Salts of Weak Acids and Strong Bases. Salts of this type hydrolyze to give basic solutions. This may be explained by considering a solution of sodium acetate. This compound is the salt of the weak acid HAc and the strong base Na^+OH^-. When the salt is dissolved in water, the Ac^- ions must react with H_3O^+ ions until the ionization constant of HAc is satisfied. No single equation can show the mechanism of this reaction, since H_3O^+ ions are used in reacting with added Ac^- ions, and undissociated water must further ionize in order to maintain the value of K_w. This results in an increase in OH^- ions and a decrease in H_3O^+ ions. Equilibrium finally is established when both K_w and K_a are satisfied. This may be shown by the box equation

$$Na^+Ac^- \rightarrow Na^+ + Ac^-$$
$$+$$
$$2H_2O \rightleftharpoons OH^- + H_3O^+$$
$$\Updownarrow$$
$$HAc + H_2O$$

Although the mechanism of the hydrolysis requires more than a single equation, the net result is a reaction between acetate ions and water molecules:

$$Ac^- + H_2O \rightleftharpoons HAc + OH^-$$

For the purpose of developing the mathematical relation for the hydrolysis of salts of this type, consider that the salt has the general formula, B^+A^-, in which B^+ is the cation of a strong base and A^- is the anion of a weak acid. Its reaction with water may be represented as

$$B^+ + A^- + H_2O \rightleftharpoons B^+ + HA + OH^-$$

Since the B^+ ion does not enter into the reaction, it may be dropped. Then the equilibrium equation reduces to

$$A^- + H_2O \rightleftharpoons HA + OH^-$$

The equilibrium constant expression for the reaction, using concentrations, is

$$K = \frac{[HA][OH^-]}{[H_2O][A^-]} \qquad (11\text{-}39)$$

The concentration of water may be replaced by a constant, k, if the solution is dilute. Equation 11-39 may therefore be written

$$K \times k = K_h = \frac{[HA][OH^-]}{[A^-]} \qquad (11\text{-}40)$$

The product of the two constants is another, termed the *hydrolysis constant*.

Equation 11-40 may be used to calculate the OH^--ion concentration of a solution containing a given salt of this type if K_h for the reaction is known. As stated previously, equilibrium results when values of the ionization constant of the acid HA and the ion product constant K_w are satisfied. K_h, therefore, is necessarily related to these two constants, and if that relationship is determined, K_h can then be calculated directly from these two values. Since the product of $[H^+]$ and $[OH^-]$ equals K_w in any aqueous solution, it follows that

$$[OH^-] = \frac{K_w}{[H^+]}$$

The substitution of $K_w/[H^+]$ for $[OH^-]$ in Equation 11-40 gives

$$\frac{[HA]}{[H^+][A^-]} \times K_w = K_h \qquad (11\text{-}41)$$

The concentration terms in Equation 11-41 are the reciprocal of the ionization constant k_a of the weak acid HA. Therefore, substituting $1/K_a$ for $[HA]/[H^+][A^-]$ gives the relation

$$\left(\; \frac{K_w}{K_a} = K_h \; \right) \qquad (11\text{-}42)$$

Substituting K_w/K_a for K_h in Equation 11-41 yields

$$\frac{[HA][OH^-]}{[A^-]} = \frac{K_w}{K_a} \qquad (11\text{-}43)$$

An examination of the hydrolysis equation reveals that one molecule of HA is produced for each OH^- ion. Therefore [HA] equals $[OH^-]$, and one may be replaced by the other in Equation 11-43. The following is the result:

$$[OH^-]^2 = \frac{K_w[A^-]}{K_a} = K_h[A^-] \qquad (11\text{-}44)$$

and

$$[OH^-] = \sqrt{K_w[A^-]/K_a} \qquad (11\text{-}45)$$

The value of A^-, the concentration of the anion undergoing hydrolysis, is equal to c, the total concentration of the salt, if the degree of hydrolysis is not too large. Equation 11-45 then becomes

$$[OH^-] = \sqrt{K_w \times c/K_a} \qquad (11\text{-}46)$$

If the salt is considerably hydrolyzed so that $[A^-]$ differs appreciably from c, then $[A^-] = c - [OH^-]$ because for each molecule of salt hydrolyzed one OH^- is formed. In this case Equation 11-45 becomes

$$\rightarrow [OH^-] = \sqrt{\frac{K_w(c - [OH^-])}{K_a}} \leftarrow \qquad (11\text{-}47)$$

Equation 11-47 is used in preference to Equation 11-46 only if K_a is very small, 1×10^{-10} or less. As an example, consider the hydrolysis of $Na_2^+S^{2-}$, whose reaction is given by the equation

$$S^{2-} + H_2O \rightleftharpoons HS^- + OH^-$$

K_a for the HS^- is 1.2×10^{-15} at $18°C$. In this case hydrolysis is so extensive that $[A^-]$ and c differ greatly, and Equation 11-47 must be used to calculate the OH^--ion concentration. The subsequent hydrolysis of HS^- to H_2S is so small as to be negligible.

In computing the fraction of hydrolysis, it need only be remembered that each OH^- ion formed represents one molecule of salt hydrolyzed. Therefore, the fraction of hydrolysis β is

$$\beta = \frac{[OH^-]}{c} \qquad (11\text{-}48)$$

and the per cent hydrolysis will be 100 times this value.

Example 11-13. Calculate the H^+ ion concentration and the per cent hydrolysis in a $0.10M$ solution of sodium acetate at $25°C$. $K_a = 1.8 \times 10^{-5}$.

SOLUTION 1. Sodium acetate hydrolyzes according to the equation $Ac^- + H_2O \rightleftharpoons HAc + OH^-$ until the hydrolysis constant is established.

$$\frac{[HAc][OH^-]}{[Ac^-]} = K_h = \frac{K_w}{K_a}$$

Let

$$x = [OH^-] = [HAc]$$

Then

$$[Ac^-] = 0.10 - x$$

Substituting in the hydrolysis constant expression

$$\frac{x \cdot x}{0.10 - x} = \frac{1 \times 10^{-14}}{1.8 \times 10^{-5}}$$

x in the denominator is negligibly small compared with 0.10, since K_a is larger than 1×10^{-10}. Therefore,

$$x^2 = \frac{0.1 \times 1 \times 10^{-14}}{1.8 \times 10^{-5}}$$

$$x = 7.4 \times 10^{-6} = \text{concentration of } OH^- \text{ in mole per liter}$$

The ion-product expression for water may now be used to obtain the H^+ concentration.

$$[H^+] = \frac{K_w}{[OH^-]} = \frac{1 \times 10^{-14}}{7.4 \times 10^{-6}} = 1.3 \times 10^{-9} \text{ mole per liter}$$

the fraction hydrolyzed, equals

$$\frac{[OH^-]}{c} = \frac{7.4 \times 10^{-6}}{0.10} = 7.4 \times 10^{-5} = \beta$$

The per cent hydrolyzed = fraction hydrolyzed $\times$ 100 = 0.0074 per cent. This value illustrates the fact that the extent of the hydrolysis for most salt solutions is very small.

SOLUTION 2. Equation 11-46 may be used to calculate the OH^--ion concentration.

$$[OH^-] = \sqrt{\frac{K_w c}{K_a}} = \sqrt{\frac{1 \times 10^{-14} \times 0.10}{1.8 \times 10^{-5}}} = 7.4 \times 10^{-6} \text{ mole per liter}$$

The hydrogen-ion concentration and the per cent hydrolysis may be calculated as before.

11n. Hydrolysis of Salts of Weak Bases and Strong Acids. Salts of this type may be exemplified by ammonium chloride, whose net reaction with the ions of water is represented by the equation

$$NH_4^+ + H_2O \rightleftharpoons NH_3 + H_3O^+$$

Thus, it is seen that the solution becomes acid. The equilibrium is concerned with the ionization constant of the weak base NH_3 and the ion-product constant of water, and it may be represented by a box-type equation analogous to that used in 11m. If $RNH_3^+A^-$ represents any salt of the strong acid-weak base type, the equation for its hydrolysis is

$$RNH_3^+ + A^- \rightleftharpoons RNH_2 + A^- + H_3O^+$$

Since A^- takes no part in the reaction, the hydrolysis constant expression is

$$\frac{[RNH_2][H^+]}{[RNH_3^+]} = K_h \qquad (11\text{-}49)$$

K_h may be evaluated in terms of K_b and K_w in a manner similar to the method used for salts of the strong base-weak acid type in 11m. Since $[H^+]$ equals $K_w/[OH^-]$, it may be substituted for $[H^+]$, giving

$$K_w \times \frac{[RNH_2]}{[RNH_3^+][OH^-]} = K_h \qquad (11\text{-}50)$$

The concentration terms are equal to the reciprocal of K_b. Therefore, Equation 11-50 becomes

$$\frac{K_w}{K_b} = K_h \qquad (11\text{-}51)$$

and Equation 11-49 becomes

$$\frac{[RNH_2][H^+]}{[RNH_3^+]} = \frac{K_w}{K_b} \qquad (11\text{-}52)$$

Since one H^+ ion is produced for every molecule of base, RNH_2, and since c may be substituted for $[RNH_3^+]$, the equation may be changed to

$$\frac{[H^+]^2}{c} = \frac{K_w}{K_b} \qquad (11\text{-}53)$$

and

$$[H^+] = \sqrt{K_w c / K_b} \qquad (11\text{-}54)$$

If K_b is extremely small (less than 1×10^{-10}), so that an appreciable amount of c hydrolyzes, Equation 11-54 is written

$$[H^+] = \sqrt{\frac{K_w(c - [H^+])}{K_b}} \qquad (11\text{-}55)$$

The degree of hydrolysis for this type of salt is given by dividing the $[H^+]$ by c.

$$\left(\beta = \frac{[H^+]}{c} \right)$$
(11-56)

Example 11-14. Calculate the hydrogen-ion concentration and the degree of hydrolysis in a solution that is $0.050M$ in ammonium chloride at 25°C. $K_b = 1.8 \times 10^{-5}$.

SOLUTION 1. The hydrolysis equation is

$$NH_4^+ + H_2O \rightleftharpoons NH_3 + H_3O^+$$

and the expression for K_h may be written

$$\left(K_h = \frac{[NH_3][H^+]}{[NH_4^+]} = \frac{K_w}{K_b} \right)$$

The $[NH_4^+]$ is 0.050. Let x represent the $[H^+]$ and $[NH_3]$. Then

$$\frac{x \cdot x}{0.050} = \frac{1 \times 10^{-14}}{1.8 \times 10^{-5}}$$

and

$$x = 5.3 \times 10^{-6} \text{ mole of } H^+ \text{ ions per liter}$$

The degree of hydrolysis $= [H^+]/c = 5.3 \times 10^{-6}/0.050 = 1.06 \times 10^{-4}$.

SOLUTION 2. Using Equation 11-54,

$$[H^+] = \sqrt{\frac{K_w c}{K_b}} = \sqrt{\frac{1 \times 10^{-14} \times 0.050}{1.8 \times 10^{-5}}} = 5.3 \times 10^{-6} \text{ mole per liter}$$

11o. Hydrolysis of Salts of Weak Acids and Weak Bases. Salts of this type are hydrolyzed to a greater degree than the other two types because both the anion and the cation react with the ions of water to form un-dissociated acid and base. Equilibrium is attained when the values of K_a, K_b, and K_w are established. If the acid and base are of approximately equal strength, the net reaction may be expressed as

$$RNH_3^+ + A^- \rightleftharpoons RNH_2 + HA$$

In such a case the resulting solution is neutral in spite of the hydrolysis. The hydrolysis constant expression becomes

$$\left(\frac{[RNH_2][HA]}{[RNH_3^+][A^-]} = K_h = \frac{K_w}{K_a K_b} \right)$$
(11-57)

The fact that K_h is equal to K_w/K_aK_b may be shown by substituting concentration equivalents:

$$\left(\quad \frac{K_w}{K_aK_b} = \frac{\dfrac{[H^+][OH^-]}{[H^+][A^-]}}{[HA]} \times \frac{[RNH_3^+][OH^-]}{[RNH_2]} = \frac{[RNH_2][HA]}{[A^-][RNH_3^+]} \quad \right)$$

If the salt is one similar to $NH_4^+Ac^-$, in which $K_a = K_b$, and the salt is not greatly hydrolyzed, $[RNH_3^+] = [A^-] = c$ (the total concentration of the salt). Therefore,

$$\frac{[RNH_2][HA]}{c^2} = \frac{K_w}{K_aK_b} \tag{11-58}$$

Since RNH_2 and HA are formed in equal amounts,

$$\left\{ [RNH_2] = [HA] = c\sqrt{K_w/K_aK_b} \right\} \tag{11-59}$$

For each molecule of salt hydrolyzing, one molecule each of RNH_2 and HA are formed. Therefore, the degree of hydrolysis may be determined by dividing $[HA]$ or $[RNH_2]$ by c.

$$\beta = \frac{[HA]}{c} \quad \text{and} \quad [HA] = c\beta \tag{11-60}$$

Substituting in Equation 11-59 for $[HA]$,

$$\beta c = c\sqrt{K_w/K_aK_b} \quad \text{and} \quad \boxed{\beta = \sqrt{K_w/K_aK_b}} \tag{11-61}$$

Since the concentration term cancels in the above expression, note that for salts of this type the degree of hydrolysis is independent of the concentration of the salt.

Example 11-15. Calculate the degree of hydrolysis in a solution of ammonium acetate. $K_a = K_b = 1.8 \times 10^{-5}$.
Employing Equation 11-61

$$\beta = \sqrt{\frac{K_w}{K_aK_b}} = \sqrt{\frac{1 \times 10^{-14}}{(1.8 \times 10^{-5})^2}} = 5.5 \times 10^{-3}$$

If the strengths of the weak acid and weak base formed during the hydrolysis are not the same, the solution will become either acidic or basic. Provided the degree of hydrolysis is not too great, the hydrogen-ion concentration of the solution may be calculated by substituting for $[HA]$ in Equation 11-59 its numerical equivalent from the K_a expression. Thus

$$K_a = \frac{[H^+][A^-]}{[HA]} \quad \text{and} \quad [HA] = \frac{[H^+][A^-]}{K_a}$$

Therefore, since

$$[HA] = c\sqrt{\frac{K_w}{K_a K_b}} \qquad (11\text{-}59)$$

then

$$\frac{[H^+][A^-]}{K_a} = c\sqrt{\frac{K_w}{K_a K_b}} \qquad (11\text{-}62)$$

Solving Equation 11-62 for $[H^+]$ and remembering that the concentration of A^- is essentially equal to c yields

$$\left\{ [H^+] = \frac{K_a \times c}{c}\sqrt{\frac{K_w}{K_a K_b}} = \sqrt{\frac{K_w K_a}{K_b}} \right\} \qquad (11\text{-}63)$$

11p. The Ionization and Hydrolysis of Acid Salts. Acid salts may be represented by the general formula B^+HA^-, in which B^+ represents any cation. On solution the salt is assumed to be ionized completely into B^+ and HA^- ions. HA^- may act as both an acid and a base in accordance with the equations

$$HA^- + H_2O \rightleftharpoons H_3O^+ + A^{2-}$$

and

$$HA^- + H_3O^+ \rightleftharpoons H_2A + H_2O$$

The first equation represents the equilibrium for the secondary ionization of the acid H_2A, and the second, the primary ionization for the same acid. Final equilibrium results when the values of both ionization constants are satisfied. These ionic expressions are represented as follows:

$$\frac{[H^+][A^{2-}]}{[HA^-]} = K_2 \qquad (11\text{-}64)$$

$$\frac{[H^+][HA^-]}{[H_2A]} = K_1 \qquad (11\text{-}65)$$

Now

$$[A^{2-}] = [H^+] + [H_2A] \qquad (11\text{-}66)$$

That this last equality is true may be seen from a consideration of the two ionization equations. In the first, for every mole of A^{2-} formed, 1 mole of H^+ is formed. Some of the H^+, however, is used in the second equation to combine with HA^- in forming H_2A, 1 mole of H_2A being formed for every mole of H^+ reacting. Hence the quantity of H^+ formed is reduced by the quantity of H_2A formed. Solving for $[H_2A]$ in Equation 11-65 gives

$$[H_2A] = \frac{[H^+][HA^-]}{K_1} \qquad (11\text{-}67)$$

Solving for $[A^{2-}]$ in Equation 11-64 gives

$$[A^{2-}] = \frac{K_2[HA^-]}{[H^+]} \qquad (11\text{-}68)$$

Substituting the value of $[H_2A]$, given in Equation 11-67, and the value of $[A^{2-}]$, given in Equation 11-68, in Equation 11-66 gives

$$\frac{K_2[HA^-]}{[H^+]} = [H^+] + \frac{[H^+][HA^-]}{K_1} \qquad (11\text{-}69)$$

Solving for $[H^+]$,

$$[H^+] = \sqrt{\frac{K_1 K_2 [HA^-]}{K_1 + [HA^-]}} \qquad (11\text{-}70)$$

Since the ionization to form the HA^- is assumed to be complete, and if the extent of the hydrolysis is slight, $[HA^-] = c$ and

$$\left([H^+] = \sqrt{\frac{K_1 K_2 c}{K_1 + c}} \quad \right) \qquad (11\text{-}71)$$

If K_1 is small compared with c, it may be dropped from the denominator of the above expression. The c terms then cancel, and Equation 11-71 reduces to

$$\ast \left([H^+] = \sqrt{K_1 K_2} \quad \right) \qquad (11\text{-}72)$$

This equation is very useful for calculating the hydrogen-ion concentration in a solution of an acid salt, such as sodium bicarbonate, as shown by the example that follows. If K_1 is significantly large compared to c, Equation 11-71 must be employed.

Example 11-16. Calculate the H^+ concentration in a solution of $0.10M$ $NaHCO_3$ at $18°C$. $K_1 = 4.3 \times 10^{-7}$. $K_2 = 5.6 \times 10^{-11}$.

In this case, the simplified equation may be used. Substituting in Equation 11-72

$$[H^+] = \sqrt{4.3 \times 10^{-7} \times 5.6 \times 10^{-11}} = 4.9 \times 10^{-9} \text{ mole/liter}$$

11q. The Calculation of pH in Solutions of Hydrolyzed Salts

Salts of Strong Bases and Weak Acids

Salts of this type, such as sodium acetate, are basic because of hydrolysis. It has been previously shown that the OH^- concentration may be calculated from Equation 11-46 if the degree of hydrolysis is not too large.

$$\left([OH^-] = \sqrt{\frac{K_w c}{K_a}} \quad \right) \qquad (11\text{-}73)$$

Now substituting for $[OH^-]$ its equal, $K_w/[H^+]$, and solving for $[H^+]$ yields

$$[H^+] = \sqrt{\frac{K_a K_w}{c}} = K_a^{1/2} K_w^{1/2} c^{-1/2} \qquad (11\text{-}74)$$

Taking the logarithms of both sides and changing all signs results in

$$-\log [H^+] = -\tfrac{1}{2} \log K_w - \tfrac{1}{2} \log K_a + \tfrac{1}{2} \log c \qquad (11\text{-}75)$$

and

$$\left(\; pH = \tfrac{1}{2}pK_w + \tfrac{1}{2}pK_a + \tfrac{1}{2} \log c \; \right) \qquad (11\text{-}76)$$

Example 11-17. Calculate the pH of a $0.10M$ solution of sodium benzoate at $25°C$. $K_a = 6.3 \times 10^{-5}$.

$$pK_a = -\log 6.3 \times 10^{-5} = 5 - \log 6.3 = 4.20$$
$$pH = \tfrac{1}{2}pK_w + \tfrac{1}{2}pK_a + \tfrac{1}{2} \log c$$
$$= 7 + 2.1 - 0.5 = 8.60$$

Salts of Weak Bases and Strong Acids

Salts of this type, such as ammonium chloride, are acidic because of hydrolysis. It has been shown that the hydrogen-ion concentration of the solution may be calculated from the following expression if the degree of hydrolysis is not too large:

$$[H^+] = \sqrt{K_w c / K_b}$$

Taking the logarithm of both sides and changing signs gives

$$-\log [H^+] = -\tfrac{1}{2} \log K_w + \tfrac{1}{2} \log K_b - \tfrac{1}{2} \log c \qquad (11\text{-}77)$$

and

$$pH = \tfrac{1}{2}pK_w - \tfrac{1}{2}pK_b - \tfrac{1}{2} \log c \qquad (11\text{-}78)$$

This equation serves as a convenient method for calculating pH values in salt solutions of this type.

11r. The Lowry-Brønsted Interpretation of Hydrolysis. In the discussion of hydrolysis, salts were divided into four types according to the classical ideas of acids and bases. Although this classification is perhaps more familiar to the average student, the Lowry-Brønsted concept of acids and bases has proved very useful in explaining hydrolysis and will in time become even more familiar, perhaps, than the classical ideas.

According to the Lowry-Brønsted theory, salts of the strong acid-strong base type, such as Na^+Cl^-, would contain a very weak cation acid Na^+, and a very weak anion base, Cl^-. On dissolving the salt in water, Na^+ cannot donate a proton to water and it cannot receive one from water.

Similarly, the Cl^- ion has no proton to give up to water, and it is such a poor proton acceptor that it cannot take one from water. Hence the salt does not react with water, and the solution remains neutral.

Salts that are classed as the strong base-weak acid type, such as Na^+Ac^-, contain a weak cation acid, Na^+, and a strong anion base, Ac^-, according to the Lowry-Brønsted concept. Although the Na^+ neither gives nor receives a proton from water, the Ac^- ion, being a base, accepts a proton from water in accordance with the familiar equation

$$Ac^- + H_2O \rightleftharpoons HAc + OH^-$$

The solution thus becomes basic.

Salts of the weak base-strong acid type, such as $NH_4^+Cl^-$, contain a strong cation acid, NH_4^+, and a weak anion base. A solution of $NH_4^+Cl^-$ becomes acid because NH_4^+, being an acid, donates a proton to water to form NH_3 and H_3O^+.

Salts of the weak base-weak acid type, such as $NH_4^+Ac^-$, are, according to the Lowry-Brønsted theory, compounds containing a strong cation acid and a strong anion base. In $NH_4^+Ac^-$ solution water molecules compete with Ac^- ions for the acceptance of protons from NH_4^+. Similarly, water molecules compete with NH_4^+ ions to donate a proton to Ac^-. Since NH_4^+ is a stronger acid, however, and Ac^- is a stronger base than water, the net result of the hydrolysis is a reaction between NH_4^+ and Ac^- to form NH_3 and HAc until K_b and K_a are satisfied. This solution remains neutral if K_a and K_b are equal. In salts such as $Zn^{2+}(Ac^-)_2$ and $Al^{3+}(Ac^-)_3$ the cation is hydrated and the donated proton comes from one of the waters of hydration. For example, with an aluminum salt, the initial donation of a proton can be represented as

$$Al(H_2O^{3+})_6 = Al(H_2O^{2+})_5OH + H^+$$

Successive donations would result in the formation of $Al(OH)_3 \cdot 3H_2O$. The equilibrium expressions obtained by the use of the Lowry-Brønsted theory are, of course, identical with those obtained by the classical methods.

11s. Definition of a Buffer Solution. In many biological and chemical processes it is necessary that the pH of the medium be kept within fairly narrow limits. This maintenance of a specified degree of acidity is effected through the use of buffer solutions. A *buffer solution is defined as one that resists change in hydrogen-ion concentration, or pH, even though strong acid or base is added to the solution.*

11t. The Nature of Buffer Action. Pure water has almost no ability to resist a change in pH when strong acid or base is added. If a drop of hydrochloric acid is added to a liter of water at $25°C$, the pH changes from

7 to about 3.2. A drop of concentrated sodium hydroxide solution will cause a comparable change in the opposite direction. A solution of a salt such as sodium chloride is similar to pure water in its lack of ability to resist change in pH. The pH of a sodium acetate solution, however, would not be appreciably altered by a drop of hydrochloric acid. Such a solution is said to have *reserve alkalinity*.

On the other hand, a solution of ammonium chloride is affected but little by adding a small quantity of sodium hydroxide solution. It is said to have *reserve acidity*. Both reserve acidity and alkalinity are possessed by a solution containing a weak acid and one of its salts or a weak base and one of its salts. These combinations are used in preparing most buffer mixtures. A number of such mixtures with their useful pH range are given in Table 11-5.

Table 11-5. Buffer Mixtures

Components	Useful pH Range
Glycine and glycine hydrochloride	1.0–3.7
Phthalic acid and potassium acid phthalate	2.2–3.8
Acetic acid and sodium acetate	3.7–5.6
Monosodium phosphate and disodium phosphate	5.8–8.0
Boric acid and borax	6.8–9.2
Borax and sodium hydroxide	9.2–11.0
Disodium phosphate and trisodium phosphate	11.0–12.0

The ability of a buffer solution to resist a change in pH may be seen by considering an acetic acid-sodium acetate mixture, which, as noted in the table, shows buffer capacity in the pH range of 3.7 to 5.6. The solution contains a high concentration of un-ionized acetic acid and a high concentration of acetate ions. If a strong acid is added to the solution, hydrogen ions react with acetate ions to form undissociated acid until equilibrium for acetic acid is satisfied. This is shown by the following equation:

$$H_3O^+ \text{ (from added acid)} + Ac^- \rightleftharpoons HAc + H_2O$$

As a result, there is little change in the hydrogen-ion concentration of the solution. If a strong base is added, hydroxyl ions will react with hydrogen ions already in the solution, and, in order to maintain the constancy of K_a, more acid ionizes. This reaction may be represented by the equation

$$HAc + OH^- \text{ (added from base)} \rightleftharpoons H_2O + Ac^-$$

Again the hydrogen-ion concentration changes little. The above equations show that the sodium acetate combats the added hydrogen ion while the acetic acid combats the added hydroxyl ion. Consequently, it follows that the *maximum reserve against pH change is obtained when the* acid and salt are mixed in the molecular ratio of one to one.

The same type of reasoning applied above to the acetic acid-sodium acetate mixture can be applied to any of the other combinations in Table 11-5. The same type of reasoning will also show that salts of strong acids and strong bases possess no buffer capacity, since there is no tendency to form either the unionized acid or the base upon the addition of hydrogen or hydroxyl ions to their aqueous solutions.

11u. The Calculation of the pH of Buffer Mixtures. The H^+ ion concentration of a buffer mixture may be calculated by methods already studied in this chapter. The common-ion principle is involved, since a buffer consists of a weak base or acid in the presence of one of its highly ionized salts (see 11f). Consider a buffer solution containing the weak acid HA and its highly ionized salt Na^+A^-. It is necessary that the K_a for the acid be satisfied. Thus

$$K_a = \frac{[H^+][A^-]}{[HA]} \quad \text{and} \quad [H^+] = \frac{K_a[HA]}{[A^-]} \tag{11-79}$$

Taking the logarithm of both sides and changing all signs yields

$$-\log [H^+] = -\log K_a - \log \frac{[HA]}{[A^-]} \tag{11-80}$$

Because of the common-ion action of A^- ions, $[HA]$ is almost equal to the total concentration of the acid. Also $[A^-]$ is essentially equal to the concentration of the completely ionized Na^+A^-. Equation 11-80 then becomes

$$-\log [H^+] = -\log K_a + \log \frac{\text{salt}}{\text{acid}} \tag{11-81}$$

and

$$\ast \left(\quad \text{pH} = pK_a + \log \frac{\text{salt}}{\text{acid}} \quad \right) \tag{11-82}$$

Equation 11-82, generally known as the *Henderson-Hasselbalch equation*, can be used to calculate the pH of a buffer made by mixing known concentrations of a weak acid and its salt, or to calculate the ratio in which acid and salt must be mixed in order to give a buffer of definite pH value.

Example 11-18. Calculate at $25°C$ the pH of a buffer solution made by adding acetic acid and sodium acetate until the concentration of each is 0.1 mole per liter. $K_a = 1.8 \times 10^{-5}$.

$$\text{pH} = pK_a + \log \frac{0.1}{0.1} = 4.74$$

Note again that the buffer solution in Example 11-18 has its maximum reserve power against the addition of either acid or base because acid and salt are mixed in the ratio of 1 : 1. At this point pH $= pK_a$. Therefore, in choosing a buffer mixture of specified pH with the maximum reserve power, select an acid whose pK_a value is equal or nearly equal to that of the desired pH of the solution.

An equation comparable to 11-82 can be developed for buffers made from weak bases and their salts. (Such combinations, however, are rarely used because of the volatility and instability of weak bases.)

Example 11-19 shows how a buffer of definite pH may be made by mixing primary and secondary sodium phosphate. This is one of the important buffers in physiological processes.

Example 11-19. Calculate the ratio in which $Na^+H_2PO_4^-$ and $Na_2^+HPO_4^{2-}$ must be mixed in order to give a buffer solution of pH $= 7.10$. $pK_a = 7.21$. The equilibrium reaction is

$$HPO_4^{2-} + H^+ \rightleftharpoons H_2PO_4^-$$

in which the HPO_4^{2-} ion is the base and the $H_2PO_4^-$ is the acid. Substituting in the Henderson-Hasselbalch equation (11-82) gives

$$7.10 = 7.21 + \log \frac{[\text{salt}]}{[\text{acid}]}$$

and

$$\frac{[\text{Salt}]}{[\text{Acid}]} = \text{antilog}\,(-0.11) = \text{antilog}\,\bar{1}.89 = 0.776$$

Therefore, if Na_2HPO_4 and NaH_2PO_4 are mixed in the proportion of 0.776 mole of the former to 1.00 mole of the latter, a pH of 7.10 will be obtained. Since this ratio is not very much different from a 1:1 ratio, the solution will have good buffer capacity against both acid and base.

11v. Buffer Efficiency. To study the efficiency with which a given buffer resists a change in pH on the addition of acid or base, consider a liter of an acetic acid-sodium acetate solution that is $0.1 M$ in both acid and salt. The pH of this solution is 4.74 (see Example 11-18). Now add a tenth of a mole of hydrochloric acid to the above buffer solution in ten increments of 0.01 mole each. If the pH of the solution is calculated after the addition of each increment, it becomes apparent that the buffer is acting most efficiently during the addition of the first few increments.

As HCl is added, hydrogen ions convert Ac^- ions (from Na^+Ac^-) into acetic acid according to the equation

$$Ac^- + H_3O^+ \rightleftharpoons HAc + H_2O$$

Since each added increment consists of 0.01 mole of HCl, 0.01 mole of the sodium acetate will be converted to 0.01 mole of acetic acid. So after the *first* addition of HCl, the pH of the solution is calculated by the Henderson-Hasselbalch equation:

$$pH = 4.74 + \log \frac{0.1 - 0.01}{0.1 + 0.01} = 4.65$$

After the *second* addition of HCl, the pH of the solution is

$$pH = 4.74 + \log \frac{0.1 - 0.02}{0.1 + 0.02} = 4.56$$

On adding the *third* increment, the pH becomes

$$pH = 4.74 + \log \frac{0.1 - 0.03}{0.1 + 0.03} = 4.47$$

In the same manner it can be calculated that after the *eighth* increment the pH is 3.79 and after the *ninth* increment, 3.46. These values show that the pH changes but 0.09 after each of the first three increments of HCl. Beyond this point, the change becomes gradually greater, until finally the change between the eighth and ninth increments is 0.33 pH unit. By now, most of the acetate ion is converted to acid and the solution has essentially lost its alkaline reserve.

Similar calculations could be made for the addition of 0.1 mole of Na^+OH^- in ten increments of 0.01 mole each. Such calculations would show a comparable effect but in the opposite direction. It therefore becomes apparent that the buffer is working at its maximum efficiency when the ratio of salt concentration to acid concentration is unity. The greater the variation of this ratio from unity, the less efficient the buffer.

The foregoing calculations show that the efficiency of a buffer depends on the ratio of the concentration of salt to acid and that the buffer is most efficient when the ratio is unity. They also show that a buffer solution has little buffer capacity when the ratio is larger than 10:1 or less than 1:10. Since pK_a is constant for a given acid, the pH of an acid and its salt is determined by the logarithm of the ratio of the concentration of salt to acid (Equation 11-82). Therefore, a given buffer mixture is effective through a range of about 2 pH units. This may be shown for the acetic acid-sodium acetate pair:

$$pH = 4.74 + \log \frac{10}{1} = 5.74$$

$$pH = 4.74 + \log \frac{1}{10} = 3.74$$

The buffer mixture should therefore be efficient in the pH range from 3.74 to 5.74. In laboratory practice buffers made from this pair give excellent results in the range 3.7 to 5.6, as shown in Table 11-4.

A second factor other than the salt:acid ratio is important in buffer efficiency, and this has to do with the actual concentrations of the salt and acid. Obviously the greater these concentrations the greater the reserve alkalinity and acidity. Calculations similar to those used above will show that the more concentrated buffers also operate more efficiently upon the addition of successive increments of acid or base.

11w. Buffer Action in the Blood. A number of buffers operate to keep the blood at a pH of 7.4. The action of such buffer systems is very important, since a change in pH of 0.1 pH unit from its normal value can produce serious pathological disturbances. The principal buffer pairs in the blood are

$$\left(\frac{H_2CO_3}{B^+HCO_3^-} \quad \frac{B^+H_2PO_4^-}{B_2^+HPO_4^{2-}} \quad \frac{HHbO_2}{B^+HbO_2^-} \quad \frac{HHb}{B^+Hb^-} \quad \frac{H\ protein}{B^+\ protein^-} \right)$$

Here B is used for any monovalent cation such as sodium or potassium, $HHbO_2$ is used for oxyhemoglobin, HHb for free hemoglobin, and H protein for free protein. Thus five buffer systems are operating to maintain the proper acid-base balance. Of these, the carbonate-bicarbonate and the phosphate pair are the most important.

REFERENCES

Bull, *Physical Biochemistry*, John Wiley and Sons, New York, 1951, Chapter 7.
Daniels and Alberty, *Physical Chemistry*, John Wiley and Sons, New York, 1961, Chapter 15.
Maron and Prutton, *Principles of Physical Chemistry*, The Macmillan Co., New York, 1958, Chapter 16.
Moore, *Physical Chemistry*, Prentice-Hall, Englewood Cliffs, New Jersey, 1962, Chapter 9.
Sheehan, *Physical Chemistry*, Allyn and Bacon, Boston, 1961, Chapter 7.

REVIEW QUESTIONS

1. Derive the expression for the ion-product constant of water. How does the value of the ion-product constant change with increase in temperature?
2. Explain the meaning of the terms: pH, pOH, and pK_w and show the relationship among them. A change of 1 pH unit in the acidity of a solution means a change of how much in terms of hydrogen- and hydroxyl-ion concentration?

3. Derive the expression for the ionization constant of a weak acid (*a*) in terms of molar concentration and (*b*) in terms of the degree of ionization and its total concentration.

4. Derive the expression for the ionization constant of a weak base in terms of (*a*) molar concentrations and (*b*) degree of ionization.

5. Derive an equation for calculating the pH of (*a*) a solution of a weak acid and (*b*) a solution of a weak base. What is meant by pK_a and pK_b?

6. What is meant by the common-ion effect? Show mathematically the effect of common-ion addition to solutions of weak acids and bases.

7. What is meant by a polyprotic acid? Give equations that represent the successive steps in the ionization of phosphoric acid. Give the mathematical expression for the ionization constant for each of these steps. What is the re-relationship of the total, or over-all, ionization constant of phosphoric acid and the separate constants for the successive steps.

8. Explain why ionization constants of polyprotic acids decrease in numerical value with each successive stage of ionization.

9. Derive the expression for the solubility product constant of a slightly soluble electrolyte of the type AB_2.

10. Discuss the effect of adding a common ion to a saturated solution of a difficulty soluble salt.

11. Discuss the neutral salt effect on (*a*) solutions of weak acids and bases and (*b*) solutions of slightly soluble electrolytes.

12. What is an ampholyte? What is a hybrid ion? By means of suitable equations show how an amino acid of the general formula, R—$CHNH_2$—$COOH$, reacts on addition of (*a*) a strong acid and (*b*) a strong base.

13. What is meant by the hydrolysis of salts? Explain why a salt such as potassium nitrate does not undergo hydrolysis.

14. Use words and equations to show the hydrolysis of (*a*) salts of strong acids and weak bases, (*b*) salts of weak acids and strong bases, and (*c*) salts of weak acids and weak bases.

15. Derive an expression for the hydrolysis constant for each of the salt types given in Question 14. Express this constant in (*a*) terms of concentrations and (*b*) in terms of K_a, K_b, and K_w as the case may be.

16. Use the hydrolysis constant expression to show how the addition of the acid or base formed in hydrolysis can be used to decrease the extent of the hydrolysis.

17. Derive expressions for the direct calculation of the hydrogen-ion concentration and the pH in solutions of (*a*) a salt of a weak acid and a strong base and (*b*) a salt of a strong acid and a weak base.

18. Use chemical equations to show the equilibria involved when sodium bisulfite dissolves in water. Derive the general expression used in calculating the hydrogen-ion concentration in solutions of acid salts. Under what conditions can the general expression be simplified?

19. How can hydrolysis be explained in terms of the Lowry-Brønsted acid-base concept?

20. Use words and equations to explain why a solution of a weak acid and one of its highly ionized salts has buffer capacity. Explain what is meant by the terms (*a*) *reserve acidity* and (*b*) *reserve alkalinity*.

21. Derive the Henderson-Hasselbalch equation for calculating the pH of a buffer solution of a weak acid and one of its highly ionized salts. Show how this equation can be used to calculate the relative quantities of acid and salt needed to prepare a solution of a given pH.

22. List several buffer pairs. What is meant by buffer efficiency? Distinguish between buffer efficiency and buffer capacity. For a given buffer system, what ratio of acid to salt gives the best efficiency against the addition of either strong acid or strong base?

23. Explain in words and by means of equations why a solution of a weak diprotic acid and its acid salt has buffer capacity. Illustrate with sodium bicarbonate and carbonic acid.

PROBLEMS

Note: The same assumptions used in working the examples in the text may be used in solving the following problems. Needed data are to be obtained from the tables given in the chapter.

I

1. Calculate the pH of each of the following solutions at 25°C. Assume complete ionization of strong acids and bases.
   (*a*) A solution of $0.0029M$ HCl
   (*b*) A solution containing 1.00 gram of NaOH in 800 ml of water

2. Calculate the hydroxyl-ion concentrations and the pH and pOH of the following solutions at 25°C.
   (*a*) $0.05M$ solution of trimethylamine
   (*b*) $0.14M$ solution of ammonia

3. Calculate the hydrogen and hydroxyl ion concentration of the following solutions at 25°C.
   (*a*) A solution with a pH of 10.27
   (*b*) A solution with a pOH of 8.73

4. Calculate the hydrogen-ion concentration and the degree of ionization in each of the following solutions at 25°C.
   (*a*) $0.26M$ acetic acid
   (*b*) $0.06M$ hydrocyanic acid
   (*c*) $0.25M$ lactic acid
   (*d*) $0.080M$ glycolic acid

5. Calculate the degree of dissociation and the concentration of the un-ionized acid at 25°C in the following solutions. How many grams of the acid are required to prepare 2.2 liters of each solution?
   (*a*) A solution of glycolic acid in which the hydrogen-ion concentration is 9.0×10^{-3} mole per liter
   (*b*) A solution of formic acid in which the hydrogen-ion concentration is 4.4×10^{-3} mole per liter

6. (*a*) Calculate the concentration of hydrogen ions, the pH, and the degree of dissociation at 25°C in a solution of 0.16*M* acetic acid to 1.0 liter of which has been added 0.24 mole of solid sodium acetate.
(*b*) What is the ratio of the hydrogen-ion concentration of the solution in (*a*) to that in the 0.16*M* acetic acid before the addition of sodium acetate?

7. Compute the hydrogen-ion concentration and the pH at 25°C in a solution prepared by mixing 0.40 mole of acetate ions with 0.20 mole of hydrogen ions in 600 ml of solution.

8. Calculate the concentration of all ionic species in a solution that is 0.14*M* with respect to acetic acid and 0.21*M* with respect to calcium acetate. $T = 25°C$. How many moles of each ion are present in 1500 ml of solution?

9. (*a*) Calculate the hydrogen-ion concentration and the pH of a 0.080*M* solution of H_2CO_3 at 25°C.
(*b*) Calculate the CO_3^{2-} concentration for the solution in (*a*).

10. A solution is prepared by dissolving 1.00 gram of sodium propionate and 1.00 gram of propionic acid in sufficient water to make a total volume of 500 ml. Calculate the pH of the solution and the degree of dissociation of the propionic acid. $T = 25°C$. $pK_a = 4.85$.

11. How many grams of solid sodium acetate must be added to 400 ml of 0.080*M* acetic acid in order to produce a solution with a hydrogen-ion concentration of 4.0×10^{-5} mole per liter at 25°C?

12. If the solubility of magnesium hydroxide is 2.7×10^{-3} gram per 300 ml of solution at 25°C, what is the solubility product at this temperature?

13. If the solubility product constant of lead iodide is 8.3×10^{-9} at 25°C, what is the solubility of this salt in grams per liter at this temperature?

14. The solubility product of magnesium hydroxide is 1.4×10^{-11} at 25°C. (*a*) If 0.10 gram of magnesium chloride is added to 100 ml of 0.10*M* methylamine, will a precipitate of $Mg(OH)_2$ form? (*b*) If 1.0 gram of methylammonium chloride is added to the solution in (*a*), will a precipitate of magnesium hydroxide form?

15. The hypothetical salt, M_2A (MW = 200), is soluble to the extent of 2.0×10^{-3} gram per liter at 25°C. How many milligrams of M_2A remain unprecipitated in 800 ml of solution in which the concentration of excess A^{2-} ion is 0.001*M*?

16. Calculate the hydrogen-ion concentration at 25°C in a 0.07*M* solution of H_2S.

17. Calculate the sulfide-ion concentration in a 0.060*M* hydrogen sulfide solution which is also 0.050*M* in HCl. Calculate the pH of the solution. The temperature is 25°C.

18. Calculate the hydrolysis constants of the following salts at 25°C: (*a*) $CH_3NH_3^+Cl^-$, (*b*) $NH_4^+C_2H_3O_2^-$, (*c*) K^+CN^-.

19. Calculate the concentration of each ionic species in the following solutions at 25°C: (a) 0.060M potassium benzoate, (b) 0.05M ammonium chloride. What is the degree of hydrolysis in each case?

20. Calculate the concentration of each ionic species in a solution made up by dissolving 0.10 mole of sodium chloride and 0.10 mole of ammonium chloride in sufficient water to make up a liter of solution. $T = 25$°C.

21. Calculate the degree of hydrolysis at 25°C of the following: (a) 0.50M ammonium acetate, (b) 0.05M ammonium acetate.

22. Calculate the hydrogen-ion concentration and the pH at 25°C of a 0.15M solution of potassium glycolate.

23. How much must a 0.20M solution of sodium acetate be diluted at 25°C in order to double the degree of hydrolysis?

24. Calculate the ionization constant of each of the following monoprotic acids at 25°C.
 (a) Concentration = 0.04M, pH = 5.22
 (b) Degree of ionization = 0.0050, pH = 2.88

25. Calculate the concentration of all ionic species in each of the following solutions at 25°C.
 (a) 1500 ml of 0.14M acetic acid containing 8.2 grams of sodium acetate
 (b) 1100 ml of 0.066M ammonia to which has been added 800 ml of 0.033M ammonium chloride

26. Calculate the pH, pOH, [H$^+$], and [OH$^-$] in each of the following solutions at 25°C:
 (a) 100 ml of solution containing 0.60 mole acetic acid and 0.50 mole of sodium acetate,
 (b) 12.2 grams of benzoic acid and 14.4 grams of sodium benzoate in 0.80 liter of solution,
 (c) 600 ml of a solution which is 0.20M in NH$_3$ and 0.15M in NH$_4$Cl.

27. What is the ionization constant of hydrocyanic acid if a 0.10M solution of sodium cyanide has a pH of 11.07 at 25°C?

28. The chloride salt of a weak organic base is dissolved in water to give a solution with a pH of 3.11 when the salt concentration is 0.20M at 25°C. Calculate the ionization constant of the base.

29. What is the pH and degree of hydrolysis of a 0.12M solution of sodium carbonate at 25°C?

30. What is the pH of a 0.15M solution of sodium bicarbonate at 25°C?

31. Given 200 ml of 1.00M acetic acid. To this is added 0.10 mole of sodium hydroxide. Calculate the hydrogen-ion concentration, the pOH, and the degree of ionization of the acid in the resulting solution.

32. In what molar ratio must lactic acid and sodium lactate be mixed at 25°C in order to give a buffer with a pH of 3.35?

33. It is necessary to prepare a buffer of pH = 4.85. In what ratio by volume must the following be mixed in order to prepare the solution:
  (a) 0.080M acetic acid and 0.080M sodium acetate?
  (b) 0.15M acetic acid and 0.30M sodium acetate?
  (c) 0.30M acetic acid and 0.15M sodium acetate?

34. How many grams of potassium acid phthalate must be added to a liter of 0.10M phthalic acid in order to give a buffer of pH = 3.00 at 25°C? pK_a = 2.89.

35. Given a 0.12M solution of acetic acid and a 0.12M solution of sodium acetate. Calculate the number of milliliters of sodium acetate solution that must be added to 100 ml of the acid in order to prepare a series of buffers that will give pH values in steps of 0.2 pH unit for the useful range of this buffer pair. T = 25°C.

36. Prepare a series of buffers in steps of 0.2 pH unit for the useful range of the buffer pair disodium phosphate and monosodium phosphate. Calculate, for 25°C, the number of milliliters of 0.20M disodium phosphate that must be added to 150 ml of 0.20M monosodium phosphate solution in order to prepare each of the buffer solutions.

II

1. Calculate the pH and the hydroxyl-ion concentration in each of the following solutions at 25°C:
  (a) 0.05M benzoic acid
  (b) A solution containing 0.50 gram of HCl in 100 ml of solution
  (c) A solution containing 1.40 grams of NH_3 in 400 ml of solution

2. Calculate the concentration of acid or base and the degree of dissociation in each of the following solutions at 25°C:
  (a) A solution of acetic acid in which the hydrogen-ion concentration is 1.40 × 10⁻³ mole per liter;
  (b) A solution of methylamine in which the pH is equal to 11.40;
  (c) A solution of glycolic acid in which the pH is 3.04.

3. How many grams of each of the substances in Problem II-2 are required to prepare 1400 ml of solution at 25°C?

4. Calculate the pH, pOH, and degree of dissociation of each of the following at 25°C:
  (a) 0.32M hydrocyanic acid
  (b) 0.050M carbonic acid
  (c) 0.06M pyridine

5. Calculate the hydrogen-ion concentration, the pH, and the degree of dissociation at 25°C of a 0.080M solution of benzoic acid which is also 0.090M in sodium benzoate.

6. (a) Calculate the pH and the degree of dissociation at 25°C of a solution made by dissolving 2.30 grams of formic acid in enough water to make 150 ml of solution.
  (b) To the formic acid solution in (a) are added 1.70 grams of solid sodium formate. Calculate the new pH and degree of dissociation.
  (c) Determine the ratio of the hydrogen-ion concentrations in (a) and (b).

7. A solution is prepared by adding 80 ml of $0.20M$ potassium lactate to 120 ml of $0.16M$ lactic acid. Calculate the concentration of *all* ionic species in the solution. Determine the degree of dissociation of the lactic acid. $T = 25°C$.

8. Calculate at $25°C$ the concentration of all ionic species present in a $0.07M$ solution of carbonic acid.

9. How many grams of solid sodium acetate must be added to a solution containing 1.00 gram of acetic acid in 80 ml of solution in order that the final solution have a pH of 4.95 at $25°C$?

10. Calculate the hydrogen ion concentration and the pH at $25°C$ of a solution made by mixing 100 ml of $0.24M$ potassium acetate with 50 ml of $0.33M$ hydrochloric acid.

11. The solubility of HgI_2 is 4.5×10^{-4} gram per liter at $25°C$. Calculate the solubility product of mercuric iodide at this temperature.

12. The solubility product of $Ag_2C_2O_4$ is 5.3×10^{-12} at $25°C$. Calculate the following:
(*a*) The solubility of silver oxalate in grams per liter
(*b*) The concentration of oxalate ions in a saturated solution
(*c*) The milligrams of silver ions in 750 ml of a saturated solution
(*d*) The grams of silver nitrate that would have to be added to a liter of saturated solution in order to reduce the oxalate-ion concentration to one fifth of its original value.

13. The solubility of silver carbonate is 4.1×10^{-2} grams per liter at $20°C$. How many milligrams of silver carbonate remain unprecipitated in 1200 ml of solution in which the concentration of the carbonate ion is $0.002M$?

14. Calculate the hydrolysis constants at $25°C$ of the following salts:
(*a*) K^+CN^-
(*b*) $NH_4^+NO_3^-$
(*c*) $NH_4^+C_2H_3O_2^-$

15. Calculate the degree of hydrolysis, the pH, and the pOH, at $25°C$, of a $0.10M$ solution of sodium citrate.

16. How many grams of CH_3NH_3Cl must be added to a liter of water at $25°C$ in order to give a solution that has a pH of 5.00?

17. Calculate the number of grams of ammonium chloride that must be added to a liter of water at $25°C$ to give a solution that has the same pH as a $0.10M$ solution of HCN?

18. A $0.120M$ solution of the sodium salt of a weak monoprotic acid is found to be 6.0% hydrolyzed at $25°C$. Calculate the ionization constant of the weak acid at this temperature.

19. How much should a $0.50M$ solution of potassium cyanide be diluted in order that the degree of hydrolysis be doubled at $25°C$?

20. The pH of a $0.20M$ solution of the sodium salt of a weak monoprotic acid is 10.58 at $25°C$. Calculate the ionization constant of the acid at this temperature.

21. Calculate the ionization constant of the following bases at 25°C:
(a) Concentration = 0.080M, pH = 10.20
(b) Degree of dissociation = 0.0142, pH = 12.10

22. Given a 0.15M ammonia solution and a 0.15M solution of hydrochloric acid. Calculate the pH in each of the following solutions:
(a) 100 ml of ammonia + 25 ml of hydrochloric acid
(b) 100 ml of ammonia + 50 ml of hydrochloric acid
(c) 100 ml of ammonia + 75 ml of hydrochloric acid
(d) 100 ml of ammonia + 100 ml of hydrochloric acid
(e) 100 ml of ammonia + 125 ml of hydrochloric acid

23. Calculate the pH and the degree of hydrolysis at 25°C of a 0.14M solution of sodium carbonate.

24. A sample of phthalic acid weighing 1.00 gram is dissolved in sufficient water to make 80 ml of solution. How many grams of potassium acid phthalic must be added to the solution to give a buffer of pH = 3.20 at 25°C? pK_a = 2.89.

25. One hundred milliliters of a 0.20M solution of Na_2HPO_4 are to be mixed with 0.30M NaH_2PO_4 solution in the preparation of the following buffer solutions. Calculate the volume of the NaH_2PO_4 solution that must be added in each case to give buffers of pH = 6.2, pH = 6.6, pH = 7.0, pH = 7.2. The temperature is 25°C.

26. Calculate the pH, pOH, [H^+], and [OH^-] in each of the following solutions at 25°C.
(a) Two hundred milliliters of solution containing 0.30 mole of lactic acid and 0.12 mole of sodium lactate.
(b) Two hundred and fifty milliliters of solution which is 0.11M in methylamine and 0.21M in methylammonium chloride.
(c) A solution of 800 ml volume which contains 6.10 grams of benzoic acid and 28.8 grams of sodium benzoate.

TWELVE

Conductivity

The purpose of this chapter is to study certain phenomena associated with the conductance of electricity through aqueous solutions of electrolytes. This includes a consideration of electrode reactions and the relation between the quantity of current passing through the solution and the quantity of the products formed at the electrodes, the factors affecting the conductance of aqueous solutions of electrolytes, and the experimental determination of conductance.

MECHANISM OF CONDUCTANCE

12a. Terms and Units. Before considering the mechanism of conductance, it is necessary to define the terms and units used in conductance measurements.

In the usual metallic conductor, such as a copper or silver wire, the *electric current* consists of a flow of electrons. In this textbook the direction of flow of the electrons is considered as the direction of flow of the current. For the production of a direct current, that is, a unidirectional flow of electrons, a *cell*, a combination of cells termed a *battery*, or a direct-current generator is usually employed. In either a cell or a generator there are two *poles*, and when they are connected by a conductor a stream of electrons flows in the external circuit from the *negative pole* to the *positive pole* of the cell or generator. Within the cell or generator the flow is from the positive to the negative pole and is brought about by a *potential difference* between the poles. This potential difference is due to a difference in the *electron pressure or activity* at the two poles. The potential difference is termed the *voltage* or *potential* of the cell, battery, or generator.

The magnitude of the electric current, that is, the number of electrons that will pass a given point in the circuit in a given interval of time, depends not only on the voltage but also on the *resistance* that the conductor offers to the flow of the electrons. This resistance varies with the type of material making up the conductor, the temperature, the cross section of the conductor, and the length of the conductor. For a given conductor at a given temperature the following relation holds:

$$\text{Resistance} \propto \frac{\text{length}}{\text{cross section}} \qquad (12\text{-}1)$$

In measurements involving solutions of electrolytes it is sometimes more convenient to employ the reciprocal of the resistance, called the *conductance*. From Equation 12-1, therefore, conductance can be expressed as

$$\text{Conductance} \propto \frac{\text{cross section}}{\text{length}} \qquad (12\text{-}2)$$

The preceding paragraph stated that the magnitude of the current is determined by the number of electrons passing a given point in a circuit in a unit of time. Since the charge on the electron is extremely small, the passage of a large number of electrons is necessary to produce a measurable current. Hence expressing the current in terms of number of electrons would be clumsy. Consequently, current may be expressed more conveniently by means of a unit termed the *ampere*. This is a practical unit, and by definition *an ampere is that current that will deposit 0.001118 gram of silver in 1 second.* It should be carefully noted that the current is a *rate* of flow, since it involves the time factor.

If a current of 1 ampere flows for 10 seconds, 0.001118 grams per sec × 10 sec = 0.01118 gram of silver will be deposited. The same quantity of silver would be deposited if a current of 10 amperes flowed for 1 second. The total quantity of silver deposited is a measure of the total number of electrons that have passed a given point in a circuit without regard to how long the current flows. Here, then, is a means of expressing *total quantity* of electricity, as opposed to the rate of flow or *quantity per second*. The unit of total quantity is termed the *coulomb*. A coulomb, then, *is that quantity of electricity that will deposit 0.001118 gram of silver from a solution of silver nitrate.* No specification whatever as to *how long* it takes for this quantity of silver to deposit is made. A comparison of the coulomb and the ampere shows that a current in which 1 coulomb is passing per second is a current of 1 ampere. Mathematically,

$$\text{Current (amperes)} = \frac{\text{coulombs}}{\text{time (seconds)}}$$

Electrical resistance is measured in *ohms*. The ohm, again, is a practical unit and is defined as *the resistance of a column of mercury 14.4521 grams in mass, 106.300 centimeters in length, of uniform cross section at 0°C.*

Since conductance is the reciprocal of resistance, the unit of conductance is termed the *reciprocal ohm* or *mho*.

The units of resistance and current having been defined, the unit of electromotive force may now be defined in terms of these two units. *The unit of electromotive force, the volt, is defined as the electromotive force required to send a current of 1 ampere through a resistance of 1 ohm.*

Electrical energy, like all forms of energy, has both a quantity factor (coulomb) and intensity factor (volt). *The unit of electrical energy, termed the joule (or watt-second), is defined as the energy expended when a current of 1 ampere passes for 1 second through a conductor when the applied electromotive force is 1 volt.* Mathematically, the expenditure of electrical energy is given by the following relation:

Energy (joules) = coulombs × volts = amperes × seconds × volts

The electrical units are summarized in Table 12-1.

Table 12-1. Summary of Electrical Units

Unit of	Name	Symbol
Resistance	ohm	R
Conductance	mho	L
Current	ampere	I
Electromotive force	volt	E
Quantity	coulomb	Q
Energy	joule	J

The relation among current, voltage, and resistance, *when they are expressed in the above units* and when a direct current is being considered, is given by *Ohm's law*. This law states that *the current (in amperes) flowing through a conductor is equal to the electromotive force (in volts) divided by the resistance of the circuit (in ohms).* Mathematically, it is expressed as

$$I = \frac{E}{R} \quad \text{or} \quad E = IR \tag{12-3}$$

The use of Ohm's law and the interrelation among the various units are illustrated in Example 12-1.

Example 12-1. (*a*) A certain conductor has a resistance of 10 ohms. It is placed between the poles of a cell whose potential is 5 volts. What current will pass through the conductor if the voltage remains constant at the value given?

$$I = \frac{5 \text{ volts}}{10 \text{ ohms}} = 0.5 \text{ amp}$$

(*b*) How many coulombs of electricity will pass through the conductor if this current is maintained for 20 min?

$$Q = 0.5 \text{ amp} \times 20 \text{ min} \times 60 \text{ sec per min} = 600 \text{ coulombs}$$

(*c*) What will be the energy expended during this time interval?

$$\text{Energy} = 0.5 \text{ amp} \times 20 \text{ min} \times 60 \text{ sec per min} \times 5 \text{ volts} = 3000 \text{ joules}$$

The terms defined so far have been for conductors in which the flow of current is effected by a moving stream of electrons. Such a conductor is termed a *conductor of the first class*. This class is characterized by the fact that no material changes take place with the passage of the current. There is simply a flow of electrons in the conductor when a difference of potential exists. The resistance of this type of conductor increases with an increase of temperature.

Chapter 8 points out that solutions of electrolytes also conduct the electric current. These solutions belong to *conductors of the second class* because in them the current flow is maintained by the movement of the ions (rather than electrons) towards the poles. Except for the hydrogen ion, H_3O^+, these ions have the composition and structure usually considered in ionization equilibria, as discussed in Chapters 8 and 11. In the case of the hydrogen ion the conductance is probably effected by the transfer of the proton (H^+) from one water molecule to another in a chainlike manner rather than the actual movement of the H_3O^+ ion. For this reason this ion in this chapter is designated by the symbol for the proton H^+. Unlike conductors of the first class, the resistance of conductors of the second class decreases with an increase of temperature, due in most part to a decrease in the viscosity of the electrolytic solution through which the ions must move.

Figure 12-1 shows a typical electrolytic circuit. The battery supplies electrons to the pole C and removes electrons from the pole A. Hence the pole C becomes negative in charge and the pole A becomes positive. The

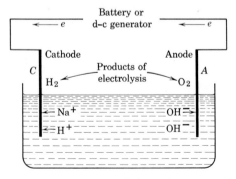

Figure 12-1. Electrolytic conductance.

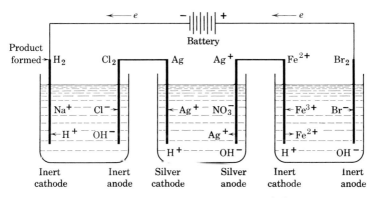

Figure 12-2. The electrolysis of aqueous solutions.

result is that the positively charged cations are attracted to the negative pole, called the *cathode*. The negatively charged anions are attracted to the positive pole, termed the *anode*. Here again it is pointed out that the transport of the charge by the hydrogen ion is effected by the passing of the proton along a series of water molecules.

12b. Electrode Reactions. Although the current in the solution is due to moving ions, a chemical reaction is necessary at the electrodes to continue the passage of current in the external circuit. The *electrode reactions* are characterized by the loss of electrons, or a process of oxidation, at the anode and a simultaneous gain of electrons, or reduction, at the cathode. Sometimes the material comprising the electrode takes part in the reaction. In other cases, the electrode is completely inert. Electrode reactions can best be studied by considering some typical examples.

Consider the electrolysis of the solutions shown in Figures 12-1 and 12-2. In Figure 12-1 the electrolyte is sodium hydroxide. This furnishes sodium ions and hydroxyl ions to the solution. Water also ionizes to a slight extent as was discussed quantitatively in the preceding chapter (Ionic Equilibrium and Buffer Action). The hydrogen ions so produced from the water can furnish protons to supplement the sodium ions in the conductance of the current toward the cathode. While the protons and sodium ions move toward the cathode, the hydroxyl ions move toward the anode. At the anode the following electrode reaction takes place:

$$4OH^- = 2H_2O + O_2 + 4e$$

At the cathode three reactions might conceivably take place. These are:

$$Na^+ + e = Na \text{ (solid)}$$
$$2H_2O + 2e = H_2 \text{ (gas)} + 2OH^-$$
$$2H^+ + 2e = H_2 \text{ (gas)}$$

To decide which takes place, we must consider the potential relationships involved, that is, which reduction takes place most readily. We must also consider which can take place most rapidly under the conditions of the experiment. The change of water to hydrogen gas and hydroxyl ions is found to be the dominant reaction. Therefore, the over-all reaction, made up of the two individual electrode reactions, is

Anode $\qquad$ $4OH^- = 2H_2O + O_2 + 4e$

Cathode $\quad$ $4H_2O + 4e = H_2 \text{ (gas)} + 4OH^-$

Over-all reaction $2H_2O = 2H_2 \text{ (gas)} + O_2 \text{ (gas)}$

The number and variety of electrode reactions are almost unlimited. They depend upon the ions present, the concentration of the ions, the nature of the solvent, the type of electrode, the temperature, and the voltage used to effect the electrolysis. The examples which follow illustrate some of the various electrode reactions.

In the Na^+Cl^- solution shown in the left-hand cell of Figure 12-2, hydrogen gas is again evolved at the cathode. At the anode, however, chloride ions are discharged to form chlorine gas, leaving OH^- ions in solution. Certain voltage relationships beyond the scope of this discussion produce the chloride-ion discharge rather than the hydroxyl-ion discharge. The electrodes used in this cell are inert, and the chlorine escapes as a gas except for the part that dissolves in the water.

In the middle cell of Figure 12-2 the electrolyte is $Ag^+NO_3^-$ and the electrodes are metallic silver. Silver plates out at the cathode and metallic silver passes into the solution as ionic silver at the anode. The passage of the current from the anode into the external circuit is caused by the electrons left on the electrode. The electrode reactions are

Cathode: $Ag^+ + e = Ag$ $\qquad$ Anode: $Ag = Ag^+ + e$

In the right-hand cell of Figure 12-2 bromide ions are discharged at the anode, producing liquid bromine, which then dissolves in the water. Iron (III) ions are reduced at the cathode to iron (II) ions. The two electrodes must be made of inert substances in order to produce the effects given. The electrode reactions are

$$Br^- = \tfrac{1}{2}Br_2 + e \qquad Fe^{3+} + e = Fe^{2+}$$

12c. Faraday's Laws. The chemical reactions occurring at the electrodes may produce solid products (plating of silver), the evolution of a gas (H_2, O_2, Cl_2), the oxidation or reduction of an ion that remains in solution ($Fe^{2+} \rightarrow Fe^{3+}$; $Ce^{3+} \rightarrow Ce^{4+}$), the conversion of a metal into an ion ($Ag \rightarrow Ag^+$; $Cu \rightarrow Cu^{2+}$), and the production of a liquid (Hg, Br_2), as well as other changes. But whatever the change may be, the quantity of product produced bears a simple relationship to the amount of electricity that has caused the change. This relationship was discovered by Michael Faraday and for this reason bears his name. His conclusions are given in *Faraday's laws of electrolysis.* His first law states that the *mass of the substance produced at an electrode by electrolysis is directly proportional to the quantity of electricity that has passed through the solution.* His second law states that the *mass of different substances produced during electrolysis is directly proportional to the equivalent weights of the substance.* Quantitatively his laws may be summarized by stating that *96,495 coulombs of electricity will yield 1 gram-equivalent of primary product, whatever its nature, at an electrode.* This quantity of electricity (rounded off at 96,500 coulombs) is known as the *faraday.* Since there are Avogadro's number of charges in a gram-equivalent of hydrogen, it follows that there are 6.02×10^{23} electrons associated with a faraday of electricity. The primary products are those first formed in an electrolysis. The laws do not apply to secondary reactions, such as the interaction of the chlorine gas with the solvent in the left-hand cell in Figure 12-2.

To determine the gram-equivalent weight, we must consider the oxidation-reduction process taking place. Write the electrode reaction and note the number of faradays accompanying the formation of a mole of product. Divide this number into the atomic or molecular weight, as the case may be, of the mole of product. We can term the number of faradays exchanged as the redox equivalent.

Faraday's laws know no exceptions provided the passage of the electricity takes place entirely by ionic conductance. The laws apply to molten electrolytes as well as to solutions and are independent of temperature and pressure. In solutions the nature of the solvent has no effect so long as it supports ionization. The laws are independent of the voltage used to produce the electrolysis. The voltage, however, must be considered in computing the energy expended in the process.

Examples 12-2 and 12-3 illustrate the application of Faraday's laws.

Example 12-2. For 1 hr a current of 50 amp is passed successively through the solutions shown in Figure 12-2. To cause this current, it was necessary to use a battery having a potential of 8 volts. Calculate (*a*) the quantity of product produced at each electrode, (*b*) the volumes of hydrogen and chlorine produced, measured under standard conditions, and (*c*) the energy expenditure necessary to effect the electrolysis.

(*a*)   Number of faradays used $= \dfrac{50 \text{ amp} \times (1 \times 60 \times 60) \text{ sec}}{96,500 \text{ amp-sec}}$

$$= 1.87$$

Gram-equivalent weights of products: hydrogen = 1.01 grams

chlorine = 35.45 grams

silver = 107.87 grams

bromine = 79.91 grams

Iron (III) to iron (II) (valence change of 1) = 55.85 grams

Weight of products:

hydrogen = 1.87 × 1.01 grams = 1.89 grams

chlorine = 1.87 × 35.45 grams = 66.29 grams

silver = 1.87 × 107.87 grams = 201.7 grams

bromine = 1.87 × 79.9 grams = 149.4 grams

iron (II) = 1.87 × 55.85 grams = 104.4 grams

(b) The weights of hydrogen and chlorine produced could be converted to moles and the volume occupied determined by the perfect gas equation. Since 1 gram equivalent of hydrogen and chlorine gas occupies 11.2 liters under standard conditions, the volume occupied by these gases should be

$$1.87 \times 11.2 \text{ liters} = 20.9 \text{ liters}$$

(c) Energy expenditure = volts × amp × time

$$= 8.0 \times 50 \times 1 \times 60 \times 60$$

$$= 1,440,000 \text{ joules (watt-sec)}$$

$$= 0.40 \text{ kw-hr}$$

Example 12-3. (a) If a current of 20 amp is passed through a bath containing Al_2O_3 in molten cryolite for 50 min, how many liters of oxygen gas measured at standard conditions would be produced? (b) How many grams of aluminum could be produced at the cathode by this quantity of electricity?

(a) Number of faradays $= \dfrac{20 \times 50 \times 60}{96,500} = 0.622$

Since oxygen is divalent, the equivalent weight is 8 grams. This amount will occupy $\frac{8}{32} \times 22.4$ liters = 5.6 liters.

Volume of oxygen produced = 0.622 × 5.6 liters = 3.48 liters

(b) Equivalent weight of aluminum = 27/3 = 9.0 grams

Quantity of aluminum produced = 9.0 × 0.622 = 5.60 grams

12d. Methods of Expressing Conductance. As shown in Equation 12-2, the conductance of a solution is proportional to the cross section and inversely proportional to the length. If each of 2 electrodes is 1 sq cm in area and if these are placed 1 cm apart, the conductance of the cubic cm of solution between them is termed the *specific conductance.* Its value furnishes much information as to the ability of the solution to conduct the electric current. Another way to express the conducting power of a solution is by means of its *equivalent conductance.* *This is defined as the conductance of that quantity of solution which contains 1 gram equivalent of the electrolyte placed between electrodes 1 cm apart, the electrodes completely covering the opposite sides of the volume of the solution.* This is illustrated in Figure 12-3. The volume between the electrodes depends upon the concentration of the solution. If the solution is $1N$, the volume would be 1000 ml, but if the solution is $0.01N$, the volume would be 100,000 ml or $1000/N$. Since the electrodes are 1 cm apart, the magnitude $1000/N$ must be numerically equal to the area of the electrodes. This, with the fact that the conductance is directly proportional to the cross section of the conductor, gives a relationship between the specific conductance and the equivalent conductance. The equivalent con-

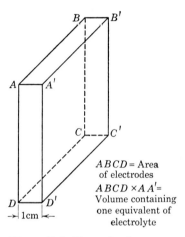

$ABCD$ = Area of electrodes

$ABCD \times AA'$ = Volume containing one equivalent of electrolyte

Figure 12-3. Electrodes for measuring equivalent conductance.

ductance (the conductance of the entire area of the electrode) is equal to the area multiplied by the conductance of 1 sq cm of the area (the specific conductance). Mathematically this can be written

$$\Lambda = \frac{1000\kappa}{c} \tag{12-4}$$

Here κ, the Greek letter kappa, is the specific conductance; Λ, the Greek letter lambda, is the equivalent conductance; and c is the concentration in equivalents per liter.

The dilution of a solution of an electrolyte will result in the further ionization of a weak electrolyte and in a lessening of the attractive forces between the ions in both strong and weak electrolytes. It follows that as a solution is successively diluted the number of ions in a weak electrolyte will increase and the activity of the ions in both weak and strong electrolytes will increase. Hence the more dilute the solution, the greater the equivalent conductance, that is, up to a point at which ionization is complete and attractive forces have become nil. Then the maximum number of ions at maximum activity is present between the electrodes shown in Figure 12-3. Further dilution produces no increase in Λ. The limiting value of Λ found on successive dilutions is termed the *equivalent conductance at infinite dilution* Λ_0.

Sometimes a term called the *molar conductance* is used. This is the conductance of that quantity of solution that contains 1 mole of electrolyte when placed between electrodes 1 cm apart. For substances in which the equivalent and molar weights are the same, the equivalent conductance and molar conductance will have the same value. The equivalent conductance values for a number of electrolytes at 25°C at various concentrations are listed in Table 12-2.

Table 12-2. Equivalent Conductance of Electrolytes in Aqueous Solutions at 25°C

Concentration (equiv/liter)	NaCl	KCl	H_2SO_4	HCl	$HC_2H_3O_2$	NH_3
0.0000	126.5	149.9	429.6	426.2	390.7	271.4
0.0005	124.5	147.8	413.1	422.7	67.7	47.0
0.001	123.7	146.9	399.5	421.4	49.2	34.0
0.01	118.5	141.3	336.4	412.0	16.3	11.3
0.10	106.7	129.0	250.8	391.3	5.2	3.6

12e. Factors Affecting Conductance. In a given conductance cell, such as one of those shown in Figure 12-5, the conductance of a solution will depend on (1) the number of ions present and (2) the speed of these ions under a given voltage drop across the electrodes.

The number of ions present will depend upon the strength (whether weak or strong) and the concentration of the electrolyte. The two electrovalent compounds (Na^+Cl^- and K^+Cl^-) shown in Table 12-2 are completely dissociated, and the two strong acids (HCl and H_2SO_4) are probably completely ionized at the concentrations shown. All four of these strong electrolytes show a greater conductance at a given concentration than the two weak electrolytes, acetic acid and ammonia. Examination of the equivalent conductance of acetic acid and ammonia at different concentrations shows the effect of dilution on the equivalent conductance, hence on the degree of dissociation. If an electrolyte is diluted sufficiently, it will finally reach a state of complete dissociation. The weaker the electrolyte, of course, the greater the dilution. Hence comparing the Λ_0 values throws no light on the extent of the dissociation at finite concentrations.

There are several factors affecting the speed of ions and, therefore, the conductance of the solution. Ionic speeds are usually calculated at *unit potential gradient*. This term is used to indicate a voltage drop of 1 volt per cm. For example, if the electrodes are 5 cm apart, it would be necessary to apply a potential of 5 volts in order to establish a condition of unit gradient. Ten volts would give a gradient of 2 volts per cm. A number of ion velocities, or mobilities, as they are termed, at unit potential gradient, for 25°C, are given in Table 12-3.

Table 12-3. Absolute Velocity of Ions at Unit Potential Gradient at 25°C

Cation	Velocity (cm/sec)	Anion	Velocity (cm/sec)
H_3O^+	0.00362	OH^-	0.00205
K^+	0.00076	SO_4^{2-}	0.00083
Ag^+	0.00064	Cl^-	0.00079
Ba^{2+}	0.00067	Br^-	0.00081
NH_4^+	0.00076	$C_2H_3O_2^-$	0.00042
Na^+	0.00052	$Fe(CN)_6^{4-}$	0.00115

In a very general way, other factors being equal, the lighter the ion per unit charge, the faster it moves under unit potential gradient, hence the better its conducting power. As previously stated, however, the hydrogen ion owes its conducting power to the ability of the proton to pass from water molecule to water molecule as it moves towards the cathode. Its high velocity must be interpreted in the light of this process. Note that the hydrogen ion and the hydroxyl ion show the best conducting ability of the cations and anions, respectively. The sulfate ion, although heavier than the chloride ion, has the greater velocity because it is doubly charged. The heavy ferricyanide ion has a comparatively high velocity as a result of its quadruple charge. The extent of hydration of an ion will affect the speed. The hydration includes not only that water actually bound to each ion in definite amounts but also the oriented solvent atmosphere that the ions tend to establish around them. This factor makes the lithium ion comparatively slow in spite of its small mass. Interionic attraction will slow up an ion. This is the principal reason why the equivalent conductances of the strong electrolytes Na^+Cl^- and K^+Cl^- decrease with increasing concentration although they are completely ionized at all concentrations. A rise in temperature increases the velocity of an ion, principally because of the decrease in the viscosity of the solution. The greater the viscosity of the solution, other factors being equal, the slower the ion moves.

THE MEASUREMENT OF CONDUCTANCE

12f. Experimental Determination of Equivalent Conductance. To determine the equivalent conductance of a given concentration of electrolyte, it is necessary only to obtain the specific conductance and apply Equation 12-4. The specific conductance could be obtained by using a conductance cell with electrodes 1 sq cm in area and 1 cm apart or by using any pair of electrodes of known dimensions and applying Equation 12-2. An exact knowledge of the size of the electrodes and their distance apart is hard to obtain by actual measurement, but the combination of these magnitudes, known as the *cell constant*, is obtained by introducing into the cell a solution of known specific conductance, usually $0.100N$ potassium chloride. The conductance is then measured and the cell constant evaluated as

κ = observed conductance $\times$ distance apart of electrodes/area

$\kappa = L \times C$

in which C is the cell constant and L, the observed conductance.

Example 12-4. By employing a given conductivity cell with $0.100N$ potassium chloride at $18°C$, an observed conductance of 0.025 mho was obtained. What is the cell constant? The specific conductance of 0.100 potassium chloride is 0.0112 mho at $18°C$.

$$C = \frac{\kappa}{L} = \frac{0.0112}{0.025} = 0.448$$

If the cell constant is known, the specific conductance of any solution can be obtained by measuring its conductance in the cell. The following steps are necessary to obtain the equivalent conductance of a solution:

1. Measure the conductance of $0.1N$ KCl (or other solution of known conductance) in the cell.
2. Calculate the cell constant.
3. Measure the conductance of the solution in the cell.
4. Using the cell constant, calculate the specific conductance.
5. By means of Equation 12-4 calculate the equivalent conductance.

The procedure is illustrated in Example 12-5.

The observed conductance is obtained by the use of an alternating-current Wheatstone bridge. Such an apparatus is shown in Figure 12-4. A high-frequency alternating current is used to prevent chemical changes at the electrodes. This current is supplied by an audio-oscillator tuned to a

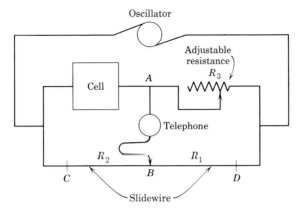

Figure 12-4. Wheatstone bridge assembly.

frequency of 1000 to 2500 cycles per second. A simple vacuum tube circuit also makes excellent oscillator. The current from the oscillator passes through the two arms of the bridge. One arm consists of a slide wire, CD, of uniform cross section and usually half a meter in length. The other arm contains the conductivity cell and an adjustable resistance, R_3, as shown in Figure 12-4. The telephone, connected at A by a fixed contact and to the slide wire by a moving contact, B, shows when a balance has been reached in the bridge. If the potentials at A and B are different, a hum is heard in the telephone. A minimum of sound indicates that A and B are at the same potential. This condition can be brought about by changing the adjustable resistance, R_3, and by changing the position of the contact B. This adjustment is usually made with B near the center of the slide wire. When a condition of balance is reached, the following relation holds:

$$\frac{R_1}{R_2} = \frac{R_3}{\text{observed resistance}}$$

Then observed conductance, the reciprocal of resistance, is obtained as follows:

$$\text{Observed conductance} = \frac{R_1}{R_3 \times R_2}$$

Since the drop wire is of uniform cross section, R_2 and R_1 can be replaced by the distances CB and DB. Then

$$\text{Observed conductance} = \frac{DB}{R_3 \times CB}$$

and

$$\text{Specific conductance} = \frac{DB}{R_3 \times CB} \times \text{cell constant} \qquad (12\text{-}5)$$

Example 12-5 illustrates how the calculations are made for a typical determination of equivalent conductance.

Example 12-5. A $0.01M$ solution of sodium chloride in the conductivity cell used in Example 12-4 at 25°C showed a condition of balance when $R = 426.3$ ohms and $CB = 235$ mm. Calculate the specific and equivalent conductance of $0.01M$ sodium chloride at 25°C. Length of slide wire = 50 cm.

From equation 12-5

$$\kappa = L \times C = \frac{265}{426.3 \times 235} \times 0.448 = 0.001185 \text{ mho}$$

and

$$\Lambda = \frac{1000 \times 0.001185}{0.01} = 118.5 \text{ mhos}$$

The cells used for conductance measurements are of various sizes and shapes, depending upon the type of solution being used and the accuracy of the results desired. They are constructed of glass with electrodes usually made of platinum. Some typical cells are shown in Figure 12-5. Best results are obtained when the electrodes are coated with a layer of finely divided platinum, termed *platinum black* because of its color. This layer of platinum black decreases polarization effects. Although the current reverses many times a second, there is a tendency for gases to form during the passage of the current. The platinum black catalyzes the reaction that prevents the accumulation of these gases.

12g. Uses of Conductance Measurements. Conductance measurements find extensive use in many chemical processes. In the preparation of distilled water the efficiency of the removal of dissolved salts can be easily followed by noting the conductance of the water. Simple Wheatstone bridges are installed for this purpose on the commercial ion-exchange stills for the preparation of distilled water of high purity. Conductivity measurements can be used to determine the solubility of salts and the extent of hydrolysis in salt solutions. In the titration of a strong acid with a strong base, the conductivity of the solution decreases because of the removal of the fast hydrogen ion and its replacement by the slower cation of the base. But at the end point all hydrogen ions are removed and further addition of base results in an increase of the hydroxyl-ion concentration. The result is an increase in the conductivity. The end

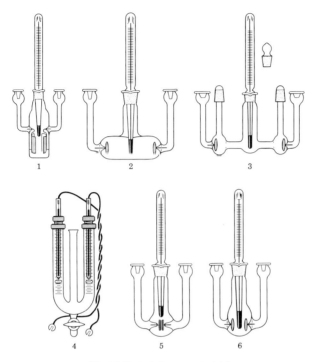

(About 1/5 actual size, approximately)

Figure 12-5. Various types of conductance cells. (Courtesy of Leeds and Northrup Company, Philadelphia, Pennsylvania.)

point of the titration, the point at which the conductance is at a minimum, can be determined by conductance measurements. This method is particularly useful in colored solutions in which indicators cannot be employed.

Conductance measurements have been used extensively to study permeability changes in living cells. An increase in the conductance of the cell contents means that ions are passing through the cell wall into the cell solution. The capacity effect of cell walls can be studied by conductance methods. Conductance measurements furnish a very convenient method for determining the absence or presence of electrolytes in protein preparations.

The approximate degree of dissociation of weak electrolytes, such as acetic acid, can be determined conductimetrically. The equivalent conductance at a particular concentration is due to the number of ions between the electrodes pictured in Figure 12-3. The equivalent conductance at infinite dilution is produced by all possible ions that may be present, since by definition this is the equivalent conductance at complete ionization. Consequently, this figure multiplied by the degree of dissociation will give the equivalent conductance at a finite concentration. For example, in a 0.001M acetic acid solution at 25°C, employing the data of Table 12-2,

$$\Lambda = \alpha\Lambda_0 \qquad 49.2 = \alpha \times 390.7 \qquad \alpha = 0.126$$

where α = degree of dissociation.

REFERENCES

Bull, *Physical Biochemistry*, John Wiley and Sons, New York, 1951, Chapter 5.

Daniels and Alberty, *Physical Chemistry*, John Wiley and Sons, New York, 1961, Chapter 13.

Maron and Prutton, *Principles of Physical Chemistry*, The Macmillan Co., New York, 1958, Chapter 15.

Moore, *Physical Chemistry*, Prentice-Hall, Inc., Englewood Cliffs, New Jersey, 1962, Chapter 9.

Sheehan, *Physical Chemistry*, Allyn and Bacon, Boston, 1961, Chapter 7.

Daniels, Williams, Bender, Alberty, and Cornwell, *Experimental Physical Chemistry*, McGraw-Hill Book Co., New York, 1962, Chapters 8 and 22.

Crockford and Nowell, *Laboratory Manual of Physical Chemistry*, John Wiley and Sons, New York, 1956, Experiment 26.

REVIEW QUESTIONS

1. What constitutes an electric current? What factors determine the magnitude of a current flowing through a conductor?

2. What factors determine the resistance of a conductor? How is resistance related to conductance? How is conductance affected by the length and cross section of the conductor?

3. What is meant by the quantity of electricity? Give the units usually employed for expressing quantity of electricity. What is meant by the magnitude of an electric current? What relationship exists between the quantity of electricity that has passed a given point in a conductor and the magnitude of the current?

4. Define the *ampere* and state its magnitude in terms of the number of grams of silver deposited in 1 sec. Define the *coulomb*. One coulomb will result in the deposition of how many atoms of silver?

5. Define the *ohm* and the *volt*. In what unit is conductance usually expressed?

6. In what units is electrical energy usually expressed? What relation exists among the magnitudes: the electrical energy produced, the magnitude of the current flowing in the conductor, the time the current flows, and the voltage necessary to produce the current?

7. State Ohm's law in words and in the form of a mathematical expression.

8. Distinguish between conductors of the first and second class. How does the conductance in each change with change in temperature?

9. What is the process of electrolysis?

10. Discuss the mechanism of electrode reactions. Give some typical reactions that take place at electrodes.

11. What are Faraday's laws? Carefully explain their meaning. What is meant by a Faraday of electricity?

12. Distinguish between specific and equivalent conductance. Derive the mathematical expression that shows their interrelationship.

13. Why does equivalent conductance increase with dilution? What is meant by equivalent conductance at infinite dilution? Why is the equivalent conductance for a given concentration of a strong electrolyte so much greater in magnitude than the same concentration of a weak electrolyte?

14. What are the factors affecting the conductance of electrolytic solutions? What factors in general determine the conducting ability of a given ion?

15. In what way does the mechanism of conductance by hydrogen ions differ from that of other ions?

16. What is meant by unit potential gradient? Explain why the speeds of various ions under a given potential gradient differ in value.

17. In connection with conductance measurements with electrolytic solutions, what is meant by the cell constant? How is its value determined? Discuss the use of the cell constant in conductance measurements.

18. Describe the Wheatstone bridge assembly usually used in conductance measurements. What data are obtained in a typical set of measurements? How are these data used in the calculation of the equivalent conductance of the particular solution?

PROBLEMS

I

1. A current of 20 amp is passed through a solution of sulfuric acid between inert electrodes for 1.5 hr. To produce this current, a potential of 10 volts is required. Calculate (*a*) the number of coulombs and the number of Faradays of electricity used, (*b*) the total energy expended, and (*c*) the number of liters of gas produced at each electrode when measured at STP.

2. A current of 2 amp is passed successively through solutions of gold (III) chloride, silver nitrate, and copper sulfate for 3 hr. How many grams of metal are plated out at the three cathodes? Assume that all the copper plated out was divalent.

3. Five hundred coulombs of electricity are passed through a solution of hydrochloric acid between inert electrodes. The time required for the passage of this quantity is 1.5 hr. Calculate (*a*) the magnitude of the current, (*b*) the volume of gas, measured at 25°C and at a pressure of 700 mm of Hg, produced at each electrode, (*c*) the number of molecules of hydrogen produced, and (*d*) the time required for the same magnitude of current to produce 0.8 gram of hydrogen.

4. What current is required to produce, in 2 hours, 3×10^{21} atoms of (a) silver, (b) aluminum, (c) copper, (d) oxygen, and (e) bromine?

5. Using Table 12-2 calculate for 25°C the specific conductance of (a) $0.001M$ KCl, (b) $0.100M$ NaCl, (c) $0.01M$ $HC_2H_3O_2$, and (d) $0.0005M$ NH_3.

6. In Table 12-2 four values for the equivalent conductance of HCl are listed for 25°C. By a plotting procedure, show that the value of the equivalent conductance at infinite dilution is 426.2 mhos as shown in the table.

7. Calculate the approximate degree of dissociation of ammonia at 25°C for each of the concentrations in Table 12-2. Plot these values against concentration.

8. Calculate the conductance and resistance of a column of $0.001N$ solution of potassium chloride at 25°C, the column being 5 cm in length and circular in cross section with a radius of 1.2 cm. Calculate the conductance for a similar column of acetic acid.

9. Plot the equivalent conductance of NaCl as given in Table 12-2 versus (a) the concentration, and (b) the square root of the concentration. By extrapolation estimate the value of Λ_0.

10. What distance will the following ions move in 2 min at 25°C under unit potential gradient: H^+, OH^-, $C_2H_3O_2^-$, Ba^{2+}? How far will these ions move in this time if the electrodes are 5 cm apart and the imposed potential is 4 volts?

11. A conductivity cell filled with $0.02M$ KCl has a resistance of 150 ohms at 18°C. At this temperature the specific conductance of $0.02M$ KCl is 0.002394 mho. Calculate the cell constant.

12. When the cell used in Problem I-11 is filled with $0.001M$ HCl, the resistance is found to be 854 ohms at 25°C. Calculate the specific and equivalent conductance of this concentration of HCl.

13. The cell used in Problem I-11 is filled with $0.01M$ ammonia. What is the conductance and resistance of the cell at 25°C?

14. With the apparatus shown in Figure 12-4 and the conductance cell used in Problem I-11, the following data were obtained with $0.001M$ NaCl: $R_1 = 200$ mm and $R_3 = 1935$ ohms. Calculate the equivalent conductance at this concentration of NaCl at this temperature.

II

1. A current of 5 amp is passed through a solution of sodium hydroxide between inert electrodes for 1.2 hr. To produce this current, a potential of 2 volts is required. Calculate (a) the number of coulombs and the number of Faradays passed through the solution, the energy expended, and the number of liters of gas produced at each electrode measured at 25°C and at 740 mm pressure.

2. A current of 2×10^{-2} amp is passed successively through solutions of nickel sulfate, gold chloride, and potassium hydroxide for 25 min. How many atoms of nickel, gold, and hydrogen will be produced at the various cathodes?

3. A current of electricity is passed through a solution of silver nitrate between silver electrodes for 3 hr. During this time 15 grams of silver are plated out on the cathode. To produce this current, 3 volts are required. What is the value of the current? What is the resistance of the solution between the two electrodes? How much electrical energy would be required under these conditions to plate out 2 lb of silver?

4. A current of electricity is passed successively through the following solutions:
   (*a*) Sodium chloride between inert electrodes
   (*b*) Silver nitrate solution between silver electrodes
   (*c*) Sulfuric acid between inert electrodes
   (*d*) Potassium hydroxide between inert electrodes
Ten liters of hydrogen gas, measured at STP, are produced at the cathode in the third solution. What products are formed at the other electrodes and what is the quantity of each?

5. What would be the conductance and the resistance at 25°C of a column of 0.10M ammonia solution, the column being 250 cm in length and 1.5 sq cm in cross section?

6. How long would a column of 0.001M sodium chloride have to be at 25°C in order to have the same resistance as a column of 0.01M ammonia 400 cm in length. The cross section of both columns is the same.

7. Calculate the approximate degree of dissociation of the various concentrations of acetic acid given in Table 12-2. Plot the degree of dissociation versus the concentration.

8. What distance will the following ions travel under unit potential gradient in 5 min at 25°C: Br^-, Ag^+, and NH_4^+? How far will each of these ions move in this time if the electrodes are 2 cm apart and the potential between the electrodes is 2.5 volts?

9. What potential gradient would be needed to cause a sodium ion to travel at a velocity of 0.00092 cm per sec at 25°C?

10. What potential gradient is required to cause a sodium ion to travel at 25°C with the same speed as the potassium ion under unit potential gradient?

11. What potential gradient is required at 25°C to cause a chloride ion to travel with a speed of 0.0015 cm per sec?

12. The resistance of a conductivity cell containing 0.10M KCl at 25°C is 18.9 ohms. The specific conductivity of this concentration of KCl at this temperature is 0.012856 mho. What is the value of the cell constant?

13. When the cell used in Problem II-12 is filled with 0.10M HCl, what would be the resistance of the cell at 25°C?

14. The resistance of the cell in Problem II-12, when filled with 0.010M acetic acid, is found to be 1491 ohms. Calculate the specific and equivalent conductance of this concentration of acetic acid at 25°C, the temperature of the measurement.

15. What would be the resistance and conductance of the cell in Problem II-12 if it is filled with $0.010M$ ammonia at 25°C?

16. With the apparatus in Figure 12-4 and the conductivity cell used in Problem II-12, the following data were obtained at 25°C when the electrolyte was $0.100M$ NaCl. Calculate the specific and equivalent conductance of this concentration of NaCl at this temperature.

$$R_1 = 240 \text{ mm} \qquad R_3 = 21.1 \text{ ohms}$$

THIRTEEN

Electromotive Force

This chapter is concerned with the galvanic cell and its place in the study of physical chemistry. The factors determining the cell potential as well as the single electrode potentials are studied in detail. Special emphasis is placed on the role of the activities of the ions and other substances in the electrode reactions. The use of the potentiometer for measuring cell potentials is described. One section deals with the thermodynamics of electrolytic cells.

THE GALVANIC CELL

13a. The Galvanic Cell. The conversion of electrical energy into chemical energy was studied in Chapter 12. In the left-hand cell of Figure 12-2 electrical energy was used to furnish the energy necessary to convert hydrogen chloride in the solution into hydrogen and chlorine gas. The quantity of electricity necessary for the decomposition was 96,500 coulombs (1 faraday) and the amount of electrical energy was EF, wherein E was the voltage necessary to effect the electrolysis. If 1 mole of sulfuric acid is decomposed, it would require 2 faradays since we are releasing 2 equivalents of hydrogen. The energy necessary would then be nEF where n is equal to 2. To plate out 1 mole of trivalent gold would require energy equal to $3EF$. As a general statement we can say that

$$\text{Electrical energy} = EnF$$

where n is the number of equivalents of product produced at the electrode.

The operation of the galvanic cell is the opposite of electrolysis in that electrical energy is produced from chemical energy. The Daniell cell in Figure 13-1 is an example of a chemical cell in which a reaction is carried out in such a manner that usable electrical energy can be obtained from the free energy change, ΔG, in the cell reaction. As the figure shows,

251

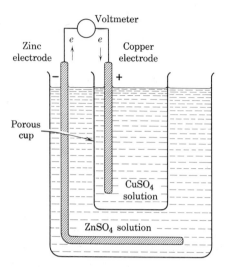

Figure 13-1. The Daniell cell.

a zinc strip dips into a dilute zinc sulfate solution and a copper strip into a concentrated copper sulfate solution. The two solutions in the cell are separated by a porous cup that prevents diffusion of the two solutions into each other but does not prevent the passage of the ions when an electric current flows. When the two metal strips are connected by an electrical conductor, electrons leave the zinc strip and flow into the outer circuit and enter the copper strip from the external part of the circuit. The passage of the electrons in the direction shown by the arrows produces a current in the connection circuit. The flow of electrons takes place because the electron pressure, or electron activity, is greater at the zinc strip than at the copper strip. The flow of electrons is accompanied by a change of metallic zinc into zinc ions and a change of copper ions into metallic copper. The two electrode reactions may be written:

$$Zn = Zn^{2+} + 2e$$
$$Cu^{2+} + 2e = Cu$$

The over-all reaction, called the *cell reaction*, is

$$Zn + Cu^{2+} = Zn^{2+} + Cu$$

and it is the free energy released in this reaction that is appearing as electrical energy. According to convention, the zinc strip is termed the *negative electrode* of the cell, since it is at this electrode that the electrons have the greater activity, and the one *from* which the electrons pass *into* the external circuit. The copper strip is the *positive electrode*, since it has the lower electron pressure or activity, and is the electrode *into* which electrons enter the cell *from* the external circuit. The number of faradays produced depends upon the number of equivalents of copper ions converted to metallic copper or the number of electrons lost and gained by the reactants and products in the cell reaction. Further, the electrons are supplied at a voltage, E, which is equal to the difference in the voltages of the two electrodes. In this particular cell this voltage is 1.1 volts under reversible conditions. The *quantity of electrical energy* supplied for each mole of zinc consumed and each mole of copper produced is

Electrical energy supplied $= EnF$

$= 2 \times 1.1$ volts $\times$ 96,500 coulombs

$= 212,300$ joules

Theoretically any oxidation-reduction reaction could be used in constructing a cell. The reaction must take place in two parts: oxidation with the liberation of electrons taking place at one electrode, and reduction with the absorption of electrons at the other electrode.

As seen in the preceding discussion of the Daniell cell, oxidation takes place at the zinc electrode as metallic zinc is converted to zinc ions and reduction takes place at the copper electrode as copper ions are changed to metallic copper.

The Daniell cell reaction could be brought about simply by placing metallic zinc directly in a copper sulfate solution. Under this set of conditions, however, the reaction would take place by direct transfer of electrons from zinc atoms to copper ions at one place, and the electron transfer could not be utilized for current production.

An oxidation-reduction reaction much more useful than that used in the Daniell cell is the one that takes place in the lead-acid storage cell commonly used in automobiles. The over-all, or cell, reaction is

$$Pb + PbO_2 + 2H_2SO_4 = 2PbSO_4 + 2H_2O$$

and the two electrode reactions are:

$$Pb + SO_4^{-2} = PbSO_4 + 2e$$
$$2e + PbO_2 + SO_4^{-2} + 4H^+ = PbSO_4 + 2H_2O$$

Another example of a reaction that can be split into two parts and used for the production of electrical energy is the formation of hydrogen chloride in aqueous solution, the reverse of the process discussed at the beginning of this section. The over-all reaction and the two electrode reactions are

$$H_2 + Cl_2 = 2H^+ + 2Cl^-$$
$$H_2 = 2H^+ + 2e$$
$$Cl_2 + 2e = 2Cl^-$$

13b. Single Electrode Potentials. Any galvanic cell is made up of two electrode systems, each characterized by a reaction capable of evolving or absorbing electrons. The electrode with the greater electron pressure or activity becomes the negative electrode or oxidizing electrode and gives up its electrons to the other electrode. It is possible for a given electrode to be the negative electrode in one combination and the positive electrode in another combination. As an example, the hydrogen electrode in a solution of hydrogen ions of unit activity may be considered. The electrode consists of a platinum foil covered with platinum black saturated with hydrogen gas at 1 atm pressure and immersed in a solution of hydrogen ions. It is described in greater detail in Chapter 14. This electrode is the positive one when used in combination with a zinc electrode immersed in a solution of zinc ions at unit activity. On the other hand, when used with a copper electrode immersed in a solution of copper ions of unit activity, the hydrogen electrode becomes the negative electrode. In these two cases the reactions are given by the following equations:

$$Zn + 2H^+ = Zn^{2+} + H_2$$
$$H_2 + Cu^{2+} = Cu + 2H^+$$

Whether a given electrode system becomes the negative electrode or the positive electrode depends upon the second electrode with which it is in combination. In other words, all electrode systems have a certain electron activity, or oxidation-reduction ability. A table can be compiled with the various electrode systems arranged in order of this ability.

The ease, however, with which metallic zinc forms zinc ions, thus creating the electron activity, depends upon the activity of the zinc ions in the solution. Similarly, the ease with which hydrogen gas forms hydrogen ions depends upon the hydrogen-ion activity and the pressure of the hydrogen gas. The oxidation-reduction ability of an electrode thus depends upon the activities of the ionic and molecular species entering into the electrode reaction. Therefore, a statement concerning the oxidizing ability of a particular electrode has no meaning unless the activities of the reactants and products involved in the electrode reaction are specified.

The values of the oxidation-reduction potentials are usually expressed as *standard oxidation potentials*. A standard oxidation potential is that of an electrode when all reactants and products are at unit activity and the electrode reaction taking place is assumed to be the *oxidation reaction*. Table 13-1 gives the standard oxidation potentials for a number of typical electrode systems. The arrangement in the table is in the order of decreasing tendency to proceed as an oxidation reaction. Consequently, if a cell is prepared by using two of the electrode systems shown in the table, the electrode system that is higher in the table will be the oxidizing electrode (negative pole) and therefore electrons will flow from it into the external circuit. The second electrode system then becomes the positive pole. Electrons are received from the external circuit, and the reaction at this second electrode will then proceed as reduction, the reverse of the change shown in the second column of the table. Conversely, from the polarity of the terminals of a cell it can be determined which reaction is the oxidation process and which is the reduction process.

Table 13-1. Standard Oxidation Potentials at 25°C on the Hydrogen Scale*

Electrode	Oxidation Reaction	E_{el}^{o} (volts)
K; K^{+}	$K = K^{+} + e$	$+2.925$
Na; Na^{+}	$Na = Na^{+} + e$	$+2.714$
Zn; Zn^{2+}	$Zn = Zn^{2+} + 2e$	$+0.763$
Fe; Fe^{2+}	$Fe = Fe^{2+} + 2e$	$+0.440$
Pb; Pb^{2+}	$Pb = Pb^{2+} + 2e$	$+0.126$
H_2; H^{+}	$\frac{1}{2}H_2 = H^{+} + e$	0.000
Ag, $AgCl(s)$; Cl^{-}	$Ag + Cl^{-} = AgCl + e$	-0.222
Cu; Cu^{2+}	$Cu = Cu^{2+} + 2e$	-0.337
Pt, O_2; OH^{-}	$2OH^{-} = H_2O + \frac{1}{2}O_2 + 2e$	-0.401
Pt; Fe^{2+}, Fe^{3+}	$Fe^{2+} = Fe^{3+} + e$	-0.771
Pt, Cl_2; Cl^{-}	$2Cl^{-} = Cl_2 + 2e$	-1.360

* The values of the potentials in this table are taken from Latimer, *The Oxidation States of the Elements and Their Potentials in Aqueous Solutions*, Prentice-Hall, New York, 1952.

The absolute values of single electrode potentials are impossible to measure, and the values given in Table 13-1 are comparative values. The reference electrode is the standard hydrogen electrode (hydrogen ions at unit activity and hydrogen gas at 1 atm pressure). This electrode is arbitrarily assigned a potential of zero, and all other potentials are expressed in terms of this value. Experimentally, then, in order to determine the magnitude of a single electrode potential, it is necessary to measure the potential of a galvanic cell made up of a standard hydrogen electrode and the electrode whose potential is to be measured. Because the hydrogen electrode is assumed to be zero, the measured electromotive force of the cell is equal to the potential of the second electrode. (If the hydrogen electrode proves to be the negative electrode, the potential of the electrode in question is by convention assigned a negative sign) On the other hand, if the hydrogen electrode proves to be the positive electrode, the potential of the electrode in question is by convention given a positive sign.) The potentials of the single electrode systems in Table 13-1 are a quantitative measure of their tendency to proceed as oxidation reactions. Figure 13-2 shows how the potentials of zinc electrode and a copper electrode are measured by the use of a standard hydrogen electrode. The function of the salt bridge is discussed later in the chapter.

Table 13-1 may be summarized as follows. The first column lists a number of electrode systems. The material making up the electrode is listed first and is followed by the ions and other substances that take part in the electrode reaction. The second column gives the reaction taking place at the electrode when the electrode system *gives up* electrons to the external circuit. The reaction taking place is one of *oxidation, and when* this reaction actually takes place in a cell the electrode in question is the *negative* electrode. The order of arrangement is that of *decreasing tendency* to proceed as *oxidation reactions* when all reactants and products are at *unit activity.* The third column gives the potentials of the single electrode systems, all reactants and products being at unit activity. Ion activities are expressed in *molalities* and the unit activity for ions is taken as $1m$. The greater the tendency to proceed as an oxidation reaction, the more positive the potential. The designation E_{el}° is used for this magnitude, the superscript $^{\circ}$ indicating that the potential is for the *standard* electrode and the subscript el indicating that the potential is for a single electrode rather than for a cell. For example, $E_{Zn,Zn^{2+}}^{\circ}$ represents the potential

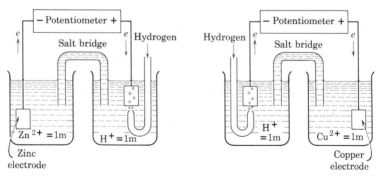

Figure 13-2. Typical galvanic cells for the measurement of oxidation potentials.

of the standard zinc electrode. These single electrode potentials are *relative* to the hydrogen electrode, the standard potential of this electrode being arbitrarily taken as zero. The values given are for 25°C.

13c. Uses of Standard Electrode Potentials. An examination of Table 13-1 shows that any given electrode system will be the negative electrode in any galvanic cell in which an electrode below it in the table constitutes the second electrode. This was shown in Figure 13-2 for the zinc and hydrogen electrodes. If the hydrogen electrode is used in combination with a copper electrode, the hydrogen electrode is the negative electrode. In other words, the more positive the electrode potential, the greater the ability of the electrode to give up electrons, hence the greater its electron pressure or activity.

The table tells exactly what the cell reaction will be for any given combination of electrodes. Consider a cell made up of a lead electrode and a chlorine electrode. Since the standard potential of the lead electrode is $+0.126$ volt and of the chlorine electrode is -1.360 volts, the lead electrode is the negative electrode and will evolve electrons. The chlorine electrode will absorb electrons. Therefore, the two electrode reactions are

$$Pb = Pb^{2+} + 2e$$
$$Cl_2 + 2e = 2Cl^-$$

and the over-all cell reaction is

$$Pb + Cl_2 = Pb^{2+} + 2Cl^-$$

The table also furnishes the data for the immediate calculation of the potential of a galvanic cell made up of two standard electrodes. With the Daniell cell combination of a zinc electrode and a copper electrode, for example, the cell voltage is given by the difference of the two individual electrode potentials. In this case

$$E^\circ_{cell} = E^\circ_{Zn;Zn^{2+}} - E^\circ_{Cu;Cu^{2+}} = 0.763 - (-0.337) = 1.100 \text{ volts}$$

With a zinc-lead combination the voltage is

$$E^\circ_{cell} = E^\circ_{Zn;Zn^{2+}} - E^\circ_{Pb;Pb^{2+}} = 0.763 - 0.126 = 0.637 \text{ volt}$$

Thus to calculate the potential of a cell made up of two standard electrodes, it is first necessary to determine which is the negative electrode. This is the electrode that has the largest oxidation potential, as given in Table 13-1. From its potential is subtracted the potential of the second electrode, as illustrated in the two preceding examples. The superscript $^\circ$ used with a cell potential signifies that the cell is made up of two standard electrodes. The potential of such a cell is termed its *standard potential*.

The discussion of the calculation of electrode and cell potentials when reactants and products are not in their standard states (unit activity) is the subject matter of the next section of this chapter.

13d. The General Expression for the Oxidation Potential of a Single Electrode. In a later section of this chapter in which the thermodynamics of the galvanic cell are treated in some detail it will be found that the oxidation potential of a single electrode, whatever may be the activities of the reactants and products of the electrode reaction, may be written in the following general manner

$$E_{el} = E_{el}^{\circ} - \frac{RT}{nF} \ln \frac{Ox}{Red} \tag{13-1}$$

In this equation Ox denotes the product of the activities of the substances in the oxidized state in the electrode reaction, each raised to a power equal to the number of times the substance occurs in the equation as written. Red denotes the product of the reactants; ln indicates that the logarithm of the Ox/Red ratio is to the base e rather than the base of 10. R is the universal gas constant (see 2h), and n is the number of electrons involved in the reaction. The use of this equation in calculating single electrode potentials is illustrated in the following examples. The activities are expressed in molalities, although molarities could be used in the dilute solutions usually employed without materially affecting the calculations. Unless otherwise stated, all activities in the examples and problems are in molalities.

Example 13-1. Calculate the oxidation potential of the hydrogen electrode when the hydrogen gas is at 1 atm pressure and the hydrogen ions have an activity of $0.080m$. Temperature $= 25°C$.

The electrode reaction is

$$H_2 = 2H^+ + 2e$$

and

$$E_{el}^{\circ} = 0$$

Substituting in Equation 13-1,

$$E_{el} = 0 - \frac{RT}{2F} \ln \frac{a_{H^+}^2}{a_{H_2}} = - \frac{8.31 \times 298 \times 2.30}{96,500} \log 0.080$$

In electrical units $R = 8.31$ joules per degree per mole and $\ln x = 2.3 \log x$, in which log indicates the logarithm to the base 10. The pressure of the hydrogen gas being 1 atm, its activity is 1; and

$$E_{el} = -0.0592 \log 0.080 = +0.0649 \text{ volt}$$

Thus it is seen that the voltage of this electrode is increased above the standard potential value by a decrease in the hydrogen-ion concentration. This makes it easier for ions to pass into solution. The electrode therefore shows a greater electron activity than the standard electrode.

Example 13-2. Calculate the oxidation potential of a copper electrode at 25°C in a solution which is 0.12m in cupric ions.

The metallic copper has an activity of 1. $n = 2$. Hence

$$E_{el} = E^{\circ}_{Cu;Cu^{2+}} - \frac{8.31 \times 298 \times 2.30}{2 \times 96,500} \log 0.12$$

$$= -0.337 - \frac{0.0592}{2} \times (-0.920) = -0.310 \text{ volt}$$

Note again that reducing the activity of the positive ion increases the voltage of the electrode (-0.310 is larger than -0.337).

Example 13-3. Calculate the oxidation potential of an electrode consisting of a platinum foil immersed at 25°C in a solution in which the ferric-ion activity is 0.020 and the ferrous-ion activity is 0.100.

From Table 13-1
$$E^{\circ}_{Fe^{2+};Fe^{3+}} = -0.771 \text{ volt}$$

Since the electrode reaction is

$$Fe^{2+} = Fe^{3+} + e$$

$$E_{el} = -0.771 - \frac{8.31 \times 298 \times 2.30}{96,500} \log \frac{0.020}{0.100}$$

$$= -0.771 + 0.041 = -0.730 \text{ volt}$$

In these problems the term 2.30 RT/F has a value of 0.0592 volt, or 59.2 millivolts (mv), at 25°C. Since this term will occur many times in electrochemical calculations, it is well for the student to have its value (and, of course, the way it is calculated) firmly in mind at all times.

13e. The Calculation of the Potential of Chemical Cells. The galvanic cells considered so far in this chapter have been examples of *chemical cells.* This term is applied to those cells whose operation depends on a chemical reaction. In some cases, to separate the reaction into two parts, two different solutions are necessary. In others, only one solution is used. Certain of the conventions used in electrochemistry are now discussed. For the cell in Figure 13-2(*a*), the following is used to represent its construction and action:

$$Zn; \; Zn^{2+}(a = 1) \overset{e\rightarrow}{\|} H^{+}(a = 1); \; H_2(1 \text{ atm}), Pt$$

The zinc is written on the left because it is the electrode *from* which the electrons pass to the external circuit. That the movement of electrons is from the left to the right in the external circuit is shown by the arrow. The semicolon indicates a phase boundary, in one case between the metallic zinc and the solution of zinc ions, and in the other case between the hydrogen gas adsorbed in the platinum black of the electrode and the solution of hydrogen ions. Whenever two phases are in contact, a potential is set up. This potential has been studied extensively in this chapter in connection with electrodes. Also, whenever two solutions are in contact, as the two solutions in the above cell, a potential is set up at the boundary. The reason for this potential and the method of calculating its value are complicated. Fortunately, it is not necessary to be concerned with this potential because the effects of this potential can be made vanishingly small by connecting the two solutions by means of a *salt bridge*. A salt bridge consists of a tube filled with a solution whose ions have approximately the same velocity. Potassium chloride fulfills this requirement. This is the electrolyte used in the bridge of the zinc-hydrogen cell. A KCl salt bridge, however, cannot be used in a cell containing silver ions because there would be interaction between the chloride ions and the silver ions. Ammonium nitrate is used in such a cell. The two vertical bars between the two solutions indicate that the junction potential can be considered as being eliminated by means of a salt bridge.

When a cell is so represented, the potential of the cell is equal to the difference between the potentials of the two half cells—that is, the potential between the left electrode and the right electrode:

$$\left(E_{cell} = E_{left} - E_{right} \right) \tag{13-2}$$

For the cell given, since each substance is in its standard state,

$$E_{cell} = E^{\circ}_{cell} = E^{\circ}_{Zn;Zn^{2+}} - E^{\circ}_{H_2;H^+} = +0.763 - 0 = 0.763 \text{ volt}$$
$$T = 25°C$$

Example 13-4. Calculate the potential of the following cell at 25°C:

$$Zn; Zn^{2+}(a = 0.10) \parallel H^+(a = 0.01); H_2(1 \text{ atm}), Pt$$
$$E_{cell} = E_{left} - E_{right}$$

$$E_{cell} = \left(E^{\circ}_{Zn;Zn^{2+}} - \frac{0.0592}{2} \log 0.10 \right) - (E^{\circ}_{H_2;H^+} - 0.0592 \log 0.01)$$

$$= (0.763 + 0.0296) - (0 + 0.1184) = 0.674 \text{ volt}$$

Example 13-5. Calculate the potential of the following cell at 25°C:

$$\text{Fe, Fe}^{2+}(a = 0.02) \parallel \text{Cl}^-(a = 0.1); \text{Cl}_2(1 \text{ atm}), \text{Pt}$$

$$E_{\text{cell}} = E_{\text{left}} - E_{\text{right}}$$

$$E_{\text{cell}} = \left(E^\circ_{\text{Fe, Fe}^{2+}} - \frac{0.0592}{2}\log 0.02\right) - \left(E^\circ_{\text{Cl}_2;\text{Cl}^-} - 0.0592 \log\frac{1}{0.1}\right) \leftarrow$$

$$= (+0.440 + 0.050) - (-1.360 - 0.0592) = 1.909 \text{ volts}$$

The general expression for the single electrode potential can be used to obtain the general expression for the potential of a chemical cell. The derivation, however, will be carried out for a special case, and the resulting formula generalized to obtain an expression applicable to any cell. Consider the cell given in Example 13-4. The potential of the cell is given by the expression

$$E_{\text{cell}} = E^\circ_{\text{Zn};\text{Zn}^{2+}} - \frac{RT}{2F}\ln\frac{a_{\text{Zn}^{2+}}}{a_{\text{Zn}}} - \left(E^\circ_{\text{H}_2;\text{H}^+} - \frac{RT}{2F}\ln\frac{a^2_{\text{H}^+}}{a_{\text{H}_2}}\right)$$

A combination of terms gives

$$E_{\text{cell}} = (E^\circ_{\text{Zn};\text{Zn}^{2+}} - E^\circ_{\text{H}_2;\text{H}^+}) - \frac{RT}{2F}\ln\frac{a_{\text{Zn}^{2+}} \times a_{\text{H}_2}}{a^2_{\text{H}^+} \times a_{\text{Zn}}}$$

Replace the difference between the two standard electrode potentials by the symbol E°_{cell}. This is the standard electrode potential of the cell. Observe that the product terms in the cell reaction

$$\text{Zn} + 2\text{H}^+ = \text{Zn}^{2+} + \text{H}_2$$

are in the numerator of the logarithmic term. The reactant terms are found in the denominator. The general formula may then be written

$$\left(E_{\text{cell}} = E^\circ_{\text{cell}} - \frac{RT}{nF}\ln\frac{\text{products}}{\text{reactants}}\right) \tag{13-3}$$

in which E°_{cell} is the difference between the two standard electrode potentials; n is the number of electrons transferred when the reaction takes place as written; the word *products* denotes the product of the activities of the products, as given by the reaction, each raised to the proper power; and the word *reactants* denotes the same for the reactants. The use of this equation is illustrated in the following examples.

Example 13-6. Calculate the potential of the cell in Example 13-4, using Equation 13-3:

$$Zn + 2H^+ = Zn^{2+} + H_2$$

$$E_{cell} = 0.763 - 0 - \frac{0.0592}{2} \log \frac{0.1 \times 1}{1 \times 0.01^2}$$

$$= 0.763 - 0.0888 = 0.674 \text{ volt}$$

Example 13-7. Calculate the potential of the cell in Example 13-5, using Equation 13-3:

$$Fe + Cl_2 = Fe^{2+} + 2Cl^-$$

$$E_{cell} = E_{cell}^\circ - \frac{0.0592}{2} \log \frac{0.02 \times 0.1^2}{1 \times 1}$$

$$= 1.800 + 0.1095 = 1.909 \text{ volts}$$

In these calculations the question of which electrode is the negative electrode can be determined by calculating the single electrode potentials. Whichever has the greater positive potential is the negative, or left, electrode. The negative electrode can be established experimentally by determining which electrode has to be connected to the negative binding post of the potentiometer, in order to secure a reading. This electrode is the negative, or left, electrode.

13f. The Calculation of the Potential of Concentration Cells. The cells discussed in 13e were termed chemical cells because the free energy obtained in the form of electrical energy was produced from a chemical reaction. Cells can also be constructed by using two similar electrode systems, each with different activities of the reacting substances. An example of such a cell is shown in Figure 13-3. The two solutions may be

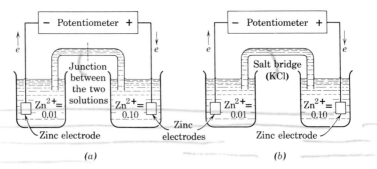

(a)   (b)

Figure 13-3. Concentration cells reversible with respect to zinc ions: (a) with junction potential, (b) without junction potential.

allowed to be in direct contact with each other as shown in Figure 13-3(*a*) or they may be connected by a salt bridge as shown in Figure 13-3(*b*). In the first case a potential will exist at the junction of the two liquids as well as at each of the two electrodes. In the second case the salt bridge reduces junction potentials to a vanishingly small value. The considerations that follow apply only to cases in which a salt bridge is used and junction effects eliminated.

In Figure 13-3(*b*) the two electrodes are of zinc and the ion activities have values of 0.1 and 0.01*m*. The cell is therefore formulated in the following manner:

$$Zn; Zn^{2+}(a = 0.010) \parallel Zn^{2+}(a = 0.100); Zn$$

and the potentials of the two electrodes are calculated as

$$E(Zn = 0.1m) = 0.763 - \frac{0.0592}{2} \log 0.1 = 0.763 + 0.0296$$

$$= +0.793 \text{ volt}$$

$$E(Zn = 0.01m) = 0.763 - \frac{0.0592}{2} \log 0.01 = 0.763 + 0.0592$$

$$= +0.822 \text{ volt}$$

The over-all cell potential would be

$$E_1 - E_r = 0.822 \text{ volt} - 0.793 \text{ volt} = 0.029 \text{ volt}$$

A cell consisting of two similar electrodes immersed in solutions of the same ion, but at different activities, is termed a *concentration cell*. The free energy change that furnishes the electrical energy comes from the work of dilution. As the cell furnishes this energy, zinc ions move *into* the solution from the negative electrode and *out of* the solution at the positive electrode. This process continues until the activity of the zinc ion is the same around both electrodes. At this point the voltage of the cell is reduced to zero. Concentration cells are said to be reversible with respect to cations when the potential difference at the two electrodes is due to a difference in activity of a particular cation and the electrode reactions consist of cations being either given to or evolved from the electrodes. If the concentration cell is one in which the potential difference is due to the difference in activities of an anion, and the electrodes evolve or take up these anions, the cell is said to be reversible with respect to anions. A cell consisting of two chlorine gas electrodes in solutions of chloride ions of different activity would be reversible with respect to the chloride anion.

In a cell reversible with respect to cations the electromotive force of the cell would be given by the following expression:

$$E_{cell} = \left(E_{el}^\circ - \frac{RT}{nF} \ln a_1\right) - \left(E_{el}^\circ - \frac{RT}{nF} \ln a_r\right)$$

$$= \frac{RT}{nF} \ln \frac{a_r}{a_1} \qquad (13\text{-}4)$$

In a cell reversible with respect to anions the electromotive force would be given by the following expression:

$$E_{cell} = \left(E_{el}^\circ - \frac{RT}{nF} \ln \frac{1}{a_1}\right) - \left(E_{el}^\circ - \frac{RT}{nF} \ln \frac{1}{a_r}\right) = \frac{RT}{nF} \ln \frac{a_1}{a_r} \quad (13\text{-}5)$$

In both Equations 13-4 and 13-5 it was assumed that a salt bridge was used between the two solutions so that the junction potential between the two half cells was essentially zero.

Example 13-8. Calculate the potentials of the following concentration cells at 25°C:

CELL 1. Cu; $Cu^{2+}(a = 0.040) \parallel Cu^{2+}(a = 0.080)$; Cu

This cell is reversible with respect to cations. Therefore Equation 13-4 is employed, and

$$E = \frac{RT}{2F} \ln \frac{0.080}{0.040} = \frac{0.0592}{2} \log 2 = \frac{0.0592}{2} \times 0.301 = 0.0089 \text{ volt}$$

CELL 2. Ag, AgCl; $Cl^-(a = 0.76) \parallel Cl^-(a = 0.38)$; AgCl, Ag

This cell is reversible with respect to anions. Therefore Equation 13-5 is applicable, and

$$E = \frac{RT}{F} \ln \frac{0.76}{0.38} = 0.0592 \log 2 = 0.0178 \text{ volt}$$

THE MEASUREMENT OF CELL POTENTIALS

13g. The Potentiometer and Its Use. The commonest use of galvanic cells in everyday life is to supply electrical energy for various purposes, such as lighting, heating, and operating motors. In medical and biological work their most important use is in analytical procedures such as the determination of hydrogen-ion activity and pH. In such a determination the cell potential is measured and the desired activity of the particular ion is determined from the formula for the cell potential. Current cannot be taken from the cell in such a measurement because part of the potential of the cell would then be taken up in the potential drop through the cell itself, due to its internal resistance. The measuring instrument would then indicate a potential less than the actual potential of the cell. Also, if current is drawn from the cell, chemical changes will take place under usual conditions and a change in the activities of the substances involved will result. Therefore accurate results could not be obtained. Thus it is necessary to carry out the measurements in such a way that a minimum of current is taken from the cell.

The instrument used for this purpose is termed a *potentiometer*. With this instrument the imposed external potential necessary to *prevent* current from flowing from the cell is determined. This imposed potential is equal in magnitude to the potential of the cell. If care is taken during the measurement, the current taken from the cell is vanishingly small and the activities of the ions in the cell are not appreciably altered in the measurement. The electromotive force of the cell thus remains constant, and its value can be determined with a very high degree of precision.

Potentiometers vary in their complexity, depending on the precision of the work for which they are designed. Figure 13-4 shows a diagram of a simplified potentiometer. This potentiometer is adequate to illustrate the basic principle of the instrument and the manner in which it is employed.

An examination of the diagram shows that there are two fundamental circuits. One of them includes the battery, *C*, the adjustable resistance, *D*, and the entire length of the resistance wire, *IJ*. The second circuit includes the galvanometer, *G*, the variable length of the resistance wire, *IF*, the double throw switch, *E*, the key, *H*, and either the standard cell, *A*, or the cell of unknown potential, *B*, depending on the position of the

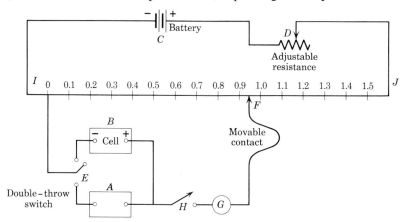

Figure 13-4. Diagram of a simplified potentiometer circuit.

switch, E. The two circuits are so wired together that the voltage from the second circuit is applied across the resistance wire, IJ, in opposition to the voltage applied from the first circuit. This is shown by the fact that the minus pole of the battery in the first circuit and the minus pole of the cell in the second circuit have a common contact at I. The resistance wire is divided into 15 sections of uniform resistance. One of these, not shown in the diagram, is further subdivided.

Consider circuit $IEAHGF$. This circuit contains the standard cell, A, which furnishes a constant known potential, and is so wired into the circuit that its voltage is exactly 1 volt across the contacts, IF. If F is at the 1.0 stop, the voltage drop across each of the subdivisions would, of necessity, be 0.1 volt. Whether current flows through this circuit, as indicated by the galvanometer, G, depends upon whether or not the voltage supplied by the battery, C, across the same length of resistance wire, IF, is exactly 1 volt. If it is, the cell cannot push electrons through the circuit being considered. This will be shown by the failure of the galvanometer to deflect. If the battery, C, is furnishing a voltage of less than 1 volt, current will flow in the $IEAHGF$ circuit, and the galvanometer will show a deflection. On the other hand, if the battery, C, is furnishing a voltage of more than 1 volt, current will be forced through the circuit under consideration, and the galvanometer will deflect in the other direction.

The function of the circuit $IEAHGF$ is to help in the establishment of such a current from the battery, C, in the first circuit, $CIFJD$, that the potential drop across each sub-division is 0.1 volt. The drop along the entire wire will then be 1.5 volts. This is done by placing the contact, F, at the 1.0 position. The double pole switch at E is placed in the standard cell circuit. The key, H, is tapped, and the movement of the galvanometer noted. A swing means that the voltage imposed by the battery, C, across IF is either greater or less than 1 volt. The adjustable resistance, D, is changed, and again the key is depressed. If the swing is in the opposite direction, the resistance has been changed too much. By tapping the key and adjusting D, the so-called working current in IJ can be adjusted so that the drop across IF is 1 volt, hence the drop across each subdivision is 0.1 volt. Key H is tapped rather than held down because the latter procedure would result in a drawing of current from the standard cell. Hence there would be an alteration in its voltage.

With the current in $CIFJD$ so regulated that the drop in potential across each subdivision is 0.1 volt, the standard cell is cut out of the circuit and replaced by the cell of unknown voltage, B. Depression of H will result in a deflection of the galvanometer until the contact, F, has been moved to such a position that the voltage drop from the battery, C, is exactly equal to the voltage of the cell. Then no deflection will be obtained on the galvanometer. The movement of contact, F, is effected by the movement of dials on the face of the instrument, and at the point of balance the voltage is read directly from the positions of the dials.

The steps in the use of the instrument may be summarized as follows:

1. With E on standard cell and F at 1.0, the current from the battery is adjusted by means of the adjustable resistance until no current flows in the standard circuit. This produces a voltage drop of 0.1 volt across each of the subdivisions of the resistance wire.

2. The double pole switch is placed in the cell position and F moved until no deflection is noted on the galvanometer. The voltage of the cell is then equal to the distance, IF, which is read from the positions of the dials.

In this procedure it is necessary to have a standard cell whose potential is constant and reproducible. It must be rugged in construction and should be affected but little by temperature change. The standard cell usually employed is the saturated Weston standard cell shown in Figure 13-5. One leg contains mercury over which is placed a paste of mercurous sulfate. The other leg contains an amalgam of cadmium and mercury. This is a one-fluid cell, and the electrolyte is a saturated solution of cadmium sulfate. In preparing the cell excess crystals of $CdSO_4 \cdot 8/3 H_2O$ are placed over the solid electrode materials, as shown in the diagram. The reaction that can take place in this cell is

$$Cd + Hg_2SO_4 = CdSO_4 + 2Hg$$

Its potential is approximately 1.0183 volts at 25°C, and with care it will maintain a constant voltage for many months.

THE THERMODYNAMICS OF GALVANIC CELLS

13h. Fundamental Equations. We shall start with certain equations given in Chapter 10. These are:

$$\Delta G° = -RT \ln K \tag{10-14}$$

$$\Delta G = \Delta G° + RT \ln \frac{\text{products}}{\text{reactants}} \tag{10-12}$$

$$\Delta G = \Delta H - T \Delta S \tag{10-8}$$

To these will be added the following without any attempt at derivation

$$\frac{d(\Delta G)_p}{dT} = -\Delta S = -\frac{d(EnF)_p}{dT} = -nF\left(\frac{dE}{dT}\right)_p \tag{13-6}$$

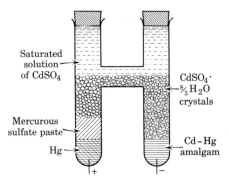

Figure 13-5. Weston cadmium standard cell.

Since the free energy change in a galvanic cell is equal to $-EnF$ we may write the preceding four equations in this manner

$$E°nF = RT \ln K \tag{13-7}$$

$$EnF = E°nF - RT \ln \frac{\text{products}}{\text{reactants}}$$

$$E = E° - \frac{RT}{nF} \ln \frac{\text{products}}{\text{reactants}} \tag{13-8}$$

$$EnF = -\Delta H + nFT \left(\frac{dE}{dT}\right)_p \tag{13-9}$$

The last equation is the Gibbs-Helmholtz equation. In this equation the term, dE/dT, is the rate of change of the electromotive force of the cell with a change in temperature. The subscript p indicates that the change is at constant pressure. Less precisely the term is the change in electromotive force for $1°$ change in temperature.

13i. Applications of the Fundamental Equations. We shall consider the use of these equations by some typical examples. The values for the free energies of formation and the entropies of the reactants and products are given in Tables 10-2 and 10-1.

Example 13-9. From free energy data calculate the electromotive force of the following cell at 25°C. The value of $\Delta H°$ for the cell reaction is -9661 cal at 25°C. Calculate the value of $\Delta S°$ for the reaction at this temperature.

$$\text{Pt, } H_2(1 \text{ atm}); \ H^+(a = 1), \ Cl^-(a = 1); \ AgCl, \ Ag$$

The cell reaction is

$$AgCl\,(s) + \tfrac{1}{2}H_2 = Ag\,(s) + Cl^- + H^+$$
$$\Delta G^\circ = -31,350\ \text{cal} + 26,224\ \text{cal} = -5126\ \text{cal}$$
$$\Delta G^\circ = -E^\circ nF = -5126\ \text{cal} \times 4.184\ \text{joules/cal}$$
$$E^\circ = \frac{5126 \times 4.184}{96,500} = 0.2222\ \text{volt}$$

Equation 10-8 will be used to calculate the entropy change.

$$\Delta G^\circ = \Delta H^\circ - T\Delta S^\circ$$
$$\Delta S^\circ = \frac{5126 - 9661}{298} = -15.2\ \text{E.U.}$$

Example 13-10. Given the following cell at 25°C.

$$Pt,\ H_2(1\ \text{atm});\ \ H^+(a = 0.03),\ Cl^-(a = 0.02);\ \ AgCl,\ Ag$$

Calculate (a) the electromotive force of the cell, and (b) the free energy change accompanying the cell reaction. In solving this example note that the activities of the hydrogen gas, the silver chloride, and the silver all have a value of unity since they are in their standard states. We shall use the data from Example 13-9 and we shall employ Equation 13-8.

(a) $E = 0.2222$ volt

$$-\ \frac{1.99\ \text{cal/mole/degree} \times 4.184\ \text{joules/cal} \times 2.303 \times 298^\circ}{96,500\ \text{coulombs}}$$
$$\times \log\,(0.03 \times 0.02)$$

$$E = 0.4129\ \text{volt}$$

(b) $\Delta G = -EnF = -\ \dfrac{0.4129 \times 96,500}{4.184} = -9523\ \text{cal}$

Example 13-11. Calculate the potential of the following cell at 25°C from free energy data.

$$Zn;\ Zn^{2+}(a = 1) \parallel H^+(a = 1);\ H_2(1\ \text{atm}),\ Pt$$

The reaction taking place in this cell when it supplies current is

$$Zn + 2H^+ = Zn^{2+} + H_2$$

This reaction is somewhat unusual in that three of the substances, H^+, Zn, and H_2 are in their standard states and all have a standard free energy value of zero. Hence

$$\Delta G^\circ = \Delta G^\circ(Zn^{2+}) + \Delta G^\circ(H_2) - \Delta G^\circ(Zn) - 2\Delta G^\circ(H^+)$$
$$= -35,180 + 0 - 0 - 0 = -35,180 \text{ cal}$$

Since

$$\Delta G^\circ = -E^\circ nF$$

$$E^\circ = -\frac{-35,180 \text{ cal} \times 4.184 \text{ joules/cal}}{2 \times 96,500 \text{ coulombs}} = +0.763 \text{ volt}$$

The potential of the cell is, of course, simply the potential of the standard zinc electrode.

Example 13-12. Given the following cell

$$\text{Pb, PbCl}_2; \text{ HCl}(1m); \text{ AgCl, Ag}$$

The value of the electromotive force at 25°C is 0.4900 volt. The rate of change of the electromotive force with temperature is 0.000186 volt/degree. Calculate ΔG, ΔH, and ΔS for the cell reaction. In the solution of this example we shall use Equations 10-8, 13-6, and 13-9. According to Equation 13-6

$$\frac{d(\Delta G)_p}{dT} = -\Delta S = -nF\left(\frac{dE}{dT}\right)_p$$

$$\Delta S = \frac{2 \times 96,500 \times 0.000186}{4.184} = 8.58 \text{ E.U.}$$

$$\Delta G = -EnF = -\frac{0.4900 \times 2 \times 96,500}{4.184} = -22,603 \text{ cal}$$

$$\Delta G = \Delta H - T\Delta S$$

therefore

$$\Delta H = -22,603 + 8.58 \times 298 = -20,046 \text{ cal}$$

Example 13-13. Given the reaction

$$\text{Zn} + \text{Cu}^{2+} = \text{Zn}^{2+} + \text{Cu}$$

The value of ΔH° for the above reaction is $-51,820$ cal at 25°C. Devise a cell that could be used to determine ΔG°, ΔS°, dE/dT, and the value of the equilibrium constant at 25°C. The cell that can be used is the Daniell cell. It is formulated as follows:

$$\text{Zn; Zn}^{2+}(a = 1) \parallel \text{Cu}^{2+}(a = 1); \text{Cu}$$

The value of $E°$ can be calculated from the standard electrode potentials as given in Table 13-1.

$$E° = 0.763 \text{ volt} - (- 0.337) = 1.100 \text{ volts}$$

and

$$\Delta G° = -E°nF = -1.100 \times 2 \times 96,500 = -212,300 \text{ joules}$$
$$= -212,300/4.184 = -50,740 \text{ cal}$$

$$\Delta S° = \frac{\Delta H° - \Delta G°}{T} = \frac{-51,820 + 50,740}{298} = -3.63 \text{ E.U.}$$

$$\Delta S° = nF \frac{dE°}{dT} = -3.63 \times 4.184 = -15.19 \text{ joules/degree}$$

$$\frac{dE°}{dT} = -\frac{15.19}{2 \times 96,500} = -7.9 \times 10^{-5} \text{ volt/degree}$$

since

$$\Delta G° = -RT \ln K = -50,740 \text{ cal}$$

$$\log K = \frac{50,740}{1.99 \times 298 \times 2.303} = 37.15$$

$$K = 1.4 \times 10^{37}$$

13j. Derivation of the Expression for the Single Electrode Potential. In 13d it was stated that the derivation for the expression for the oxidation potential

$$E_{el} = E°_{el} - RT/nF \ln \text{Ox/Red} \qquad (13\text{-}10)$$

would be obtained later in the chapter. We shall now demonstrate the correctness of this expression by applying Equation 13-8 to a typical cell. Let this cell be

$$\text{Pt, H}_2; \text{H}^+ \parallel \text{Fe}^{2+}, \text{Fe}^{3+}; \text{Pt}$$

The equation for the reaction taking place when this cell furnishes current is

$$\text{H}_2 + 2\text{Fe}^{3+} = 2\text{H}^+ + 2\text{Fe}^{2+}$$

Applying Equation 13-8, we have

$$E_{cell} = E_1 - E_r = E°_{cell} - \frac{RT}{2F} \ln \frac{a_{H^+}^2 a_{Fe^{2+}}^2}{a_{H_2} a_{Fe^{3+}}^2}$$

$$E_{cell} = (E°_{H_2,H^+} - E°_{Fe^{2+},Fe^{3+}}) - \frac{RT}{2F} \ln \frac{a_{H^+}^2}{a_{H_2}} - \frac{RT}{2F} \ln \frac{a_{Fe^{2+}}^2}{a_{Fe^{3+}}^2}$$

$$E_{cell} = \left(E°_{H_2,H^+} - \frac{RT}{F} \ln \frac{a_{H^+}}{a_H^{1/2}} \right) - \left(E°_{Fe^{2+},Fe^{3+}} - \frac{RT}{F} \ln \frac{a_{Fe^{3+}}}{a_{Fe^{2+}}} \right)$$
$$\qquad\qquad (1) \qquad\qquad\qquad\qquad\qquad\qquad (2)$$

Expression (1), E_1, is the oxidation potential of the hydrogen gas electrode and has the form shown in Equation 13-10 for the reaction taking place at this electrode. Expression (2), E_r, is the oxidation potential expression for the Fe^{2+}, Fe^{3+} electrode. Thus we have demonstrated for two special electrodes the exactness of Equation 13-10. The same reasoning can be used to show that this equation is applicable to any electrode and is a general expression for the oxidation potential of all single electrodes.

REFERENCES

Bull, *Physical Biochemistry*, John Wiley and Sons, New York, 1951, Chapter 6.

Daniels and Alberty, *Physical Chemistry*, John Wiley and Sons, New York, 1961, Chapter 14.

Maron and Prutton, *Principles of Physical Chemistry*, The Macmillan Co., New York, 1958, Chapter 17.

Moore, *Physical Chemistry*, Prentice-Hall, Englewood Cliffs, New Jersey, 1962, Chapter 10.

Sheehan, *Physical Chemistry*, Allyn and Bacon, Boston, 1961, Chapter 7.

Daniels, Williams, Bender, Alberty, and Cornwell, *Experimental Physical Chemistry*, McGraw-Hill Book Co., New York, 1962, Chapters 9 and 22.

Crockford and Nowell, *Laboratory Manual of Physical Chemistry*, John Wiley and Sons, New York, 1956, Experiments 28, 29, and 30.

REVIEW QUESTIONS

1. Discuss the use of the galvanic cell as a device for producing electrical energy from the free energy change that accompanies the cell reaction. What relationship exists among the electrical energy that can be obtained from a chemical cell, the voltage of the cell, and the term, n, associated with the reaction taking place?

2. Sketch two galvanic cells, each with a hydrogen electrode dipping into a solution of hydrogen ions. In one cell the second electrode is one using a metal above hydrogen in the electromotive series dipping into a solution of its ions, and in the second a metal below hydrogen in the electromotive series dipping into a solution of its ions.

3. Which are the positive electrodes and which are the negative electrodes in the two cells in Question 2. When the ions are at unit activity and the hydrogen gas is at one atmosphere pressure, what are the values of the electromotive forces of the cells at 25°C? Write the electrode reactions that take place at each of the electrodes when these cells furnish current. Write the over-all cell reaction in each cell.

4. Give the equations for the electrode reactions in a number of typical half cells.

5. What characteristics must a chemical reaction possess in order for its reactants and products to be useful in the construction of a galvanic cell?

6. Write several reactions involved in the operation of galvanic cells. Write the two electrode reactions in each case.

7. What is meant by the oxidation potential of a half-cell? What is meant by the standard oxidation potential of a half cell? Discuss the basis upon which the electrode systems are arranged in the electromotive force table.

8. Why are the potentials in the electromotive series based on an assigned value of zero for the standard hydrogen electrode? Show that calculated cell potentials are unaffected by the fact that the standard hydrogen electrode has arbitrarily been assigned a value of zero.

9. Discuss the expression that gives the potential of a single electrode when the activities of the reactants and products differ from unity.

10. How are single electrode potentials used in obtaining the potential of a galvanic cell? What sign conventions are used in electromotive force calculations and the formulation of galvanic cells?

11. Derive a general expression for the electromotive force of a galvanic cell from the expressions for the single electrode potentials.

12. What is a salt bridge? Why is it used? What determines the suitability of a substance for preparing a salt bridge?

13. What is a concentration cell? What type of process in such a cell produces the electrical energy?

14. Derive the general expression for the potential of a concentration cell without junction potential (a) when the cell is reversible with respect to cations and (b) when the cell is reversible with respect to anions.

15. Explain in detail the operation and use of the potentiometer. Why is it necessary to use the principle of the potentiometer in measuring cell potentials?

16. Describe the Weston standard cell. What chemical reaction accounts for the operation of the cell?

17. List the three general thermodynamic equations used in the study of the thermodynamics of galvanic cells. Give the equation for the way in which the free energy change varies with temperature change.

18. By substituting for ΔG the equivalent expression, $-EnF$, derive from the four equations of Question 17 the three equations most useful in the thermodynamic study of galvanic cells. Which of these equations is termed the Gibbs-Helmholtz equation? How are these equations used in the study of galvanic cells?

19. From the general expression for the electromotive force of a galvanic cell derive the general expression for single electrode potentials.

PROBLEMS

I

1. Calculate the oxidation potentials of the following hydrogen electrodes at 25°C.

	H^+ Activity	Pressure of Hydrogen Gas
(a)	1.0	1.32 atm
(b)	0.082	1.0 atm
(c)	0.082	740 mm
(d)	2.1×10^{-4}	750 mm

2. Calculate the oxidation potentials of the following electrodes at 25°C.

(a) Zn, Zn^{2+} ($a = 1.4 \times 10^{-3}$)
(b) Pt, Fe^{2+} ($a = 0.12$), Fe^{3+} ($a = 0.048$)
(c) Pt, O_2 (0.90 atm), OH^- ($a = 0.10$)
(d) Cu, Cu^{2+} ($a = 0.38$)

3. Calculate the single electrode potentials in each of the following cells. What is the cell potential in each case? $T = 25°C$.

(a) A zinc electrode immersed in a solution in which the activity of the zinc ion is $0.01m$ and a copper electrode in which the activity of the copper ions is $0.002m$.

(b) A lead electrode immersed in a solution of lead ions of activity 0.35 and a silver electrode immersed in a solution in which the activity of the silver ions is 0.18. The standard potential of the Ag, Ag^+ electrode is -0.800 V.

4. Calculate the potential of the following cells at 25°C.

(a) A hydrogen gas electrode and an oxygen gas electrode immersed in pure water. The pressure of both gases is 1 atm.

(b) A hydrogen gas electrode and an oxygen gas electrode immersed in pure water. The pressure of both gases is 720 mm.

(c) A zinc electrode and a chlorine gas electrode immersed in a solution of zinc chloride. The activity of the zinc ions is 0.001. The pressure of the chlorine gas is 1 atm.

5. Calculate the change in the potential at 25°C of each of the following electrodes when the activity of the particular ion is changed from 1.2×10^{-3} to 0.12.

(a) Ag, AgCl electrode in a solution of chloride ions
(b) Pt, O_2, electrode in a solution of OH^- ions
(c) Pt, Cl_2, electrode in a solution of chloride ions

6. A Daniell cell has a potential of 1.040 volts at 25°C. What is the ratio of the activities of the copper and zinc ions in the cell? If the activity of the zinc ion is $0.05m$, what is the activity of the copper ion?

7. A Daniell cell has a potential of zero at 25°C. If the activity of the zinc ion is $0.20m$, what is the activity of the copper ion?

8. Calculate the single electrode potentials and the cell potential at 25°C for the cell:

$$Pb, Pb^{2+} (a = 0.0018) \parallel Fe^{2+} (a = 0.200), Fe^{3+} (a = 0.150); Pt$$

9. Given a cell consisting of a hydrogen gas electrode and a silver-silver chloride electrode dipping into a solution of HCl at 25°C. What would be the electromotive force of the cell if the hydrochloric acid is of such a concentration that the activities of the hydrogen and chloride ions are 0.040 each and the pressure of the hydrogen gas is 740 mm?

10. A cell consisting of a hydrogen electrode and a zinc electrode in solutions of the respective ions at 25°C has an electromotive force of 0.620 volt. The hydrogen gas has a pressure of 760 mm and the hydrogen-ion activity is $1.25 \times 10^{-3}m$. What is the activity of the zinc ion?

11. Given a cell consisting of a copper electrode in a solution of copper ions of molality equal to 2.4×10^{-3} and a bright platinum electrode in a solution of Fe (II) and Fe (III) ions at $25\,°C$. The activity of the Fe (II) is 0.45. The cell has a potential at this temperature of 0.414 volt. What is the activity of the Fe (III) ion? The copper electrode has the larger oxidation potential.

Note: In the following concentration cells and in those given in Part II assume that the effect of the junction potential has been eliminated by means of a salt bridge.

12. Given two silver-silver chloride electrodes immersed in solutions of chloride ions with activities of 0.288 and 0.185. What is the electromotive force of the cell at $25\,°C$?

13. Calculate the potential of a concentration cell made up of two zinc electrodes immersed in solutions of zinc ions with activities of 0.402 and 0.182. Assume a temperature of $25\,°C$.

14. A concentration cell reversible with respect to zinc ions has a potential of 0.065 volt at $25\,°C$. The activity of the zinc ion at the positive electrode is 0.030. What is the activity of the zinc ion at the other electrode?

15. Given a cell consisting of a silver-silver chloride electrode and a hydrogen electrode immersed in a hydrochloric acid solution. The value of $E°$ for this cell is $+0.2224$ volt at $25\,°C$. The change in the electromotive force with temperature is -0.0007 volt per degree. Calculate $\Delta G°$, $\Delta S°$, and $\Delta H°$ from the data supplied in this problem.

16. Given a cell consisting of a zinc electrode immersed in a solution of zinc ions and a silver electrode immersed in a solution of silver ions. The temperature is $25\,°C$ and the ion activities are both unity. Write the equation for the reaction taking place in the cell when the cell furnishes current. From the data of Tables 10-1 and 10-2 and the fact that the entropy of zinc at $25\,°C$ is 9.95 cal per mole per degree, calculate $\Delta G°$, $\Delta H°$, and $\Delta S°$ for the cell reaction at $25\,°C$. Calculate the equilibrium constant for the reaction and the rate of change of the electromotive force of the cell per degree of temperature at $25\,°C$.

17. From the data of Problem I-16 calculate the electromotive force of the following cell at $25\,°C$.

$$\text{Zn, Zn}^{2+} (a = 0.12) \parallel \text{Ag}^+ (a = 0.25), \text{Ag}$$

18. Given a cell consisting of a silver, silver chloride electrode and a chlorine gas electrode immersed in a $1m$ solution of HCl saturated with silver chloride. The cell reaction is:

$$2Ag + Cl_2 \rightarrow 2AgCl$$

The cell potential is 1.1362 volts at $25\,°C$ and the change of potential with temperature is -0.00060 volt per degree. Calculate ΔH, ΔG, and ΔS for the cell reaction.

II

1. Calculate the oxidation potentials of the following electrodes at $25\,°C$:

(a) Pt, O_2 ($P = 750$ mm), OH^- ($a = 0.250$)

(b) Pt, Fe^{2+} ($a = 0.150$), Fe^{3+} ($a = 0.260$)
(c) Cu, Cu^{2+} ($a = 0.880$)
(d) Ag, AgCl, Cl^- ($a = 0.620$)
(e) Pb, Pb^{2+} ($a = 2.3 \times 10^{-3}$)

2. Calculate the oxidation potential of the following hydrogen electrodes at 25°C:

	H^+ Activity	Pressure of Hydrogen Gas
(a)	0.037	1.0 atm
(b)	0.840	735 mm
(c)	3.6×10^{-7}	765 mm

3. Given a hydrogen gas electrode at 25°C with a solution 0.455m in hydrogen-ion activity. The pressure of the hydrogen gas is 740 mm. If the gas pressure is changed to 760 mm, what change would have to be made in the activity of the hydrogen ions in order for the electrode potential to remain unchanged?

4. Calculate the electromotive force of the following cells at 25°C.

(a) Pt, H_2 (1 atm), pure water, O_2 (1 atm), Pt
(b) Zn, Zn^{2+} ($a = 0.205$) Fe^{2+} ($a = 0.125$), Fe

5. What is the electromotive force at 25°C of a cell consisting of a zinc electrode in a solution in which the activity of the zinc ion is 1.24×10^{-4} and a hydrogen gas electrode dipping into a solution whose pH is 5.00? The pressure of the hydrogen gas is 740 mm.

6. In a cell similar to the one in Problem II-5 the pressure of the gas is 1 atm and the pH is 3.2. The cell potential is 0.5664 volt at 25°C. What is the activity of the zinc ion?

7. Calculate the electromotive force of a cell at 25°C consisting of a platinum electrode in a solution of Fe (II) ions and Fe (III) ions of equal activity and a lead electrode immersed in a solution of lead ions with an activity of 0.070?

8. Calculate the electromotive force of a concentration cell at 50°C consisting of two zinc electrodes immersed in solutions of zinc ions of 0.020 and 0.060 activity.

9. Given the cell in Problem II-8. The zinc-ion activity around the positive electrode is 0.020 as in the previous problem. What would have to be the activity of the zinc ion around the other electrode at 25°C if the electromotive force of the cell is to be the same at this temperature as the electromotive force of the cell in II-8?

10. Given a concentration cell reversible with respect to cobalt (II) ions at 25°C. The activities of the ions are 0.050 and 0.180. What is the electromotive force of this cell at this temperature?

11. Given a cell consisting of two hydrogen gas electrodes immersed in a solution of hydrogen-ion activity equal to 2.80×10^{-2}. The pressure of the hydrogen gas at one electrode is 750 mm and that at the other electrode is 780 mm. What is the electromotive force of the cell at 25°C?

12. The following cell has an electromotive force of 0.4900 volt at 25°C.

$$\text{Pb, PbCl}_2 \ (s), \ \text{HCl} \ (1m) \ \text{AgCl} \ (s), \ \text{Ag}$$

$\Delta E/\Delta T = 0.000186$ volt per degree. The cell reaction is

$$\text{Pb} + 2\text{AgCl} \rightarrow \text{PbCl}_2 + 2\text{Ag}$$

Calculate ΔG, ΔS, and ΔH for this reaction at 25°C.

13. Construct a cell that will give the value of $\Delta G°$ for the following reaction

$$\text{Zn} \ (s) + \text{Fe}^{2+} \rightarrow \text{Zn}^{2+} + \text{Fe} \ (s)$$

Given the following values for the entropies of the reactants and products at 25°C.

$$\text{Zn} = 9.95 \text{ E.U.} \qquad \text{Fe}^{2+} = -27.1 \text{ E.U.} \qquad \text{Zn}^{2+} = -25.45 \text{ E.U.}$$

$$\text{Fe} = 6.49 \text{ E.U.}$$

Calculate the following for 25°C:

(a) $\Delta H°$ for the cell reaction
(b) The equilibrium constant for the cell reaction
(c) The standard electromotive force of the cell
(d) $\Delta G°$ for the cell reaction
(e) $\Delta S°$ for the cell reaction

FOURTEEN

The Determination of
Hydrogen-Ion Concentration

The importance of hydrogen-ion measurement and control in chemical and biological systems was pointed out in Chapter 11. Because of this importance, the needs for rapid and accurate methods for the determination of pH are essential.

There are two general methods for determining the pH of a given solution: (1) colorimetric, by means of indicators, and (2) potentiometric, by measuring the electromotive force of a cell in which hydrogen ions take part in the cell reaction. This chapter is concerned with the various electrodes and cells that may be employed for the potentiometric determination of pH and with the colorimetric procedures that may be used. Included is a discussion of the theory of indicators and the factors determining their selection and use. Some typical titration curves concerned with pH measurements are discussed.

THE POTENTIOMETRIC DETERMINATION OF pH

14a. General Considerations. It was shown in Chapter 13 that a cell is composed of two electrode systems, or half cells, and that the electromotive force of the cell is the difference in the single electrode potentials. It was shown further that the potential of each half cell may be calculated from its standard potential by means of Equation 13-1.

A cell to be used for pH measurements must consist of a *pH-indicating electrode* and a *reference electrode*. The reference electrode must have a known and constant potential and the pH-indicating electrode must indicate accurately the hydrogen-ion concentration in the solution.

14b. The Hydrogen Electrode. The hydrogen gas electrode is the electrode used for the precise measurement of hydrogen-ion concentration. It is constructed by welding a small sheet of platinum foil, usually about a half centimeter square, to a platinum wire sealed through the end of a glass tube. This glass tube is surrounded by a gas space formed by another tube sealed to the glass tube at the top, and flared to a bell around the platinum electrode. A side arm permits the entrance of hydrogen into the gas space, and openings in the bell allow its escape. The openings are so located that the electrode is in contact with the hydrogen gas about half the time. The details are shown in Figure 14-1. The platinum foil is coated with a layer of finely divided platinum, termed *platinum black* because of its color. This platinum black serves a double function. It adsorbs the hydrogen gas, and this, in effect, produces a "solid" hydrogen electrode. The platinum black also speeds up the equilibrium between hydrogen gas and hydrogen ions, thus making the potential much more reproducible.

The potential of the hydrogen electrode may be expressed in the following way:

$$E = -\frac{RT}{2F}\ln\frac{a_{H^+}^2}{a_{H_2}} = \frac{2.303RT}{F}\,\text{pH} + \frac{RT}{2F}\ln a_{H_2} \qquad (14\text{-}1)$$

At 25°C this equation reduces to

$$E = 0.0592\,\text{pH} + 0.0296\log a_{H_2} \qquad (14\text{-}2)$$

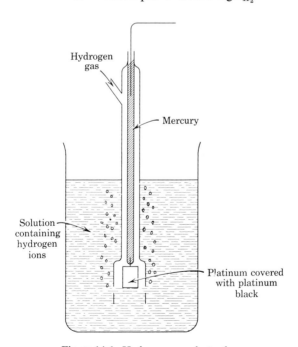

Figure 14-1. Hydrogen gas electrode.

Since the activity of the hydrogen gas is expressed in atmospheres, the last term of Equation 14-2 becomes zero at 1 atm. It is impractical, however, to deliver hydrogen gas to the electrode at a pressure of exactly 1 atm because of varying barometric pressures and the effect of the vapor pressure of the solution. Except for highly precise research work, normal variations in hydrogen pressure due to these two causes have a negligible effect on the determination of pH. This is shown in Example 14-1.

Example 14-1. The potential of a hydrogen electrode is 0.232 volt at 25°C. The hydrogen gas is at a pressure of 740 mm. What error is made in the calculation of pH by assuming the hydrogen pressure to be 1 atm?

Using Equation 14-2 and assuming the pressure to be 1 atm,

$$E = 0.0592 \text{ pH} + 0.0296 \log a_{H_2} = 0.232 = 0.0592 \text{ pH} + 0$$
$$\text{pH} = 3.920$$

Using Equation 14-2 and the actual hydrogen pressure,

$$0.232 = 0.0592 \text{ pH} + 0.0296 \log \frac{740}{760}$$
$$\text{pH} = 3.924$$

Thus the correction is 0.004 pH unit.

It is shown in Example 14-1 that a 20-mm variation in the hydrogen gas pressure affects the calculated pH by only 0.004 pH unit at 25°C. Since the vapor pressures of aqueous solutions are of the order of magnitude of 20 mm, this effect on the total hydrogen pressure is negligible. The hydrogen electrode is seldom used as a reference electrode in laboratory practice because other reference electrodes are much easier to construct and operate. The difficulties attending the use of the hydrogen electrode may be summed up as follows:

1. Purified hydrogen gas must be delivered to the surface of the platinum black electrode. This requires a complicated purification train to remove the last trace of oxygen and other possible impurities.

2. The electrodes are prepared by the electrodeposition of platinum black on the electrode surface from a solution of chloroplatinic acid. To obtain an evenly deposited and firmly coherent coat, the plating current must be carefully regulated. Since the platinum black tends to flake off with use, periodic replating is necessary. Also, many solutions contain ions and other substances that, upon adsorption on the platinum surface, render it inactive, or "poison" the electrode.

3. The hydrogen electrode may not be used in a solution containing ions of metals that are below hydrogen in the electromotive series. Interaction with the hydrogen will take place and the metal will be deposited

on the electrode surface. Also the hydrogen electrode may not be used in solutions containing strong oxidizing agents.

14c. The Calomel Electrode. The calomel electrode is a convenient and practical reference electrode. Once properly prepared, it can be used indefinitely without further attention. One of the many forms of the calomel electrode is shown in Figure 14-2. Connection is made to the external circuit by a side arm containing mercury that is connected to the material in the electrode proper by a platinum wire sealed in the bottom of the main electrode vessel. This wire leads into a pool of mercury in the bottom of the half cell. The mercury in turn is covered with a paste of mercury and mercurous chloride (calomel). Over this is placed a solution of potassium chloride saturated with mercurous chloride. The potassium chloride solution may be of any strength, but the usual concentrations are tenth normal, normal, or saturated. A side arm, filled with the KCl solution, furnishes the connection to the electrode system with which it is to be used.

The saturated calomel electrode is formulated as

$$KCl\,(sat.);\ \ Hg_2Cl_2,\ Hg$$

The electrode reaction taking place in the half cell written in the usual manner is

$$2Hg + 2Cl^- = Hg_2Cl_2 + 2e$$

and the potential is given by the expression

$$E = E^\circ - \frac{RT}{2F}\ln\frac{a_{Hg_2Cl_2}}{a_{Hg}^2 \times a_{Cl^-}^2}$$

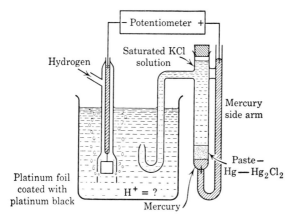

Figure 14-2. Calomel-hydrogen cell.

Since the activities of the mercurous chloride and the mercury are both unity, the expression reduces to

$$E = E° - \frac{RT}{F} \ln \frac{1}{a_{Cl^-}} \qquad (14\text{-}3)$$

The potentials of the tenth normal, normal, and saturated calomel electrodes may be measured by determining their potential against the standard hydrogen electrode. The combination used for the normal calomel electrode may be written as

$$\text{Pt, H}_2(1 \text{ atm}); \ \text{H}^+(a = 1) \parallel \text{KCl}(1N); \ \text{Hg}_2\text{Cl}_2, \text{Hg}$$

The calomel electrode is always the positive electrode when used in combination with the hydrogen electrode. Hence electrons flow into the calomel electrode from the external circuit. The potential of the cell is equal numerically to the potential of the electrode, and, since the calomel electrode is the positive electrode, its oxidation potential, like the standard copper electrode potential, has a negative sign.

The oxidation potentials so obtained at 25°C are

tenth normal calomel electrode	−0.334 volt
normal calomel electrode	−0.280 volt
saturated calomel electrode	−0.246 volt

The variation in the potentials of the three calomel electrodes with changing chloride-ion activity is in accordance with Equation 14-3.

14d. The Silver-Silver Chloride Electrode. The silver-silver chloride electrode is one of the most convenient and easily constructed of all the reference electrodes. It is particularly useful in commercial pH meters that employ the glass electrode as the pH-indicating electrode. The silver-silver chloride electrode is prepared by sealing one end of a small platinum wire through a glass tube. The wire in turn is plated with silver, which, in turn, is covered with a thin layer of silver chloride. This dips into a solution of a fixed and known chloride-ion concentration. The electrode reaction is:

$$\text{Ag} + \text{Cl}^- = \text{AgCl} + e$$

The standard oxidation potential of this electrode is −0.222 volt at 25°C.

14e. The Hydrogen-Calomel Cell. The hydrogen electrode may be used as a pH-indicating electrode along with a calomel reference electrode. Such a cell is shown in Figure 14-2 and is written

$$\text{Pt, H}_2(1 \text{ atm}); \ \text{H}^+(a = \text{unknown}) \parallel \text{KCl}(\text{sat.}); \ \text{Hg}_2\text{Cl}_2, \text{Hg}$$

Example 14-2 shows how the data obtained with such a cell are used to calculate pH.

Example 14-2. The potential of the cell shown above is 0.527 volt at 25°C. What are the hydrogen-ion activity and the pH of the unknown solution?

The electrode potential of the saturated calomel electrode is -0.246 volt. Therefore, this is the value of the right half cell or E_r. Therefore,

$$0.527 = -0.0592 \log H^+ - (-0.246)$$
$$\log H^+ = -4.75 = \bar{5}.25$$
$$H^+ = 1.78 \times 10^{-5} \text{ mole/liter}$$
$$pH = -(\log 1.74 \times 10^{-5}) = 4.75$$

14f. The Glass Electrode. It has been found experimentally that a potential exists at the interface between certain special glasses and a solution containing hydrogen ions. The value of the potential is a function of the hydrogen-ion activity and the nature of the particular glass used. In other words, the glass functions in the same manner as the hydrogen electrode. Now, if the glass in the form of a membrane is so arranged that it separates two solutions of different hydrogen-ion activity, a potential is developed between the two solutions. This potential is given by the same formula used to calculate the potential of a hydrogen concentration cell without junction potential. See Equation 13-4.

$$E = \frac{RT}{F} \ln \frac{a_1}{a_2}$$

The problem of measuring this potential is solved by employing two reference electrodes, one on each side of the membrane. The potentials of these electrodes are constant, and if the activity of the hydrogen ions on one side of the glass membrane is fixed, the over-all electromotive force of the system becomes a function solely of the pH of the second solution.

The usual procedure is to use the glass electrode in the form of a bulb sealed to the bottom of a glass tube. The reference electrodes are usually the silver-silver chloride electrode and the calomel electrode. A typical glass electrode system is shown in Figure 14-3. The glass membrane is a thin-walled bulb of small size. Within the bulb is a solution of hydrochloric acid, which furnishes a constant pH on one side of the glass membrane and a constant chloride-ion activity for the silver-silver chloride electrode within the bulb. The saturated calomel electrode dips into the solution of unknown pH, which is outside the glass membrane. The glass electrode itself may be represented as:

reference electrode; solution of known pH;

glass; solution of unknown pH

The over-all glass-electrode system in the figure may be represented in this manner:

Ag, AgCl; solution of known pH; glass;

solution of unknown pH, KCl (sat.); Hg_2Cl_2, Hg

Four sources contribute to the over-all potential of this cell: the calomel electrode, the unknown pH solution and the glass membrane, the glass membrane and the solution of known pH, and the silver-silver chloride electrode. The potential of the liquid junction between the KCl solution of the calomel electrode and the solution of unknown pH is essentially zero. All of these contribute a constant potential to the cell except the unknown pH glass source. The cell voltage may therefore be represented by the relation

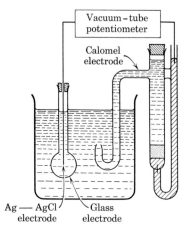

$$E_{\text{cell}} = E_{\text{g}}^{\circ} - \frac{RT}{nF} \ln a_{\text{H}^+}$$

At 25°C this reduces to

$$E_{\text{cell}} = E_g^{\circ} + 0.0592 \text{ pH}$$

Figure 14-3. Glass electrode assembly.

In this expression E_g° includes the potentials of the calomel and silver-silver chloride electrodes and any effects due to dissimilarities in the surface of the glass on the two sides of the membrane. This constant, E_g°, can be determined for a given system by placing a solution of known pH in the vessel containing the glass electrode and measuring the over-all potential.

The theory of the glass electrode is rather complicated and in some respects not completely understood. Certainly, the action of the electrode depends upon the fact that hydrogen ions exist in the glass and can be transferred through it from one solution to another. The activity in the glass and the ease of transfer depend upon the nature of the glass, and so it is found that some glasses are much better than others for the preparation of glass electrodes.

The glass electrode possesses many advantages over the other pH-indicating electrodes. It can be used in strong oxidizing solutions that react with hydrogen. It may be used in unbuffered solutions without affecting their pH. Micro glass electrodes have been developed so that it is possible to measure the pH of very small quantities of solution. These electrodes are particularly useful in biological work. The usual glass electrodes may be used in solutions with pH values ranging from 0 to 9. Electrodes composed of special glasses can be used for measurements up to a pH of 12. Above pH 12, however, other cations affect the potential of the glass interface and thus render the electrode useless.

The very high resistance of the glass membrane is one difficulty, and for this reason it cannot be used with the ordinary potentiometer. Potentiometers using vacuum tubes, however, have been developed that make the operation of the glass electrode both rapid and precise.

ACID-BASE INDICATORS

14g. The Theory of Acid-Base Indicators. Certain weak acids and bases, termed acid-base indicators, change their color over a range of pH. Below the lower limit the indicator shows one color and above the upper limit of the pH range the indicator shows a different color. Methyl orange, for example, shows its full acid color (red) when added to a solution whose pH is 3 or below, and it shows its full basic color (yellow) at a pH of 4.2 or above. At pH values between the full acidic and basic colors methyl orange shows colors intermediate between red and yellow. Phenolphthalein gives its full basic color (red) when added to a solution of pH 10 and above and its acid color (colorless) at pH 8.5 and below. Thus indicators give a color change over a distinct pH range, usually about 2 pH units. Since this range may be wholly on the acidic or wholly on the basic side of neutrality, an *indicator may be defined as a substance that exhibits a color change over a distinct pH range.*

Indicators are substances capable of existence in at least two different structural forms, each of which shows a different kind of color absorption. The equilibrium between the two color forms must be affected by the hydrogen-ion concentration of the solution. Let us consider two typical acid-base indicators.

Consider *p*-nitrophenol, an indicator that is colorless in acid solution and yellow in basic solution:

I	II	III
Normal or pseudo acid (colorless)	Aci- or ionogenic form (yellow)	Ion (yellow)

Solid *p*-nitrophenol is colorless. In solution this colorless or pseudo form of the acid exists in a tautomeric equilibrium with the ionogenic (ion-forming) form, which is highly ionized. In strong alkaline solution the equilibrium is shifted completely to the right and the solution is yellow. In acid solution equilibrium is shifted to the left so that the colorless form predominates.

For phenolphthalein the following equilibria are involved in the trans-formation from colorless to red:

I	II	III
Pseudo or normal form (colorless)	Ionogenic form (red)	Ion (red)

Let us now apply the mass law considerations to the equilibria involved in a solution of phenolphthalein. If HIn represents the pseudo or normal form of the indicator and HIn' represents the ionogenic form, the indicator equation may be written

$$\text{HIn} \rightleftharpoons \text{HIn}' \xrightarrow{H_2O} H^+ + In^-$$

Color A (pseudo or normal)   Color B (ionogenic)   Color B (ion)

The equilibrium constant expression for the shift from the pseudo to the ionogenic form is

$$K_1 = \frac{[\text{HIn}']}{[\text{HIn}]} \qquad (14\text{-}4)$$

and the expression for the ionization of the ionogenic form is

$$K_2 = \frac{[H^+][In^-]}{[\text{HIn}']} \qquad (14\text{-}5)$$

If the two equations are multiplied together, the HIn' terms cancel. Therefore,

$$\frac{[H^+][In^-]}{[\text{HIn}]} = K_1 \times K_2 = K_{In} \qquad (14\text{-}6)$$

Note that K_{In} *is not a true ionization constant*, since it is the product of the ionization constant of the ionogenic form and the equilibrium constant for the shift from the pseudo to the ionogenic form. Since the final constant embraces the constants for whatever number of equilibria are involved in the indicator transformation, K_{In} is termed the *apparent ionization constant* of an indicator. Finally, note that the constant for the tautomeric shift from the pseudo to the ionogenic form of an indicator must be small. Otherwise, both indicator colors would be present in large quantities regardless of the pH of the solution.

Methyl orange and a number of other important indicators are weak bases. It is the usual practice, however, to treat all indicators as acids for quantitative purposes. This is possible through the operation of the ion-product constant of water. $K_w/[H^+]$ may be substituted for $[OH^-]$ in the equilibrium expression, and the indicator constant includes the ion-product constant of water.

14h. Examples of Neutralization Indicators. For an indicator to be useful, its acid color must be distinctly different from its alkaline color, and the colors should be stable so that they will not fade on standing. At present, several hundred compounds have been prepared that may be regarded as satisfactory indicators, although only a few dozen are in common use for acid-base titrations and for the colorimetric determination of pH. Both the acid and salt forms of most indicators have distinctive colors and so are known as *two-color indicators*. A *one-color indicator* exhibits color in only one of its two forms. Phenolphthalein is the most common example of this latter type, being colorless in acid solution.

Indicators may be classified according to their structures. Some of the more important classes are the phthaleins, the sulfonephthaleins, the azo indicators, the nitro indicators, and certain triphenylmethane dyes. Table 14-1 gives the common name, the chemical name, the useful pH range, and the acid and base colors of some of the more commonly used indicators.

14i. Quantitative Relationships in Solutions of Indicators. According to Equation 14-6, the apparent ionization constant of an indicator may be represented by the expression

$$\frac{[H^+][In^-]}{[HIn]} = K_{In} \qquad (14\text{-}7)$$

Solving for the hydrogen-ion concentration in 14-7 yields

$$[H^+] = K_{In} \cdot \frac{[HIn]}{[In^-]} \qquad (14\text{-}8)$$

Table 14-1. Some of the More Useful Indicators

Common Name	Chemical Name	Useful pH Range	pK_{In}	Color Change	
				Acid	Alkaline
o-Cresol red	o-Cresolsulfonephthalein	0.2–1.8	—	Red	Yellow
m-Cresol purple	m-Cresolsulfonephthalein	1.2–2.8	1.51	Red	Yellow
Thymol blue	Thymolsulfonephthalein	1.2–2.8	1.50	Red	Yellow
Tropeolin 00	Sodium diphenylaminoazo-p-benzene sulfonate	1.3–3.2	—	Red	Yellow
Bromophenol blue	Tetrabromophenolsulfonephthalein	3.0–4.6	3.98	Yellow	Purple
Methyl orange	Sodium dimethylaminoazo-p-benzene sulfonate	3.1–4.5	3.7	Red	Yellow
Bromocresol green	Tetrabromo-m-cresolsulfonephthalein	3.8–5.4	4.67	Yellow	Blue
Methyl red	Dimethylaminoazobenzenecarboxylic acid	4.4–6.3	5.1	Red	Yellow
Chlorophenol red	Dichlorophenolsulfonephthalein	4.8–6.4	5.98	Yellow	Red
Bromocresol purple	Dibromo-o-cresolsulfonephthalein	5.2–6.8	6.3	Yellow	Purple
Bromothymol blue	Dibromothymolsulfonephthalein	6.0–7.6	7.0	Yellow	Blue
Phenol red	Phenolsulfonephthalein	6.4–8.2	7.9	Yellow	Red
Cresol red	o-Cresolsulfonephthalein	7.0–8.8	8.3	Yellow	Red
m-Cresol purple	m-Cresolsulfonephthalein	7.4–9.0	8.32	Yellow	Purple
Thymol blue	Thymolsulfonephthalein	8.0–9.6	8.9	Yellow	Blue
Phenolphthalein	Phenolphthalein	8.0–9.8	9.4	Colorless	Red
Thymolphthalein	Thymolphthalein	9.3–10.5	9.9	Colorless	Blue
Alizarine yellow	Sodium salt of p-nitraniline-azosalicylic acid	10.1–12.1	—	Yellow	Lilac

Taking the logarithm of both sides of the equation, changing signs, and defining pK_{In} as the negative of the logarithm of the indicator constant gives

$$pH = pK_{In} + \log \frac{[In^-]}{[HIn]} \qquad (14\text{-}9)$$

If an indicator is added to a solution whose pH is such that half of the indicator is in the acid form and half in the salt form, the indicator shows its *neutral color* or *middle tint*. That is, the color of the solution is that given when 50 per cent of the indicator is in its acidic form, HIn, and 50 per cent is in its basic form, In^-. At this point, the ratio of In^-/HIn becomes unity, and the last term of Equation 14-9 becomes zero. Then

$$pH = pK_{In} \qquad (14\text{-}10)$$

Suppose, for example, that a given indicator has a constant of 1×10^{-6}. Since pK_{In} is the negative logarithm of this value, pK_{In} equals 6. If a small quantity of this indicator is added to a solution of pH = 6, the indicator becomes 50 per cent transformed and the color of the solution is that characteristic of the middle tint of the indicator. Since most indicators change color gradually from full acid color to full base color over a pH range of about 2, this indicator would probably show its full acid color at pH 5 and its full base color at pH 7.

If an indicator exists wholly in its acid form, it may be assumed that the eye cannot perceive a color change until about 10 per cent is transformed into the salt form. Thus, if 1 part of an indicator is in its salt form (In^-), and 10 parts are in the acid form, substitution in Equation 14-9 yields

$$pH = pK_{In} + \log \frac{1}{10} = pK_{In} - 1 \qquad (14\text{-}11)$$

Furthermore, after about 90 per cent of the indicator is transformed into the salt form, the eye can perceive no further change in color even if the solution is made more alkaline. Assuming 1 part to be in the acid form and 10 parts to be in the salt form, substitution in Equation 14-9 gives

$$pH = pK_{In} + \log \frac{10}{1} = pK_{In} + 1 \qquad (14\text{-}12)$$

An examination of Equation 14-11 reveals that an indicator should show its full acid color when the pH of the solution is 1 unit less than pK_{In}. Similarly, 14-12 shows that an indicator should show its full basic color when the pH is 1 unit greater than pK_{In}. Since most indicators do, in fact, show a color range of about 2 pH units, the assumption that about

10 per cent of an indicator must be transformed before there is a perceptible color change is justified.

THE DETERMINATION OF pH BY COLORIMETRIC METHODS

14j. The Determination of pK_{In} and Approximate pH Values. In order to determine pK_{In} for a given indicator, it is necessary only to determine the pH at which an indicator exhibits its middle tint because at that point pH equals pK_{In}. The principle of the determination may best be shown by an arrangement similar to that given in Figure 14-4. Tube A consists of two flat-bottomed glass tubes, a and b, both of the same length and one placed on top of the other. The same quantity of indicator is added to a and b, and one is made acidic enough to transform all the indicator into the acid form, while the other is made basic enough to transform all the indicator into its base color. If tube A is observed from above, the light emerging from the tube has passed through its entire length and therefore has traversed a solution of the indicator which is half in its acid form and half in its base form. Hence the observed color is the middle tint of the indicator. Tube B is equal in length to tube A and is filled with a buffer solution of known pH containing the same quantity of indicator as tube A (a and b combined). When a buffer solution is introduced into tube B, of such a pH that the colors from tubes A and B match, pH equals pK_{In}. The above is a simplified picture of the determination of an indicator constant, but better methods of determining pK_{In} will be discussed in the section to follow.

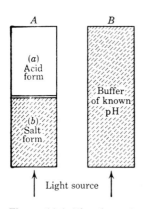

Figure 14-4. The determination of pK_{In}.

Since each indicator has its own characteristic color-change range, it is a relatively simple matter to determine the approximate pH of a solution under examination. A drop or two of indicator solution is added to a small portion of the unknown to see whether the indicator shows its acidic or basic color. If the indicator, for example, shows its basic color, a second indicator of higher pH range is added to a second portion of the unknown. This is continued until an indicator is found that exhibits its approximate middle tint in the immediate neighborhood of the pH of the unknown. At this point, the pH value of the unknown solution must approximate the numerical value of pK_{In}. Such a procedure takes only a few minutes if a series of indicator solutions is available but serves at best to establish the pH value of the unknown solution to within ± 1 pH unit.

The approximate pH of a solution may also be determined by a *universal indicator*, which is a mixture of several indicators designed to give a definite color at any given pH. Kolthoff's universal indicator consists of five indicators that give a red color at pH 2, red-orange at 3, orange at 4, yellow-orange at 5, lemon-yellow at 6, yellow-green at 7, green at 8, blue-green at 9, and violet at 10. Other satisfactory universal indicators have been prepared, and some are put up in the form of papers.

Although the procedures described above are adequate for the determination of approximate pH values, more exact methods are usually required. They are described in the following sections.

14k. The Bjerrum Wedge Comparator. The *wedge comparator* shown in Figure 14-5 is of historical interest but does present a very simple method for determining the pH of an unknown solution. It consists of a rectangular glass trough, usually about 12 in. long, 1 in. wide, and 4 in. high. A glass plate placed diagonally in the trough divides it into two wedge-shaped halves. A solution made acid enough to transform the chosen indicator into its acid form, HIn, is placed in one compartment. The same quantity of indicator is placed in the second compartment in a solution basic enough to transform the indicator into its salt form, In⁻. The comparator is illuminated from the rear by a source of diffused light and is viewed from the front. As the eye moves across the front of the comparator, a gradual transition in indicator color from full acidic to full basic color is observed. Thus it is possible to observe the color tint corresponding to any desired ratio of acid to base color. Looking through the exact center gives the tint when the indicator is half transformed—0.5 in the HIn form and 0.5 in the In⁻ form. The ratios, as calculated from the depth of the two solutions through which the light passes, are marked on the face of the comparator.

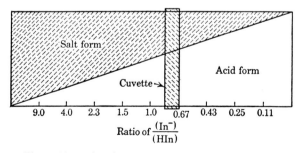

Figure 14-5. The Bjerrum wedge comparator (*top view*)

The unknown solution is contained in a narrow glass cell, or cuvette, equal in length to the width of the comparator trough. The same concentration of indicator is added, and the cuvette is moved along the top of the comparator until the color in the cuvette matches that in the comparator below. At this point, the ratio of In^- to HIn in the cuvette is the same as that at the match point in the comparator below. Hence the pH of the unknown may be calculated by substituting this ratio of $[In^-]/[HIn]$ in Equation 14-9.

$$pH = pK_{In} + \log \frac{[In^-]}{[HIn]}$$

Much better results are obtained if an indicator is chosen in which the value of pK_{In} is numerically close to the pH of the unknown. A color match is then obtained somewhere near the center of the comparator, where a small change in pH causes a large change in indicator tint.

The pK_{In} of an indicator may be determined in the wedge comparator by reversing the process described above. A buffer of known pH is placed in the cuvette, the ratio of $[In^-]/[HIn]$ is measured, and pK_{In} is calculated from Equation 14-9.

14l. Color Standards. If a large number of pH determinations are to be made, it is often convenient to prepare a series of color standards, that is, a series of buffered solutions of known pH each differing from the next by a constant pH increment, usually 0.1 or 0.2 pH unit. The solutions usually extend through the ranges of several indicators. A given amount of each buffer solution is contained in a test tube, and the proper amount of indicator is added to each. The indicators chosen for the color standards should be stable so that the standards may be preserved for some time. The unknown is treated with the same concentration of the proper indicator, and a color match is obtained.

It is possible to obtain the pH of a solution without buffered solution color standards by preparing a series of stable comparison solutions. Mixtures of colored inorganic salts are used to obtain these comparison standards. Iron (III) chloride and cobalt (II) nitrate mixtures, for example, are satisfactory standards for neutral red, methyl orange, and tropeolin 00. Inorganic comparison solutions are advantageous for routine work, but it is advisable to test them frequently against buffered solutions of the indicator.

Colored glasses are sometimes used instead of stable comparison solutions, and various devices have been developed to aid in color matching between an unknown solution containing an indicator and glass standards. Figure 14-6 shows a commercial type of pH comparator using liquids for

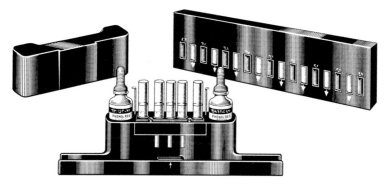

Figure 14-6. Commercial comparator using liquid standards (Taylor comparator). (Courtesy W. A. Taylor and Co.)

color standards while Figure 14-7 shows an instrument using glass standards.

14m. The pH Colorimeter.   A number of colorimeters employing precise optical systems have been devised for the colorimetric determination of pH. Two light beams that have passed through known and unknown solutions are made to converge in an optical system so that they may be seen side by side, each constituting half a circular field. The cups for

Figure 14-7. Commercial comparator using glass standards. (Courtesy Hellige, Inc.)

holding the solutions in one such colorimeter are shown in Figure 14-8. *A* and *A′* are stationary plungers. Cups *B*, *C*, and *D* are cylindrical glass containers with flat glass plates as the bottoms. Cups *C* and *D* are stationary, whereas cup *B* may be moved by a rack and pinion from the bottom of cup *C* to the bottom of plunger *A*, a distance usually of 100 mm. The distance from the bottom of cup *D* to the bottom of plunger *A′* is also 100 mm. Cup *B* contains a solution made acid enough to transform the indicator into its acid form and cup *C* is alkaline enough to transform the indicator into its salt form. Cup *D* is filled with the unknown solution, to which is added a quantity of indicator equal to that contained in *B* and *C* together. Cup *B* is then moved up and down until a color match is obtained. The two beams of light seen in the eye-piece have passed through 100 mm of solution in each arm of the colorimeter. The light reaching plunger *A*, however, has passed through a ratio of $[In^-]/[HIn]$ that may be varied at will by raising or lowering cup *B*. This ratio is easily calculated from the scale reading.

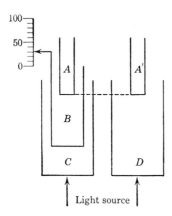

Figure 14-8. Cup arrangement. pH colorimeter.

At the color match point, the ratio must be the same in both known and unknown solutions so that the pH of the unknown may be calculated from Equation 14-9.

14n. The Use of the Spectrophotometer. A spectrophotometer consists of an optical system that provides a narrow band of monochromatic light and a vacuum tube amplifying circuit for measuring the amount of light absorbed by a system. A much greater accuracy can be obtained with such an instrument than by the methods previously discussed. A spectrophotometer is more sensitive to a change in color tint, and the use of monochromatic light eliminates the error of *dichromatism*, which is pronounced in some indicator systems. Certain indicators change color tint when the depth of the solution is changed, and they are said to be dichromatic. Apparently the reason for the change is that the tint is due to the presence of two or more colors, the relative intensities of which are altered as the depth of solution is changed. If monochromatic light is used, only one band of light is provided for absorption by the solution.

14o. Errors in Colorimetric Methods. Since indicators are themselves weak acids or bases, their addition to solutions produces a change in pH.

Since the indicator concentration is always small, the effect is very slight except in unbuffered solutions. An attempt to determine the pH of distilled water colorimetrically, however, might result in an error of 1 or 2 pH units. Since most biological fluids have buffer capacity, a pH change due to the addition of indicator would probably be inappreciable.

It is assumed in colorimetric work that two solutions of the same hydrogen-ion activity will have the same color if the same concentration of an indicator is added to each. This assumption is not necessarily true, however, if one of the solutions contains an appreciable concentration of salts. *The effect on indicator color caused by the presence of electrolyte is called the salt error.* The salt error may be explained by remembering that the color of an indicator is determined by the relative *concentrations* of the acid and salt forms, while the indicator equilibrium is governed by the *activities* of the acid and salt forms. Thus if enough electrolyte is added to change the ratios of the activities of the acid and salt forms, the indicator equilibrium is shifted, and the concentrations of the two forms are altered even though the pH may remain the same. If the ionic strength of the solution is known, the extent of the salt effect may be calculated.

The presence of proteins or amino acids may give rise to an error in the colorimetric determination of pH. Such an error, called the *protein error*, is due to the amphoteric nature of these substances, which allows them to react with both acidic and basic indicators. The extent of the protein error varies with the indicator. Hence it is advisable to check the determined pH results of any given type protein solution with a hydrogen or glass electrode before establishing a routine colorimetric pH method.

USE OF INDICATORS IN NEUTRALIZATION REACTIONS

14p. Titration of a Strong Acid with a Strong Base. In quantitative analysis indicators are used to determine the equivalence point of acid-base titrations. Since indicators have various pH ranges and since the equivalence point for an acid-base pair varies with the relative strength of the acid and base, the selection of proper indicators is important. This subject can best be discussed by considering the pH changes occurring in typical acid-base titrations.

The titration of a strong acid with a strong base may be illustrated by the reaction of hydrochloric acid and sodium hydroxide. Twenty-five milliliters of $0.1M$ HCl is diluted to 75 ml and titrated with $0.1M$ NaOH. Table 14-2 shows the change in hydronium-ion concentration and pH after successive additions of sodium hydroxide. The equivalence point occurs after the addition of 25 ml of base, at which point the volume of the

Table 14-2. pH Change on Titrating HCl and NaOH

(25 ml of 0.1M HCl is diluted to 75 ml and titrated with 0.1M NaOH)

Ml of NaOH	Volume of Solution	[H⁺]	pH
0.00	75.0	0.0333	1.48
5.00	80.0	0.0250	1.60
10.00	85.0	0.0176	1.75
15.00	90.0	0.0111	1.96
20.00	95.0	0.00526	2.28
23.00	98.0	0.00204	2.69
24.00	99.0	0.00101	3.00
24.50	99.5	0.000503	3.30
24.75	99.8	0.000251	3.60
24.85	99.9	0.000150	3.82
24.95	100.0	0.000050	4.30
24.99	100.0	0.000010	5.00
25.00	100.0	1.00×10^{-7}	7.00
			(equiv. point)
25.01	100.0	1.00×10^{-9}	9.00
25.10	100.1	1.00×10^{-10}	10.00
25.20	100.2	5.00×10^{-11}	10.30
25.50	100.5	2.01×10^{-11}	10.70
26.00	101.0	1.01×10^{-11}	11.00
27.00	102.0	5.10×10^{-12}	11.29
30.00	105.0	2.10×10^{-12}	11.68

solution is 100 ml. The hydronium-ion concentration at each point was calculated on the assumption that any unneutralized acid or excess base is 100 per cent ionized.

The calculated values shown in Table 14-2 for the hydrogen-ion activity and pH could easily be checked by immersing a pH-indicating electrode along with the salt-bridge arm of a calomel reference electrode in the titrating beaker and measuring the potential of the cell. From the measured potential, hydrogen-ion activity and pH are calculated as outlined earlier in this chapter. These measured values would differ only slightly from the calculated values. Note that the pH of the solution changes slowly at first on adding base, rising only to 5.00 after 24.99 ml of base has been added. On adding the next two successive 0.01-ml portions, the pH jumps first to 7.00 and then to 9.00, a change of 4 pH units. A plot of pH versus milliliters of NaOH is shown in Figure 14-9, the vertical portion of the curve showing the large change in pH on adding a small volume of titrating solution at the equivalence point. Such a plot is called a *titration curve*.

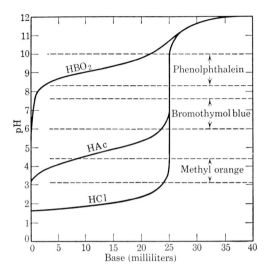

Figure 14-9. Titration curves of acids.

An indicator is suitable for a given titration only if it changes color at or very near the equivalence point. Now the pH change on titrating a strong acid with a strong base is so great near the equivalence point that any one of a large number of indicators may be used. Any indicator, in fact, whose effective range is spanned by the pH values in the vertical part of the titration curve is suitable. For example, any indicator listed in Table 14-1 lying between methyl orange and thymolphthalein would be suitable for the titration of a strong acid with a strong base under proper concentration conditions.

As was stated above, pH changes during a titration may be determined by measuring the potential of a cell made by combining a pH-indicating electrode with a reference electrode. A titration curve prepared from such data not only is useful in indicator selection but also may be used for an accurate determination of the equivalence point in a titration. If the molarity of the hydrochloric acid solution were unknown, it could readily be calculated. A perpendicular dropped from the center of the steep portion of the curve shows that 25.00 ml of 0.1 M NaOH was necessary to titrate the sample. Titrations in which the equivalence point is determined from the electromotive force of a cell are called *potentiometric titrations*. Such titrations are often used even in routine work, especially when the unknown has enough color to interfere with an indicator.

14q. Titration of a Weak Acid with a Strong Base. The titration of a weak acid with a strong base may be illustrated by the reaction between

Table 14-3. pH Changes on Titrating HAc with NaOH
(25 ml of 0.1M HAc is diluted to 75 ml and titrated with 0.1M NaOH)

M of NaOH	Volume of Solution	H$^+$	pH
0.00	75.0	7.74 × 10^{-4}	3.11
2.50	77.5	1.62 × 10^{-4}	3.79
5.00	80.0	7.24 × 10^{-5}	4.14
10.00	85.0	2.75 × 10^{-5}	4.56
15.00	90.0	1.20 × 10^{-5}	4.92
20.00	95.0	4.50 × 10^{-6}	5.35
23.00	98.0	1.56 × 10^{-6}	5.81
24.00	99.0	7.50 × 10^{-7}	6.12
24.50	99.5	3.67 × 10^{-7}	6.44
24.90	99.9	7.24 × 10^{-8}	7.14
24.95	100.0	3.66 × 10^{-8}	7.44
24.98	100.0	1.54 × 10^{-8}	7.84
24.99	100.0	7.20 × 10^{-9}	8.14
25.00	100.0	2.69 × 10^{-9}	8.57
			(equiv. point)
25.025	100.0	4.00 × 10^{-10}	9.40
25.10	100.1	1.00 × 10^{-10}	10.00
25.20	100.2	5.00 × 10^{-11}	10.30
25.50	100.5	2.01 × 10^{-11}	10.70
26.00	101.0	1.01 × 10^{-11}	11.00
27.00	102.0	5.10 × 10^{-12}	11.29
30.00	105.0	2.10 × 10^{-12}	11.68

acetic acid and sodium hydroxide. Table 14-3 shows the change in pH on titrating 25 ml of 0.1M HAc, diluted to 75 ml, with 0.1M NaOH. Hydrogen-ion concentration and pH calculations at various points during the titration are more complicated in this case, but they may be accomplished by the methods given in Chapter 11. Before any base is added, the hydrogen-ion concentration is calculated from the ionization constant expression of acetic acid, in which [H$^+$] = $\sqrt{K_a c}$. From the first addition of NaOH to the equivalence point, the solution contains a buffer mixture of HAc and Na$^+$Ac$^-$ in which [H$^+$] does not equal [Ac$^-$]. The Ac$^-$ concentration, however, is essentially equal to the concentration of Na$^+$Ac$^-$, and proper substitution in the ionization-constant expression of acetic acid allows the calculation of [H$^+$]. The Henderson-Hasselbalch modification is used for this calculation. At the equivalence point the solution is simply a water solution of Na$^+$Ac$^-$, and the hydrolysis-constant expression must be used. Beyond the equivalence point the OH$^-$ concentration is due solely to the excess of Na$^+$OH$^-$. This excess is completely ionized.

The titration curve of $0.1M$ HAc with $0.1M$ NaOH is shown in Figure 14-9. Note that the vertical portion of the titration curve is about half as high as that obtained with HCl, and that this vertical portion does not begin until about pH 6.5, whereas that for the HCl curve begins at about $pH = 3$. The explanation for this difference lies in the buffering action of the Ac^- ion. This ion is present in increasingly higher concentration as the equivalence point is approached in the HAc titration. It is produced by the reaction

$$HAc + Na^+OH^- \rightarrow Na^+ + Ac^- + H_2O$$

Even though HAc is present up to the equivalence point, its ionization is repressed by Ac^- ions and the pH is high even though the solution is acid. No such buffering action is caused by the Cl^- ions in the HCl titration. Beyond the equivalence point neither the HAc nor the HCl solution has any buffering power towards excess base. Hence both curves reach the same height and flatten out together. A suitable indicator for this titration must change color at or near the equivalence point. Hence phenolphthalein, thymol blue, or any other indicator whose pK_{In} value is near 8.57 may be used. If methyl orange ($pK_{In} = 3.7$; pH range $= 3.1 - 4.5$) were used, the indicator, would change to its basic color before half the HAc was titrated.

Figure 14-9 also shows a titration curve for boric acid, HBO_2, with NaOH. This plot shows that the titration of boric acid ($K_a = 6.0 \times 10^{-10}$) is not feasible, since there is no sharp break or inflection point in the curve. In other words, boric acid is so weak and the hydrolysis and buffering power of the borate ion are so great that there is no sharp change in the pH at the equivalence point. Hence an indicator does not change from one color to the other on adding a small amount of NaOH at or near the equivalence point, and the observer fails to detect the exact end point. Experience shows that the titration of an acid whose K_a value is less than about 1×10^{-7} is not feasible.

14r. Titration of a Weak Base with a Strong Acid. Figure 14-10 is plotted from the data obtained on titrating 25 ml of $0.1M$ NH_3 diluted to 100 ml, with $0.1M$ HCl. The pH at the equivalence point is 5.5, and a suitable indicator for the titration should have a pK_{In} value near this point. Methyl red, bromocresol green, and methyl orange are satisfactory.

Figure 14-10 also shows a curve plotted from potentiometric data obtained on titrating sodium carbonate with hydrochloric acid. This curve shows two inflection points, one representing the transformation of the carbonate ion into the bicarbonate ion and the other representing the titration of the bicarbonate ion into carbonic acid. Thus the transformation of CO_3^{2-} into HCO_3^- is complete at a pH of about 8.5, and the

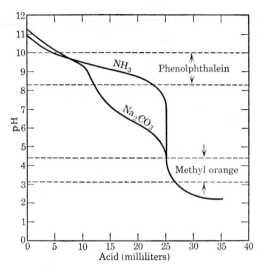

Figure 14-10. Titration curves of ammonia and sodium carbonate.

HCO_3^- is completely transformed at pH 4.3. It is possible to use phenol-phthalein to detect the first end point and then add methyl orange to obtain the second.

14s. Titration of a Weak Acid with a Weak Base. Table 14-4 gives the calculated pH values at various intervals during the titration of 100 ml of 0.1M HAc with 0.1M NH$_3$. The equivalence point occurs after 100 ml of ammonia is added.

Figure 14-11 shows a titration curve plotted from the data in Table 14-4. This curve shows clearly that the pH change near and at the equivalence

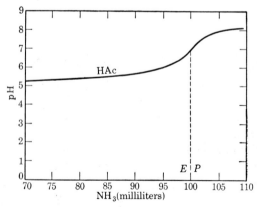

Figure 14-11. Titration curve of acetic acid with ammonia.

Table 14-4. pH Changes on Titrating Acetic Acid with Ammonia*

(100 ml of 0.1M HAc is titrated with 0.1M NH$_3$)

Ml of NH$_3$	[H$^+$]	pH
0.00	1.3×10^{-3}	2.89
50.00	1.8×10^{-5}	4.75
90.00	2.0×10^{-6}	5.70
98.00	3.7×10^{-7}	6.43
99.00	2.2×10^{-7}	6.65
99.60	1.42×10^{-7}	6.85
99.80	1.20×10^{-7}	6.92
99.90	1.12×10^{-7}	6.96
100.00	1.00×10^{-7}	7.00
Excess ammonia		
100.10	9.14×10^{-8}	7.04
100.20	8.38×10^{-8}	7.08
100.40	7.08×10^{-8}	7.15
101.00	4.50×10^{-8}	7.35
102.00	2.70×10^{-8}	7.57

* Most of the data in this table are taken from Kolthoff and Furman, *Potentiometric Titrations*, John Wiley and Sons, 1931, page 35.

point is so slight that it is impossible to make an accurate determination of the equivalence point with an indicator. That is, the indicator color would change so gradually that an exact end point is impossible. Here the solution has buffer capacity on *both* sides of the equivalence point because of the presence of NH$_4^+$ and Ac$^-$ ions. These are formed during the titration in the reaction

$$HAc + NH_3 \rightleftharpoons NH_4^+ + Ac^-$$

When excess acid is present, its ionization is represented by Ac$^-$ ions. When excess base is added, its ionization is repressed by NH$_4^+$ ions. Hence the change in pH on adding titrating solution at the equivalence point is slight. Therefore only strong acids or bases are used to make standard solutions for the determination of a weak acid or a weak base.

REFERENCES

Bull, *Physical Biochemistry*, John Wiley and Sons, New York, 1951, Chapters 6 and 7.
Daniels and Alberty, *Physical Chemistry*, John Wiley and Sons, New York, 1961, Chapter 14.

Maron and Prutton, *Principles of Physical Chemistry*, The Macmillan Co., New York, 1958, Chapter 17.

Moore, *Physical Chemistry*, Prentice-Hall, Englewood Cliffs, New Jersey, 1962, Chapter 10.

Sheehan, *Physical Chemistry*, Allyn and Bacon, Boston, 1961, Chapter 7.

Daniels, Williams, Bender, Alberty, and Cornwell, *Experimental Physical Chemistry*, McGraw-Hill Book Company, New York, 1962, Chapter 9.

Crockford and Nowell, *Laboratory Manual of Physical Chemistry*, John Wiley and Sons, New York, 1956, Experiments 31 and 32.

Willard, Merritt, and Dean, *Instrumental Methods of Analysis*, D. Van Nostrand Co., New York, 1958.

Reilley and Sawyer, *Experiments for Instrumental Analysis*, McGraw-Hill Book Co., 1961, Chapters 2 and 6.

REVIEW QUESTIONS

1. Describe the characteristics that must be possessed by a reference electrode in order for it to be efficient. List the most common reference electrodes.

2. What is a pH-indicating electrode and what characteristics must it possess for it to be suitable in the measurement of pH?

3. Describe the construction and use of the hydrogen-gas electrode.

4. Show by formula the effects of the hydrogen-ion activity and the pressure of the hydrogen gas on the potential of the hydrogen electrode. What causes a variation in hydrogen gas pressure in the ordinary gas electrode set-up? Is this pressure variation a serious factor in the usual determination of pH? Demonstrate mathematically the correctness of your answer.

5. Describe in detail the construction and use of a calomel reference electrode. What concentrations of potassium chloride are usually used in calomel electrodes?

6. Give the chemical equation that represents the reaction taking place in the calomel electrode. Show mathematically how changes in the potassium chloride concentration affect the potential of the calomel electrode.

7. Describe in detail the silver-silver chloride electrode. What reaction takes place at this electrode when it receives electrons from the external circuit?

8. A cell consists of two hydrogen gas electrodes both with hydrogen gas furnished at 1 atm pressure. Write a formula for the electromotive force of such a cell. Is a cell of this type practical for the ordinary determination of pH? Explain your answer.

9. A cell is prepared that consists of a saturated calomel electrode and a tenth normal calomel electrode. Which of these will be the negative electrode? What is the electromotive force of such a combination?

10. Consider three cells, each made up of a hydrogen gas electrode immersed in solutions of the same pH, but with normal, tenth normal, and saturated calomel electrodes as the second electrode. What are the numerical differences in the potentials of these three cells at 25°C?

11. Describe the glass electrode and discuss its use as a pH-indicating electrode. What are its advantages and disadvantages?

12. Give the simple formula used for the electromotive force of a glass electrode assembly and state what potentials make up the constant terms of the expression.

13. Give a precise definition of a neutralization indicator.

14. Discuss equilibrium relationships and the significance of the equilibrium constant in indicator equilibria. Why is K_{In} an "apparent dissociation constant" instead of a true dissociation constant?

15. An indicator which is a weak base may be treated as a weak acid for purposes of expressing the indicator constant. Show by a mathematical procedure that it is possible to treat this indicator as an acid for quantitative purposes.

16. Show that the pH of a solution is numerically equal to pK_{In} when the indicator is half transformed into the salt form.

17. Explain what is meant by (*a*) a one-color indicator, (*b*) a two-color indicator, and (*c*) the middle tint of an indicator.

18. Show clearly why most indicators have a useful pH range of about 2 pH units.

19. Explain how a series of indicators of known pK_{In} values may be used to determine the approximate pH of a solution. What is a universal indicator?

20. Describe the use of the wedge comparator for determining pH and indicator constants.

21. Describe the general procedure for preparing a set of color standards. How may these be used in the determination of pH?

22. Describe the cup arrangement in a pH colorimeter and explain how this instrument may be used to determine the pK_{In} of an indicator.

23. Explain why significant errors may result if an attempt is made to determine the pH of unbuffered solutions by colorimetric methods. What is dichromatism? What is meant by salt error and protein error?

24. What is a titration curve? Show how the data for a typical titration curve using various combinations of acids and bases may be calculated.

25. Explain why the vertical portion of the titration curve is longer for HCl than for HAc when each is titrated with a strong base. Include the buffering action of the acetate ion in your discussion.

26. The titration of an acid or base with a constant smaller than 1×10^{-7} is said not to be feasible. By means of calculations show that this statement is correct.

27. Explain why a weak acid should not be titrated with a weak base. Bring the buffering action of the salt into your discussion.

28. Explain why most of the indicators in Table 14-1 between methyl orange and phenolphthalein can be used in the titration of HCl with NaOH. Which of these could not be used for the titration of acetic acid with sodium hydroxide? Why?

29. Choose several indicators from Table 14-1 for the titration of a weak base with HCl and explain your choice.

30. Choose several indicators from Table 14-1 for each of the following titrations:

  (*a*) Lactic acid ($K_a = 1.4 \times 10^{-4}$) with KOH
  (*b*) Benzoic acid ($K_a = 6.3 \times 10^{-5}$) with Ba(OH)$_2$
  (*c*) Methylamine ($K_b = 4.4 \times 10^{-4}$) with HCl

PROBLEMS

I

1. Calculate the hydrogen-ion concentration and the pH in the solution around each of the following electrodes at 25°C.

  (a) Pt, H_2 (1 atm), H^+(?) $E_{el} = 0.364$ volt
  (b) Pt, H_2 (1.5 atm), H^+(?) $E_{el} = 0.364$ volt
  (c) Pt, H_2 (640 mm), H^+(?) $E_{el} = 0.388$ volt

2. A cell consists of two hydrogen electrodes, one immersed in a solution which is 0.200m in hydrogen ions and the second electrode surrounded by a solution of unknown pH. The pressure of the hydrogen gas at each electrode is 1 atm and the temperature is 25°C. The cell potential is 0.582 volt. Calculate the pH of the unknown solution.

3. Calculate the potentials of the following cells at 25°C.

  (a) Pt, H_2 (720 mm), H^+ (0.03m) $\|$ H^+ (0.3m), H_2 (700 mm), Pt
  (b) Pt, H_2 (760 mm), H^+ (0.003m) $\|$ H^+ (0.03m), H_2 (700 mm), Pt

4. A cell is made up of a hydrogen electrode and a normal calomel electrode. The hydrogen gas pressure is 1 atm and the temperature is 25°C. The electromotive force of the cell is 0.725 volt. Calculate the pH of the solution, the hydroxyl ion concentration, and the pOH of the solution.

5. A cell consisting of a hydrogen electrode and a saturated calomel electrode is to be used in the determination of the ionization constant of the hypothetical weak acid, HA. A 0.200m solution of the acid is used. The solution also is 0.200m in the salt, NaA. With the hydrogen gas pressure at 1 atm and the temperature at 25°C, the electromotive force of the cell is 0.544 volt. Calculate the ionization constant of the acid.

6. A hydrogen gas electrode and a normal calomel electrode are used to make a cell in which the electrolyte has a pH of 10.42. The hydrogen gas has a pressure of 740 mm of mercury. What is the potential of the cell at 25°C? What would be the potential of the cell if the gas pressure is 1 atm?

7. The electromotive force of a cell made by combining a hydrogen electrode and a saturated calomel electrode is 0.582 volt at 25°C. (a) If the hydrogen gas pressure is 1 atm, what is the pH of the solution in the cell? (b) If the potentiometer reads 4 millivolts too low, what pH would be recorded? (c) If the hydrogen gas pressure were really 740 mm, what pH would be recorded?

8. Given the following cell:

  Pt, H_2 (1 atm), H^+ = (?), Cl ($a = 0.1$), AgCl, Ag

Calculate the pH of the solution in the cell if the potential of the cell at 25°C is 0.668 volt.

9. A glass electrode is immersed in a solution of pH = 5.00. Connections are made in the usual way with a saturated calomel electrode. If the potential of the cell at 25°C is 0.194 volt, what is the value of E_g° of the glass electrode system? A silver-silver chloride electrode is used within the glass electrode system.

10. A cell consisting of a glass electrode and a saturated calomel electrode is to be used to measure the pH of an unknown solution. If the value of E_g° for the glass electrode is -0.100 volt and the potential of the cell assembly is found to be 0.242 volt, what is the pH of the solution? Data are for 25°C.

11. A cell is set up using a saturated and a normal calomel electrode. What is the electromotive force of the cell at 25°C? Which is the positive electrode? What is the ratio of the activities of the chloride ions at the two electrodes?

12. The match point in a wedge comparator was obtained when the light had passed through 60 per cent of the indicator in the salt form and 40 per cent in the acid form. Calculate the pH of the solution if the indicator is: (*a*) bromo-cresol green, (*b*) thymol blue, and (*c*) phenol red.

13. In order to determine the pK_{In} of phenol red, a buffer solution of pH equal to 8.00 is placed in a cuvette and the proper concentration of phenol red is added. A color match is obtained with a suitable wedge comparator at the point where 45 per cent of depth through which the light passes is composed of the acid form of the indicator. Calculate the pK_{In} of phenol red.

14. In a potentiometric titration 100 ml of 0.200*m* acetic acid is titrated with 0.200*m* sodium hydroxide. Calculate the pH (*a*) when the acid is one tenth neutralized, (*b*) when the acid is 25 per cent neutralized, (*c*) when the acid is 99 per cent neutralized, (*d*) at the equivalency point, and (*e*) when an excess of 5 ml of sodium hydroxide has been added.

15. If the titration given in I-14 is followed with a hydrogen electrode (gas at 1 atm) and a saturated calomel electrode, calculate the potentials of the cell at the various points given in I-14. Temperature = 25°C.

16. Confirm the various values of pH and hydrogen-ion concentration given in Table 14-3.

II

1. Calculate the pH and the hydrogen-ion concentration in the solutions around the following electrodes at 25°C:
   (*a*) Pt, H_2 (1 atm), $H^+ = (?)$ $E_{el} = 0.401$ volt
   (*b*) Pt, H_2 (0.8 atm), $H^+ = (?)$ $E_{el} = 0.401$ volt

2. Calculate the potentials of the following electrodes at 25°C:
   (*a*) Pt, H_2 (1 atm), H^+ ($a = 0.0134$)
   (*b*) Pt, H_2 (1.1 atm), H^+ (pH $= 9.84$)

3. What would be the potentials of the following cells at 25°C:
   (*a*) Pt, H_2 (900 mm), $H^+ = (0.18m)$ || $H^+ = (0.018m)$, H_2 (600 mm), Pt
   (*b*) Pt, H_2 (600 mm), $H^+ = (0.018m)$ || $H^+ = (0.18m)$, H_2 (900 mm), Pt

4. What would be the potentials of the following cells at 25°C? See problem II-2.
   (*a*) Pt, H_2 (1 atm), $H^+ = (a = 0.0134)$ || saturated calomel electrode
   (*b*) Pt, H_2 (1 atm), $H^+ = (pH = 9.84)$ || normal calomel electrode

5. A cell is made up of a hydrogen electrode and a tenth-normal calomel electrode for the purpose of determining the pH of a solution. The hydrogen pressure is 1 atm and the temperature is 25°C. If the potential of the cell is 0.625 volt, calculate the pH and the hydroxyl-ion concentration of the solution.

6. A cell is made up consisting of two hydrogen electrodes connected by a salt bridge. Calculate the potential of the cell at 25°C if the hydrogen pressure at each electrode is 1 atm and the hydrogen-ion activities are $9.1 \times 10^{-7}m$ and $0.0050m$. Which electrode is the positive electrode?

7. The potential of a cell consisting of a hydrogen electrode and a normal calomel electrode is 0.602 volt at 25°C. What is the pH around the hydrogen electrode if the hydrogen gas pressure is (a) 730 mm and (b) 1 atm?

8. A cell is made up of a hydrogen electrode and silver-silver chloride electrode as follows:

$$\text{Pt, } H_2 \text{ (1 atm), } H^+ = (?), \text{ KCl (0.10}m\text{), AgCl, Ag}$$

Calculate the pH of the solution if the potential of the cell at 25°C is 0.613 volt.

9. In order to determine E_g° for a glass electrode system, the electrode is connected in the usual way with a saturated calomel electrode. The potential of the cell is 0.249 volt at 25°C when the electrolyte has a pH of 7.00. What is the value of E_g° at this temperature? A silver-silver chloride electrode constitutes a part of the glass electrode assembly. What would be the potential of this assembly if a solution of pH equal to 4.48 were used?

10. A glass electrode assembly used with a saturated calomel electrode has an E_g° value of -0.107 volt at 25°C. Calculate the pH of a solution which gives a potential of 0.304 volt at 25°C.

11. A cell employs a $1.0N$ and a $0.1N$ calomel electrode. What is the value of the cell potential at 25°C? What is the ratio of the chloride-ion activities in the two solutions?

12. Using a wedge comparator in the colorimetric determination of pH, the match point was obtained when the light passed through 65 per cent of the indicator in the acid form and 35 per cent in the salt form. Calculate the pH of the solution when the indicator is (a) bromothymol blue, (b) methyl orange, and (c) cresol red.

13. A buffer solution of pH = 4.00 is placed in a cuvette and the proper concentration of bromophenol blue is added. A color match is obtained with a suitable comparator at the point where 54 per cent of the depth through which the light passes is composed of the salt form of the indicator. Calculate the pK_{In} of bromophenol blue.

14. Fifty milliliters of $0.160m$ ammonia is titrated with 0.160 hydrochloric acid. Prepare a table similar to Table 14-3 showing the hydrogen-ion concentration and the pH corresponding to various additions of the acid. Calculate the potentials obtained from a cell using a hydrogen electrode and a tenth-normal calomel electrode at 25°C and employing the solutions obtained in the various steps in the titration. Draw a figure similar to those shown in the text in which milliliters of acid are plotted on the horizontal axis, and pH and potential are plotted on the vertical axis.

FIFTEEN

Oxidation-Reduction
Potentials

The subject of electrode potentials is discussed in Chapter 13 and colorimetric and potentiometric methods for the determination of pH are discussed in Chapter 14. In this chapter the determination of oxidation-reduction potentials by the use of indicators, as well as by potentiometric methods, will be discussed. Special reference is made to biological systems.

OXIDATION-REDUCTION SYSTEMS

15a. Redox Potentials in Typical Couples. In Chapter 13 the process of oxidation as the loss of electrons and reduction as the gain of electrons was discussed in detail. Whether electrons are evolved or absorbed in a given electrode reaction depends upon the potential of the electrode in question and the potential of the electrode with which it is in combination when acting as one of the electrodes in a galvanic cell. Of course, a given oxidation-reduction reaction may take place elsewhere than in a galvanic cell. Zinc will replace hydrogen ions when added to an acid solution in a beaker, and hydrogen gas will replace copper ions when the gas is passed into a solution of cupric ions under the proper conditions.

Most of the electrode systems in Table 13-1 are characterized by the fact that one or more of the products or reactants make up part of the electrode proper. For example, in the Zn, Zn^{2+} combination Zn constitutes the electrode and is also involved in the electrode reaction. Even in the case of the hydrogen gas electrode, as pointed out in Chapter 14, hydrogen gas can be considered as the electrode, the platinum black serving simply to adsorb the gas. This creates, in effect, an electrode of hydrogen similar in properties to the zinc electrode. The Fe^{2+}, Fe^{3+} system is different in that the electrode is a metal foil that acts as an inert metallic conductor for giving electrons to, or accepting them from, the solution.

Whether the platinum electrode is present or not, a solution containing ferric and ferrous ions has a definite potential. The oxidized and reduced forms of the substances making up the oxidation-reduction system do not form part of the electrode proper, as is the case with gases and solids. The term *redox system* is used for such pairs. A redox system, then, consists of a solution containing two substances in different states of oxidation, these substances constituting the reduced and oxidized forms of an electrode system. Such pairs of substances are termed *couples*. A redox system has a definite potential which is termed the *redox potential* (reduction-oxidation potential of the system).

In cases such as the Fe^{2+}, Fe^{3+} or Sn^{2+}, Sn^{4+} couples, the electrode reaction is relatively simple compared with couples such as the MnO_4^-, Mn^{2+} and the $Cr_2O_7^{2-}$, Cr^{3+}, in which the electrode reaction is more involved. A number of the commoner redox potentials in inorganic systems are given in Table 15-1. These are *standard redox potentials;*

Table 15-1. Standard Redox Potentials of Some Redox Combinations at 25°C*

Couple	Reaction	Redox Potential, volts
Ce^{3+}, Ce^{4+}	$Ce^{3+} = Ce^{4+} + e$	−1.610
Mn^{2+}, MnO_4^-, H^+	$Mn^{2+} + 4H_2O = MnO_4^- + 8H^+ + 5e$	−1.520
Fe^{2+}, Fe^{3+}	$Fe^{2+} = Fe^{3+} + e$	−0.771
Sn^{2+}, Sn^{4+}	$Sn^{2+} = Sn^{4+} + 2e$	−0.150
Ti^{3+}, Ti^{4+}	$Ti^{3+} = Ti^{4+} + e$	−0.04

* The values of the potentials in this table are taken from Latimer, *The Oxidation States of the Elements and Their Potentials in Aqueous Solutions*, Prentice-Hall, New York, 1952.

that is, they are potentials when all reactants and products are in their standard states.

15b. The Calculation of Redox Potentials. Since redox couples are special cases of electrode systems, the redox potential is calculated in exactly the same manner as the oxidation potentials discussed in Chapter 13, Equation 13-1.

$$E_{el} = E_{el}^{\circ} - \frac{RT}{nF} \ln \frac{Ox}{Red}$$

is employed for this purpose. Such a calculation is illustrated in Example 15-1. This example includes also the method of calculating the potential of a cell consisting of two redox electrodes.

Example 15-1. (a) Calculate the redox potential of a solution containing the following ions: $Fe^{3+} = 0.02m$, $Fe^{2+} = 0.40m$. Temperature = 25°C.

$$E = -0.771 - 0.0592 \log \frac{0.02}{0.40} = -0.694 \text{ volt}$$

(b) Calculate the redox potential of a solution containing the following ions: $MnO_4^- = 0.50m$, $Mn^{2+} = 0.02m$, $H^+ = 0.80m$. Temperature = 25°C.

$$E = -1.520 - \frac{0.0592}{5} \log \frac{0.50 \times 0.80^8}{0.02} = -1.527 \text{ volt}$$

(c) The two redox systems in (a) and (b) are used to form a galvanic cell. Which will be the negative electrode? Formulate the cell and write the cell reaction. Calculate the cell potential.

The ferrous-ferric electrode will be the negative electrode and will give up electrons to the permanganate-manganous electrode. In other words, the ferrous ion will be oxidized by the permanganate system. Hence the cell will be

Pt; Fe^{2+} ($a = 0.40$), Fe^{3+} ($a = 0.02$) $\|$

MnO_4^- ($a = 0.50$), Mn^{2+} ($a = 0.02$), H^+ ($a = 0.80$); Pt

The cell reaction will be

$$5Fe^{2+} + MnO_4^- + 8H^+ = 5Fe^{3+} + Mn^{2+} + 4H_2O$$

The cell potential can be calculated by subtracting the potential of the permanganate-manganous electrode from the potential of the ferrous-ferric electrode.

$$E_{cell} = E_{left} - E_{right} = -0.694 - (-1.527) = 0.833 \text{ volt}$$

The potential can also be calculated from Equation 13-3.

$$E = E_{cell}^\circ - \frac{RT}{nF} \ln \frac{\text{products}}{\text{reactants}}$$

$$= E_{Fe^{2+};Fe^{3+}}^\circ - E_{MnO_4^-;Mn^{2+}}^\circ - \frac{RT}{5F} \ln \frac{a_{Fe^{3+}}^5 \times a_{Mn^{2+}} \times a_{H_2O}^4}{a_{Fe^{2+}}^5 \times a_{MnO_4^-} \times a_{H^+}^8}$$

$$E = -0.771 + 1.520 - \frac{0.0592}{5} \log \frac{0.02^5 \times 0.02 \times 1^4}{0.40^5 \times 0.50 \times 0.80^8}$$

$$= 0.749 + 0.084 = 0.833 \text{ volt}$$

15c. Organic Redox Systems. Many organic systems show redox potentials. Consequently, if a bright platinum electrode is immersed in a solution containing the reduced and oxidized forms, a potential is developed and the system can be made a part of a galvanic cell. One such system is the hydroquinone-quinone system, often employed in the determination of pH. Another example is the diphenylbenzidene-diphenylbenzidene violet system.

The reactions for the two systems are

$$C_6H_4(OH)_2 = C_6H_4O_2 + 2H^+ + 2e$$

$$\underset{\text{Hydroquinone}}{} \quad \underset{\text{Quinone}}{}$$

$$\underset{\text{Diphenylbenzidene}}{C_6H_5{\cdot}NH{\cdot}C_6H_4{\cdot}C_6H_4{\cdot}NH{\cdot}C_6H_5} = \underset{\text{Diphenylbenzidene violet}}{C_6H_5{\cdot}N:C_6H_4:N{\cdot}C_6H_5} + 2H^+ + 2e$$

These two equations, as well as those for other organic redox systems, follow the general equation

$$\text{Red} = \text{Ox} + 2H^+ + 2e$$

The general expression for the redox potential is therefore

$$E = E^\circ - \frac{RT}{2F} \ln \frac{a_{\text{Ox}} \times a_{\text{H}^+}^2}{a_{\text{Red}}}$$

$$= E^\circ - \frac{RT}{2F} \ln \frac{a_{\text{Ox}}}{a_{\text{Red}}} + \frac{RT}{F} \cdot \text{pH} \qquad (15\text{-}1)$$

The standard redox potential is usually given for a definite pH rather than for a solution in which the hydrogen-ion activity is one. In such a case the symbol E° is replaced by $E^{\circ\prime}$. Unless otherwise noted, the value of $E^{\circ\prime}$ is given for a neutral solution, that is, one in which the pH is 7. Equation 15-1 then reduces to

$$E = E^{\circ\prime} - \frac{RT}{2F} \ln \frac{a_{\text{Ox}}}{a_{\text{Red}}} \qquad (15\text{-}2)$$

Usually there is no mathematical relationship between the pH of the solution and the value of $E^{\circ\prime}$. Therefore all values of $E^{\circ\prime}$ have to be determined experimentally.

Many of the organic redox systems are characterized by the fact that the reduced and oxidized forms of the substances have different colors. The color of the solution will therefore depend not only on the pH but also on the ratio of the Ox and Red activities. These, in turn, will determine the potential of the system in accordance with Equation 15-2. Such substances, therefore, can often be used as *redox indicators*. The colors produced by these indicators in various solutions can be used to determine the potentials of the solutions, just as the color of acid-base indicators can be used to find the pH of solutions. Note that in a number of cases the indicators can act as acid-base indicators as well as oxidation-reduction indicators. This must be carefully considered in setting up the conditions under which any one of these indicators is used and the purpose for which it is being used. The use of redox indicators is discussed further in the next section. A number of redox indicators, along with their standard oxidation potentials at various pH values, are given in Table 15-2.

Table 15-2. Standard Redox Potentials of Some Oxidation-Reduction Indicators at Various pH Values at 30°C

Indicator pH =	5.8	6.2	7.0	7.4	8.2
o-Bromophenol indophenol	−0.308	−0.284	−0.230	−0.200	−0.137
Toluylene blue	−0.173	−0.151	−0.115	−0.101	−0.075
Methylene blue	−0.056	−0.039	−0.011	−0.002	−0.090
Indigo trisulfonate	+0.016	+0.039	+0.081	+0.099	+0.174
Indigo disulfonate	+0.057	+0.081	+0.125	+0.143	+0.174

THE DETERMINATION OF REDOX POTENTIALS

15d. Potentiometric Method. The potentiometric determination of redox potentials is, in most cases, very simple. It is necessary only to immerse a bright platinum electrode in the solution and to determine its potential against a reference electrode, usually the normal calomel electrode. Such a procedure gives excellent results in most inorganic redox systems. An adaptation of the method is used in potentiometric oxidation-reduction titrations. Iron, for example, may be titrated with permanganate solution and the progress of the oxidation followed by measuring the potential of a cell, one electrode of which is a platinum foil immersed in the beaker in which the titration is being carried out. When the cell potential is plotted against the volume of the titrating solution, a curve is obtained that is similar in shape to the curves obtained in acid-base titrations. The abrupt change in potential indicates the end point.

In organic systems and biological fluids the same general procedure is followed whenever possible. A platinum electrode is immersed in the fluid being studied, and its potential is measured against a reference electrode. Such a procedure is illustrated in Example 15-2.

Example 15-2. The voltage of the following cell at 30°C is 0.3500 volt.

What is the potential of the solution? The potential of the normal calomel electrode at this temperature is -0.2788 volt.

$$\text{Pt; solution} \parallel \text{normal calomel electrode}$$

$$E_{cell} = E_{left} - E_{right} = E_{left} - (-0.2788 \text{ volt}) = 0.3500 \text{ volt}$$

$$E_{left} = 0.0712 \text{ volt} = \text{redox potential}$$

Oxygen from the air will react with the redox system of many fluids to cause erroneous results. This can be prevented by measuring the potential in a closed system with some oxygen-free inert gas, such as purified nitrogen, bubbling through the solution.

15e. Colorimetric Method. As stated in 15c, certain organic substances known as redox indicators can be used for the determination of the redox potentials of solutions. A number of such indicators are listed in Table 15-2. In the selection of an indicator for a particular determination the redox potential of the indicator should be close to that of the solution being measured. The indicator should exist in two forms of such colors and such intensities that the natural color of the solution cannot influence unduly that of the indicator. A high color intensity is desirable, so that only a small quantity of indicator is necessary. Large quantities cause material changes in the concentrations of the reduced and oxidized substances in the solutions, and the results obtained would not be a true value of the original redox potential.

When making such a determination, a small quantity of the indicator is added to the solution. Interaction between the indicator and the solution takes place until the potentials of the two solutions are equal. If the amount of indicator is small compared to the quantity of the reduced and oxidized forms of the substance being measured, there is a negligible change in the potential of the solution because of interaction with the indicator. The resulting color can then be compared with a set of standards similar to those used in colorimetric pH determinations. The standards must, of course, have the same pH as the solution. This method has proved of great value in the study of living cells for which no satisfactory electrode has yet been developed. The indicator is either injected into the cell or allowed to diffuse through the cell wall. The color enables us to determine the redox potential of the cell solution.

The methylene blue test has long been used in the testing of milk. Fresh milk has a redox potential of about -0.25 volt. In sterile milk this potential remains constant for several hours, but in milk in which certain bacteria are present there is a marked change in the potential as bacterial action proceeds. Methylene blue can be used to follow the change produced, and the final decolorization of the methylene blue indicates that marked bacterial action has taken place. The time necessary to carry out this test is often a serious disadvantage, and in the rapid grading of milk the indicator resazurin has to a considerable extent replaced the use of methylene blue.

The calculations involved in the colorimetric determination of the redox potential are shown in Example 15-3.

Example 15-3. In the determination with methylene blue of the redox potential of a sample of milk at 30°C, it was found by color comparison that 60 per cent of the indicator was in the reduced form. The pH of the sample was 6.2. What is the redox potential of the sample?

In Table 15-2 it is shown that $E^{\circ\prime}$ for methylene blue at a pH of 6.2 is -0.039 volt. Therefore,

$$E = -0.039 - \frac{RT}{nF}\ln\frac{0.4}{0.6} = -0.039 - 0.030\log 0.667$$

$$= -0.039 + 0.005 = -0.034 \text{ volt}$$

The equivalent points in oxidation-reduction titrations can be determined with the proper redox indicators, just as the end point in acid-base titrations can be determined with the proper hydrogen-ion indicator. A special case is the titration of ferrous iron with permanganate solution. Not only does the permanganate oxidize the iron, but it also indicates by a characteristic color change when the titration is complete. Such titrations are used not only in routine inorganic oxidation-reduction determinations but also in a number of biological determinations. For example, the ascorbic acid (vitamin C) content of blood can be determined by titration with 2,6-dichlorobenzenoneindophenol. Just as in the permanganate titration, this indicator not only effects the oxidation of the ascorbic acid but also indicates by a color change when the titration is complete.

In many redox systems the reaction is sluggish, so that the establishment of equilibrium is slow in a titration involving oxidation and reduction. Thus erratic results are obtained if the progress of the process is followed by either electrometric or colorimetric means. This condition can often be remedied by adding a very small amount of a more active redox system. Any redox system that in small amounts speeds up the equilibrium condition is called a *potential mediator*. An example of this type of action is found in the reduction of fumaric to succinic acid. The equation for this reaction is

$$(CH \cdot COOH)_2 + 2H_3O^+ + 2e = (CH_2COOH)_2 + 2H_2O$$

The reduction is effected by the enzyme, succinic dehydrogenase, which is found in muscle tissue. To measure the potential of a mixture of succinic and fumaric acids it is necessary to carry out the reduction in the presence of methylene blue. This substance acts as a potential mediator, probably by serving as a carrier for the hydrogen ions activated by the enzyme. The mediator transports these ions from their source in the solution to the fumaric acid.

REFERENCES

Bull, *Physical Biochemistry*, John Wiley and Sons, New York, 1951, Chapters 6 and 8.
Daniels and Alberty, *Physical Chemistry*, John Wiley and Sons, New York, 1961, Chapter 14.
Maron and Prutton, *Principles of Physical Chemistry*, The Macmillan Co., New York, 1958, Chapter 17.
Moore, *Physical Chemistry*, Prentice-Hall, Englewood Cliffs, New Jersey, 1962, Chapter 10.
Sheehan, *Physical Chemistry*, Allyn and Bacon, Boston, 1961, Chapter 7.
Daniels, Williams, Bender, Alberty, and Cornwell, *Experimental Physical Chemistry*, New York, 1962, Chapter 9.
Latimer, *The Oxidation States of the Elements and their Potentials in Aqueous Solutions*, Prentice-Hall, New York, 1952.

REVIEW QUESTIONS

1. Explain what is meant by the term *redox system*. What is a redox couple? Discuss redox potentials.

2. What is the role of the bright platinum electrode in the measurement of redox potentials?

3. Discuss the calculation of a given redox potential from the electromotive force of a cell made up of the redox system and one of the usual reference electrodes.

4. Define a redox indicator. Give some examples of oxidation-reduction indicators. By means of suitable formulas show the effect of pH change on the potential of typical redox indicator systems.

5. Discuss the characteristics that a redox indicator must have in order to be suitable for the determination of the potential of a given solution.

6. Describe the colorimetric determination of the redox potential of a given solution. What precautions must be observed in the process?

7. Explain the use of redox indicators in oxidation-reduction titrations. What characteristics must a redox indicator have in order to be suitable for a given titration? How can a substance function as both the titrating agent and as the indicator?

8. What are potential mediators and why are they necessary in certain redox determinations?

9. Discuss the general procedure for the determination of the redox potential of a system by potentiometric methods. Discuss the calculation of the redox potential from the data of such a determination.

PROBLEMS

I

1. Calculate the potential of each of the following solutions at 25°C:
   (a) Sn^{4+} ($a = 0.20$), Sn^{2+} ($a = 0.60$)
   (b) Ce^{4+} ($a = 0.14$), Ce^{3+} ($a = 0.080$)
   (c) MnO_4^- ($a = 0.30$), Mn^{2+} ($a = 0.12$), pH $= 4.00$
   (d) Ti^{4+} ($a = 0.18$), Ti^{3+} ($a = 1.4 \times 10^{-4}$)
   (e) MnO_4^- ($a = 0.10$), Mn^{2+} ($a = 0.80$), H^+ ($a = 1.00 \times 10^{-2}$)

2. A cell is prepared by using a saturated calomel electrode and a bright platinum electrode dipping into each of the solutions in problem I-1. What potential is obtained in each case if the temperature is 25°C?

3. The electromotive force of a cell consisting of a bright platinum electrode dipping into a solution of ferrous-ferric ions combined with a normal calomel electrode is 0.564 volt at 25°C. What is the ratio of the activities of the ferrous and ferric ions? If the activity of the ferrous ion is 0.15, what is the activity of the ferric ion?

4. Calculate the electromotive force at 25°C of the following cell:

   Pt | $Cr_2O_7^{2-}$ (0.24), Cr^{3+} (0.080m), H^+ (0.0010m) || saturated calomel electrode

   Assume activities and molalities are identical. $E°$ for the dichromate-chromium III pair is -1.36 volts.

5. What would be the electromotive force of the cell in I-4 if the hydrogen-ion concentration is tripled in value? What would be the electromotive force if the hydrogen-ion activity is increased one-hundred fold?

6. Methylene blue solution is added in small quantities to a buffer solution of pH $= 5.8$. Under these conditions 30 per cent of the methylene blue is found to be in the oxidized form. What is the redox potential of the solution? $T = 30°C$.

7. Indigo trisulfonate is added to a solution buffered at pH $= 7.40$ at 30°C. Calculate the potential of the solution if it is known that 45 per cent of the indicator is in the reduced form.

8. Given a solution buffered at 7.0. To this is added a small quantity of indigo trisulfonate. What percentage of the indicator is in the reduced form if the solution has a redox potential of 0.074 volt?

9. What is the electromotive force of a cell at 30°C consisting of the solution in problem I-6, in which a bright platinum electrode is immersed, and a normal calomel electrode. At 30°C the potential of a normal calomel electrode is -0.283 volt.

II

1. Calculate the potentials of each of the following solutions at 25°C.
   (a) MnO_4^- ($a = 0.15$), Mn^{2+} ($a = 0.10$), pH $= 4.00$
   (b) MnO_4^- ($a = 0.15$), Mn^{2+} ($a = 0.10$), pH $= 1.00$
   (c) Fe^{3+} ($a = 0.30$), Fe^{2+} ($a = 0.70$)

2. Cells are constructed by combining each of the above solutions with a tenth normal calomel electrode. Calculate the potential at 25°C for each of these cells.

3. The potential of a solution in which the permanganate ion activity is 0.200 and the manganous ion activity is 0.300 is found to be -1.420 volts at 25°C. What is the value of the hydrogen-ion activity in this solution?

4. The electromotive force of a cell consisting of a solution of Ce^{4+} and Ce^{3+}, in which is immersed a bright platinum electrode, and a saturated calomel electrode is 0.780 volt. The temperature is 25°C. What is the activity of the cerous ion if the activity of the ceric ion is 0.15?

5. A cell is constructed consisting of a normal calomel electrode and a bright platinum electrode dipping into a solution containing ferric ions and ferrous ions both at an activity of 0.10. What is the potential of this cell at 25°C. At this temperature the normal calomel electrode has a potential of -0.280 volt.

6. Two bright platinum electrodes are used to construct a cell, one electrode dipping into a solution of ferric ions at an activity of 0.020 and ferrous ions at an activity of 0.040, and the other dipping into a solution containing ceric ions at an activity of 0.030 and cerous ions at an activity of 0.040. What is the potential of this cell at 25°C?

7. A small quantity of toluylene blue is added to a solution buffered at a pH of 5.8. Calculate the potential of the solution if it is known that 25 per cent of the indicator is in the oxidized form. The temperature is 30°C.

8. What is the potential of a cell made from the solution in problem II-7, into which is dipping a bright platinum electrode and a normal calomel electrode. The temperature is 30°C, at which temperature the potential of the calomel electrode is -0.283 volt.

SIXTEEN

Reaction Kinetics. Catalysis

The general topic of reaction rates is discussed in this chapter. The subject matter includes a brief discussion of the techniques used in reaction kinetic studies. The concept of reaction order is discussed and the simpler mathematical equations used in reaction kinetics are developed and discussed. Special emphasis is given to catalytic action and the theory of catalysis. The role of activation energy in reaction kinetics is presented.

1. REACTION KINETICS

16a. Reaction Kinetics. The study of rates at which reactions take place and effects of environmental conditions, including the role of concentrations of reactants, constitutes the subject matter of *reaction kinetics.*

The subject of reaction velocity is a familiar one. It has to do with the speed with which a reacting system approaches a state of equilibrium. Some reactions take place in an essentially instantaneous manner. For example, if a solution of silver nitrate is added to a solution of a soluble chloride, an immediate and essentially complete precipitation of silver chloride results. The mixing of a solution of a strong acid with a solution of a strong base produces almost immediate neutralization. The same is true of many other ionic reactions. An explosion is an example of an instantaneous reaction. On the other hand, many reactions proceed quite slowly, some so slowly that measuring their progress is very difficult. Among the reactions whose speeds can be easily followed are the rate of interaction of acetic acid with ethyl alcohol and the inversion of sucrose to levulose and glucose.

Not only do reaction rate studies tell us about the actual speeds of reactions but they also throw light on reaction mechanisms. For example, more than one reaction may be taking place between two reactants to form different products. Kinetic studies often tell us how we may change the conditions so as to favor one of these possible reactions. Such studies tell us how to speed up certain reactions and how to slow down or prevent others. Reaction kinetics are most important in biological processes. Much of our knowledge of the reactions of enzymes have been obtained from reaction kinetic studies.

Many factors play a role in reaction kinetics. The concentrations of the reactants is one of the major factors, but, if reverse reactions can take place, the concentrations of the products can also play a role. Temperature change is a most important factor. Pressure can be a factor in reactions involving gases. Certain substances termed *catalysts* affect the speed of many reactions, some speeding up specific reactions and others slowing them down. In photochemical reactions light intensity and the wave length of the light are vital factors.

Thermodynamics can predict whether or not a reaction can take place under a given set of conditions, but it tells us nothing about how long it will take for the system to reach a final state of equilibrium or the paths by which the reaction may proceed. A mixture of hydrogen and oxygen in the proper proportions is a most unstable system thermodynamically; yet we can keep such a mixture of the two without any apparent change taking place for long periods of time. The use of the equilibrium constant in no way throws any light on the speed with which the given equilibrium will be reached.

The speed of a chemical reaction is usually expressed in terms of the number of moles of a reactant transformed in a unit volume in unit time. The speed may also be expressed in terms of the rate of formation of a product. If the unit of volume is the liter, then concentrations are in terms of molarity.

A number of techniques are available for the study of reaction rates. One general procedure is to remove portions of the reacting system from time to time and then to analyze these portions. Standard chemical procedures such as the titration of an acid or the formation of a precipitate could be used. It is better, however, to find some easily measured physical or chemical property that changes during the course of the reaction. This could be the color, the index of refraction, the optical activity, the conductivity, the hydrogen-ion concentration, or the potential of an appropriate electrode.

Removing samples for analysis has certain drawbacks. The reaction may continue in the sample so that the results obtained do not give a true concentration picture of the system at the time of the sampling. A technique for overcoming this difficulty, termed *freezing the equilibrium*, is to chill the sample as rapidly as possible after it is removed from the reaction mixture. This essentially stops the reaction and analyses can proceed without further change in concentration.

A better procedure is to follow the physical or chemical property in the reacting mixture as a whole. If the reacting mixture is a liquid and there is a measurable volume change, this change could be followed with a dilatometer. If there is a color change or a change in the absorption spectrum, perhaps the reaction could be carried out in such a way as to permit the use of a spectrophotometer. The conductance of the solution could be followed by carrying out the reaction in a conductivity cell. It is quite easy to follow the inversion of sucrose with a polarimeter. Often it is not necessary to solve for the concentration in using the reaction kinetic formulas. The property undergoing change, whether it be volume, pressure, etc., can be measured and the data used directly in the proper equations.

16b. Reaction Order. To treat reaction rates in a quantitative manner, it is necessary to consider reactions from the standpoint of *order*. If the speed of the reaction is proportional to the first power of a reacting substance, the reaction is one of the *first order*. If two concentration terms appear and each is raised only to the first power, the reaction is said to be of the *second order*. If only one concentration term appears but it is raised to the second power, the reaction again is a *second-order* one. If the total number of exponents for all the concentration terms is three, it is a *third-order reaction*. Only a few third-order reactions are known, and no known cases exist of reactions of higher than the third-order. If concentration terms do not appear in the kinetic equation, such a reaction is said to be of *zero order*. Mathematical expressions could be given at this time to illustrate the above but the procedure to be followed is to discuss each order separately, develop the mathematical expressions involved, and show how these expressions are used in reaction rate calculations.

16c. First-Order Reactions. Consider first some reactions that are of the first order, that is, reactions whose speed depends only on the first power of the concentration of the reacting substance. The equations for some typical first-order reactions follow.

$$Br_2 = 2Br \qquad\qquad (a)$$

$$N_2O_5 = N_2O_4 + \tfrac{1}{2}O_2 \qquad\qquad (b)$$

$$\text{Uranium-235} = \text{fission products} \qquad\qquad (c)$$

The rate of these reactions is proportional to the concentration of the reacting molecule, other factors being constant. This may be expressed by the simple mathematical relation

$$\text{Speed} = -\frac{da}{dt} = ka \qquad\qquad (16\text{-}1)$$

In this expression dt is an extremely small interval of time and da represents the number of moles of the reactant changing in a volume of 1 liter during that small interval of time. The concentration diminishes with time and hence a minus sign is placed before the right-hand term in the expression. The term, da/dt, is known as a differential term and is the notation characteristic of differential expressions in the calculus. If it is kept in mind that the small letter d stands for "a small amount of," such a term should be meaningful even to those students who do not have training in calculus. For example, db/dt would mean the small part of a mole of b reacting during the very small interval of time, dt.

In Equation 16-1 k is a constant that takes into account the nature of the reacting substance, the temperature, the catalyst that may be present, and any other constant factor that affects the speed of the reaction. The concentration of the reactant is given by a. The value of a, as stated, decreases with time. As a result, the speed of the reaction, da/dt, would also decrease with time. The constant k is often called the *specific rate constant* because it is numerically equal to the speed of the reaction when the concentration of the reacting substance has a value of one mole per liter. Equation 16-1 is not a very useful one for calculations involving reaction kinetics. It may, however, by the process of integration, be put into forms that are extremely useful.

In the process of integration, the first step is to separate the variables. When this is done, Equation 16-1 becomes

$$- \frac{da}{a} = k \, dt \qquad (16\text{-}2)$$

Integration yields the following equation

$$\log a = - \frac{kt}{2.303} + I \qquad (16\text{-}3)$$

In this expression I is the constant of integration. If the integration of Equation 16-2 is carried out between the limits of time equal to zero and time equal to t, with the corresponding concentration values of a^0 and a, this expression is obtained:

$$\log \frac{a^0}{a} = \frac{kt}{2.3} \qquad (16\text{-}4)$$

In these expressions k is a constant whose numerical value depends on the characteristics of the particular reaction and a^0 is the initial concentration of the reacting substance. Any first-order reaction must obey Equations 16-2, 16-3, and 16-4. Whether or not the experimental data obey these equations can be checked by three methods.

1. The value of k for a number of sets of t and a data can be calculated, and if the values are constant, the reaction is of the first order. If the calculated k's vary, the reaction is of a higher order.

2. The logarithm of the concentration can be plotted against t. As seen from Equation 16-3, the resulting curve is a straight line if the reaction is of the first order.

3a. The third method consists in the use of the so-called *half-life period*. The half-life period is the time necessary for the original concentration to be reduced one half. When this has taken place, a is equal to $\frac{1}{2}a^0$. Making this substitution in Equation 16-4,

$$\log \frac{a^0}{a^0/2} = \frac{kt_{1/2}}{2.3}$$

This reduces to

$$\log 2 = \frac{kt_{1/2}}{2.3} \tag{16-5}$$

Thus, the half-life period is independent of the initial concentration. Consequently, if the half-life period is determined experimentally for a number of different initial concentrations and if the values obtained are identical, the reaction is of the first order.

In this chapter the reactions considered are all homogeneous; that is, they are reactions taking place entirely in one phase. Examples of homogeneous gas-phase, first-order reactions follow:

Thermal decomposition of nitrogen pentoxide:

$$N_2O_5 = N_2O_4 + O$$

Thermal decomposition of azomethane:

$$CH_3N{=}NCH_3 = N_2 + C_2H_6$$

Thermal decomposition of paraldehyde:

$$(CH_3CHO)_3 = 3CH_3CHO$$

Examples of first-order reactions in solutions are:

Decomposition of H_2O_2 in the presence of iodide ions:

$$H_2O_2 = H_2O + O$$

Thermal decomposition of trinitrobenzoic acid:

$$C_6H_2(NO_2)_3COOH = C_6H_3(NO_2)_3 + CO_2$$

Thermal decomposition of nitrogen pentoxide in solution:

$$N_2O_5 = N_2O_4 + O$$

All the reactions given above are obviously first order but certain other reactions follow the first-order expression, although an inspection of the equations indicates that they should be second order. Consider the following equations. The first equation gives the change taking place when sucrose undergoes inversion in the presence of certain enzymes or in an acid solution.

$$C_{12}H_{22}O_{11} + H_2O = C_6H_{12}O_6 + C_6H_{12}O_6$$
$$\text{Glucose} \qquad\qquad \text{Levulose}$$

The concentration of the water does undergo change but in the usual solutions employed the concentration of the water remains essentially unchanged because of its high concentration in comparison with the sucrose concentration. Hence the concentration of the water can be considered as constant and the term is combined with the velocity constant. The reaction data, therefore, follow a first-order equation with the concentration of the sucrose as the only variable.

The second equation is for the hydrolysis of ethyl acetate in dilute aqueous solution.

$$CH_3COOC_2H_5 + H_2O = CH_3COOH + C_2H_5OH$$

Here the concentration of the water is so much greater than the usual concentration of the ester that the rate equations contain only the concentration of the ethyl acetate as the variable concentration term. The concentration of the water is essentially unchanged.

The uses of Equations 16-3, 16-4, and 16-5 are illustrated in Examples 16-1 and 16-2.

Example 16-1. In the decomposition of nitrogen pentoxide in the gaseous state at 35°C, Daniels and Johnston [*J. Am. Chem. Soc.* **48,** 53 (1921)] found the fractions of nitrogen pentoxide decomposed at various periods of time to be as follows:

Time (min)	Fraction Decomposed
20	0.148
40	0.274
60	0.382
100	0.551

(*a*) Calculate the value of the velocity constant. (*b*) What fraction would be decomposed at the end of 50 min? (*c*) Calculate the half-life period for this reaction.

(*a*) Any pair of the data may be used to calculate a value of the constant. If the data are absolutely accurate, all values so calculated should be equal. Usually, because of variations in the data, the values so calculated will show a slight variation. The average is taken as the best value of the constant. To solve the problem the 40 min = 0.274 pair of data is employed. Let a^0 be the initial concentration. Then the number of moles changed in a liter will be $a^0 \times 0.274$. The concentration remaining will be $a^0 - 0.274a^0 = 0.726a^0$.

Substituting in Equation 16-4

$$\log \frac{a^0}{0.726a^0} = k \frac{40}{2.3}$$

$$k = 0.0080 \text{ min}^{-1}$$

(b) Since a/a^0 is the fraction of the original concentration remaining after t min, Equation 16-4 can be written

$$- \log \frac{a}{a^0} = 0.0080 \text{ min}^{-1} \times \frac{50 \text{ min}}{2.3}$$

$$\frac{a}{a^0} = 0.670$$

The fraction decomposed is $1 - 0.670 = 0.330$. In this problem, as in other kinetic problems, the value of the constant depends upon the unit of time employed.

(c) Substituting in Equation 16-5,

$$\log 2 = \frac{k t_{1/2}}{2.303}$$

$$t_{1/2} = \frac{\log 2 \times 2.303}{0.0080}$$

$$t_{1/2} = 86.4 \text{ min}$$

Example 16-2. The data given below were obtained by Harned [*J. Am. Chem. Soc.* **45**, 1461 (1918)] for the decomposition of hydrogen peroxide in aqueous $0.02M$ KI solution at $25°C$. The reaction progress was followed by measuring the gas produced from a given volume of the reaction mixture. This volume is given in the second column. Calculate the velocity constant for the 5-, 10-, 25-, and 45-min data.

In handling such data it would be possible to calculate the concentration of the hydrogen peroxide by converting the volume of gas produced to moles. Remembering that one mole of hydrogen peroxide produces half a mole of oxygen gas, it would then be possible to calculate the number of moles of hydrogen peroxide decomposed in the given volume. The volume and the number of moles being known, the concentration could then be determined. The initial concentration could be determined from the total amount of oxygen gas evolved. This involved procedure, however, is not necessary. The initial concentration of hydrogen peroxide (a^0) is a function of the total amount of gas evolved at ($t = \infty$), just as the volume produced at time $t_{(x)}$ is a function of the concentration change. Consequently, the ratio a^0/a is determined by $c/(c - x)$.

Substituting this term in Equation 16-4 produces the k values shown in the fourth column

t (min)	x (Volume of Gas Produced)	$c - x$	k
0	0.00	57.90	...
5	7.50	50.40	0.0277
10	14.00	43.90	0.0277
25	28.80	29.10	0.0275
45	41.20	16.70	0.0276
Infinity	57.90	0	...

Radioactivity decay is a special type of first-order reaction and receives added importance because of the use of the half-life concept in connection with the radioactive disintegration of atoms. This will be discussed in detail in Chapter 19.

16d. Second-Order Reactions. The rate of a second-order reaction is proportional to the product of the concentrations of two atoms or molecules. These two molecules may be the same, as in the following reactions:

Gaseous decomposition of HCl: $2HCl = H_2 + Cl_2$
Gaseous decomposition of HBr: $2HBr = H_2 + Br_2$

or they may be different as in these reactions:
Formation of ethyl acetate in solution:

$$CH_3COOH + C_2H_5OH = CH_3COOC_2H_5 + H_2O$$

Saponification of ethyl acetate in solution:

$$CH_3COOC_2H_5 + OH^- = C_2H_5OH + CH_3COO^-$$

When the two reacting molecules are the same, the equation for the reaction is

$$-\frac{da}{dt} = ka^2 \tag{16-6}$$

When the two reacting molecules are different, the equation for the reaction rate is

$$-\frac{da}{dt} = -\frac{db}{dt} = k(a \times b) \tag{16-7}$$

If the two initial concentrations are equal, then $a = b$ and Equation 16-7 becomes identical in form with 16-6. The integration of Equation 16-7 is somewhat complicated, so for purposes of simplification all second-order reactions are considered as taking place between similar molecules; or if the molecules are different, the concentrations are considered equal.

If Equation 16-6 is integrated, two equations corresponding to Equations 16-3 and 16-4 for a first-order reaction are obtained. These are

$$\frac{1}{a} = kt + I \tag{16-8}$$

$$\frac{a^0 - a}{a^0 a} = kt \tag{16-9}$$

In these expressions k again is a constant, and a^0 is the initial concentration or concentrations of the reactant or reactants. Any second-order reaction must obey these equations, assuming, of course, that the two reacting molecules are the same or that they have the same concentration. The data may be checked by one of the following methods:

1. The value of k for a number of sets of t and a data can be calculated, and if the values so obtained are constant, the reaction is of the second order.

2. The reciprocal of the concentration can be plotted against t. If the resulting curve is a straight line, the reaction is of the second order.

3. By substituting $a^0/2$ for a in Equation 16-9, the half-life period, unlike the first-order reaction, is now a function of the initial concentration.

$$\frac{a^0 - a^0/2}{a^0 \times a^0/2} = kt_{1/2}$$

$$t_{1/2} = \frac{1}{a^0 k} \tag{16-10}$$

Consequently, if the half-life periods are determined for two different initial concentrations and these periods are found to be inversely proportional to the initial concentrations, the reaction is of the second order. It must be remembered that this half-life period relationship holds only if the two reacting molecules are of the same species or if the initial concentrations are identical. With two different reacting species at different concentrations, there would be a different half-life period for each of the reactants.

Example 16-3. The saponification of methyl acetate at 25°C was studied by Walker [*Proc. Roy. Soc.* **A78,** 157 (1906)] by mixing equal volumes of 0.02M methyl acetate and sodium hydroxide.

Time (min)	Concentration of Base Found
3	0.00743
5	0.00635
7	0.00552
10	0.00464
15	0.00363
21	0.00290

(*a*) Calculate the value of the velocity constant. (*b*) Calculate the half-life period for the reaction.

(*a*) Any set of time-concentration data may be used. Employing the 10-min value and substituting in Equation 16-9,

$$\frac{0.01 - 0.00464}{0.01 \times 0.00464} = k \times 10 \text{ min}$$

$$k = 11.5 \text{ min}^{-1} \text{ liter mole}^{-1}$$

(*b*) Substituting in Equation 16-10,

$$t_{1/2} = \frac{1}{11.5 \times 0.01} = 8.7 \text{ min}$$

16e. Third-Order Reactions. The rate-determining steps of most reactions are usually of the first or second order. There is a very limited number of third-order reactions, and there are no known reactions of a higher order.

When a reaction is greater than bimolecular, the equation as written is usually a summation of a series of much more simplified equations.

16f. Zero-Order Reactions. Experimental studies show that for certain reactions the speed is not proportional to the concentration of the re-actants. Such a reaction is termed a reaction of the *zero order,* In such a case the speed is determined by some limiting factor other than concentration. In many reactions this factor is the rate of illumination of a certain wavelength of light. This rate is determined by the number of quanta of light received by the solution per unit of time. The initial step in the reaction is the absorption of quanta of light by the reacting particles. If the concentration of the reaction substance is sufficiently large, the rate of interaction will depend solely on the rate of illumination. In some catalytic reactions the rate of reaction is determined by the amount of catalyst exposed to the reacting system. In such situations the equations for the reaction speed are

$$dx/dt = k$$

and

$$x = kt + I$$

In these equations x is the amount of a product formed in unit of time in unit volume. The velocity constant is k, which contains constants corresponding to the intensity of the light or the amount of catalyst present.

16g. Complex Reactions. The reactions so far considered have been of a simple nature, inasmuch as the speed was determined by the simple interaction of one or two molecules. In the formulation of exact rate equations complicating features must often be considered.

One such complication is found in *reversible* or *opposing reactions*. In such a reaction the products can act to reform the reactants at an appreciable speed, even at the low concentrations of product characteristic of the early stages of the reaction. The over-all speed then becomes equal to the forward speed less the reverse speed. In establishing the rate equation, the expression for the speed becomes

$$\frac{dx}{dt} = \left(\frac{dx}{dt}\right)_{\text{forward}} - \left(\frac{dx}{dt}\right)_{\text{reverse}}$$

Equations of the usual form are then set up for the forward and reverse speeds, and the resulting equation is integrated to obtain the final concentration-time formulas. An example of an opposing reaction is the interaction of nitric oxide and oxygen at high temperatures.

$$2NO + O_2 \rightleftharpoons 2NO_2$$

The expression for the over-all speed is

$$\frac{dx}{dt} = k'c_{NO}^2 c_{O_2} - k''c_{NO_2}^2$$

Complications are often introduced by *consecutive reactions*, in which a product of the initial reaction undergoes a second reaction with one of the original reactants. Esters of dibasic acids show this behavior upon hydrolysis. For example, diethyl oxalate reacts with a hydroxide base in this manner:

$$(COOC_2H_5)_2 + OH^- = (COOC_2H_5)COO^- + C_2H_5OH$$
$$(COOC_2H_5)COO^- + OH^- = (COO)_2^{2-} + C_2H_5OH$$

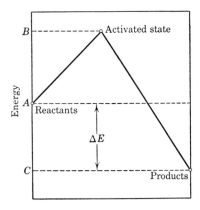

Figure 16-1. Relation between energies of activation and heat of reaction.

Another type of complex reaction is the *side reaction*, in which the reactant or reactants are capable of reacting in more than one way. For example, in the chlorination of benzene at least two reactions proceed at the same time:

$$C_6H_6 + Cl_2 = C_6H_5Cl + HCl$$
$$C_6H_6 + 3Cl_2 = C_6H_6Cl_6$$

In the study of complex reactions it is often possible to regulate the conditions of temperature, concentration, type of catalyst, and solvent in such a way as to reduce the complicating factor to a point where it no longer must be considered in establishing the rate equation.

Reactions often are quite complex. Equations become very complicated, and when solved, it is found that the reaction does not follow a whole-number order. In certain reactions the order may be, for example, 2.8. On the face of it, this may appear absurd, but this is indeed not the case. It simply indicates that the situation is a complex one and, if properly studied, would show the various complicating reactions that go to make up the over-all reaction.

16h. Effect of Temperature on Reaction Speeds. In general, the speed of a reaction is doubled for each 10-degree rise in temperature. Of particular significance to students of biology is the temperature effect in reactions occurring in plant and animal bodies. For example, the rate of beat of an insect's wings is apparently controlled by a master chemical reaction. The change in physiological activity with temperature is a reflection of the change in the velocity of this master reaction with temperature. No doubt the temperature effect on reaction velocity is the controlling factor in the increase in plant growth with increase of temperature. On the other hand, certain reactions in plant and animal bodies appear to decrease above a certain optimum temperature. Such reactions, however, are probably catalyzed by an enzyme that is destroyed at the higher temperatures. Hence it is probable that these are not exceptions to the general rule that relates temperature to reaction rate.

16i. Energy of Activation. The concept of the energy of activation will be approached from the consideration of a simple reaction in which there must be collision between the reacting particles before reaction takes place. From kinetic considerations it is a fairly easy matter to calculate the number of collisions taking place between molecules in a given quantity of the system in a given interval of time. The number of collisions can then be compared with the yield of products. Such considerations lead to the conclusion that only a small fraction of the collisions results in inter-action. The concepts of the activated state and energy of activation have been introduced to explain the small number of fruitful collisions in most chemical reactions. According to present theories, reaction takes place only when the reactants possess an additional amount of energy above that possessed by the average reactant molecules in the system. This additional energy is termed the *energy of activation.* When molecules possess energy of activation, they are said to be in an *activated state.* The energy of activation is the chief factor in determining the speed of a reaction. The greater the needed energy of activation, the fewer the molecules that possess it and the slower the reaction at a given temperature. On the other hand, the higher the temperature, the greater the number of mole-cules in the activated state, other factors being equal. Hence reaction velocities increase with temperature, as noted in 16h, and the rate of increase with temperature can be calculated mathematically. What form the energy of activation takes varies with the nature of the reaction. Sometimes it is simply a question of greater speed. At other times the additional energy effects a rearrangement of the atoms or groups in the molecule to form a more highly reactive isomer. The presence of a catalyst often produces a greater concentration of activated molecules; hence a speeding up of the reaction takes place.

Energy of activation is always positive. That is, energy must be added to produce activated molecules. The products resulting from the inter-actions of activated molecules are also activated, and they must lose this energy of activation when they change to their normal state. Whether the reaction is exothermic or whether it is endothermic depends upon the comparative values of the energy of activation of the products and the reactants. This is illustrated in Figure 16-1. In order for reactants to react, they must acquire an energy of activation equal to *AB*. After reaction the products lose their energy of activation. In the figure this is equal to BC. Here the energy of activation released by the products is greater than the energy of activation absorbed by the reactants. The net effect is an evolution of heat, which would be the heat of reaction if the reaction took place at constant volume. At constant volume no pressure-volume work is done by the system or on the system. The heat of reaction at constant volume is represented by the symbol ΔE. ΔE would be negative and the reaction at constant volume would be exothermic in the reaction illustrated in Figure 16-1. The actual value of ΔE is given by the distance AC. Had the energy of activation of the reactants been larger than the energy of activation of the products, the heat of reaction at constant volume would have been positive and the reaction would have been endothermic.

Mathematically it can be proved and experimentally it has been demonstrated that the energy of activation is related to the velocity constant by the following equations:

$$\frac{d(\ln k)}{dt} = \frac{\Delta E_a}{RT^2} \tag{16-11}$$

$$\ln k = \frac{-\Delta E_a}{RT} + I \tag{16-12}$$

$$\log \frac{k_2}{k_1} = \frac{\Delta E_a}{2.3R}\left(\frac{1}{T_1} - \frac{1}{T_2}\right) \tag{16-13}$$

To calculate the energy of activation, it is necessary only to know the velocity constant at two temperatures. A plot of these values allows the calculation of ΔE_a from the slope of the line by the use of Equation 16-12, or the two sets of values can be substituted in Equation 16-13 and the equation solved for ΔE_a.

CATALYSIS

16j. Criteria of Catalysis. It has already been stated that a *catalyst* is a substance that alters the speed of a reaction. The process of altering the speed of the reaction is termed *catalysis*. In most cases the role of the catalyst is to increase the speed of the reaction, but some are employed to slow down a reaction. These are termed *negative catalysts*.

If the catalyst and reactants form a single phase, the process is called *homogeneous catalysis*. If the catalyst constitutes a different phase, the process is termed *heterogeneous catalysis*. The catalyst itself may be a solid, a gas, or a liquid. But whatever the type of reaction and whatever the nature of the catalyst, the following characteristics are found in all catalytic processes.

1. The catalyst is unchanged in the chemical reaction. This does not mean that the catalyst may not enter into one of the steps in the reaction or even alter the way in which the reaction takes place, but at the completion of the reaction the catalyst is chemically unchanged. If it does enter into the reaction, it may be changed in physical form, for example, from platinum gauze that is smooth to that with a roughened surface, as in the gaseous reaction of ammonia with oxygen. Here the reaction is probably one taking place by chemical adsorption of one or both of the gases on the catalyst surface. An example of a gaseous catalyst that enters into a chemical reaction but comes out unchanged is nitrogen dioxide when used as a catalyst in the lead-chamber process for preparing sulfuric acid. The simple reactions are

$$NO_2 + SO_2 = NO + SO_3$$
$$NO + \tfrac{1}{2}O_2 = NO_2$$
$$\text{Net reaction } \overline{SO_2 + \tfrac{1}{2}O_2 = SO_3}$$

2. The catalyst does not affect the equilibrium position of a reversible reaction. The absence or presence of a catalyst will not affect the final equilibrium concentrations, the only effect being to increase or decrease the time necessary for attainment of the equilibrium. As a corollary, it follows that a given catalyst must affect the speed of both the forward and reverse processes in a reversible reaction to the same extent.

In certain cases it may appear that the catalyst does affect the equilibrium position and the value of the equilibrium constant. In such cases the catalyst is used in large concentration or in large quantity, and the change in the equilibrium constant is due to the effect of the catalyst on the activities of the reactants and products. An example of this is found in the ethyl alcohol-acetic acid-water-ethyl acetate equilibrium discussed in Chapter 9. If an acid is used to speed up the attainment of equilibrium, it is found that the equilibrium constant undergoes changes from the usual value of 4 used for this equilibrium. Here the acid in some manner interacts with the reactants and products to alter their effective concentrations, or activities.

3. The catalyst does not initiate the reaction. This is in reality a corollary to 2. The reaction would take place, however slowly, without the presence of the catalyst, but the course, or manner in which the reaction takes place, may be influenced by it.

A fourth criterion often listed is that only a small quantity of the catalyst is required. Although this is sometimes true, in a great many cases the quantity or concentration of the catalyst does affect appreciably the speed of the reaction. In the inversion of cane sugar the speed of the inversion is proportional to the hydrogen-ion concentration. In many gaseous reactions catalyzed by finely divided metal, or metal in the form of gauze, the extent of the exposed surface determines the speed of the reaction.

16k. Homogeneous Catalysis. Homogeneous catalysis is limited to gaseous and liquid systems. The process in such systems is probably effected in most cases by the formation of intermediate compounds. This is illustrated in 16j in the oxidation of sulfur dioxide. The catalyst is nitrogen dioxide. It oxidizes the sulfur dioxide to sulfur trioxide and in the process is reduced to nitric oxide. The nitric oxide is then reoxidized to nitrogen dioxide by the oxygen of the air.

In liquid systems there are many examples of catalysis that may be grouped under the general heading of *acid-base catalysis.* Two well-known examples are the inversion of cane sugar and the hydrolysis of various esters. Both of these reactions are catalyzed by hydrogen ions, and the strength of the acid used, as well as its concentration, determines the rate of the reaction. For example, a tenth normal solution of dichloro-acetic acid is much more effective in the inversion of cane sugar than a tenth normal solution of acetic acid. The mechanism can be explained on the basis of the Lowry-Brønsted theory. The acid donates a proton to the sugar or other substance undergoing reaction; thus, the reacting molecule is acting in the role of a proton acceptor, or base. A complex is formed, which can be designated as XH^+. It then undergoes reaction to form the products, giving up the proton to the water present to form the H_3O^+. This in turn resupplies the proton to another molecule of X. In such a series of steps the compound XH^+ constitutes the intermediate compound. This type of action is illustrated in the enolization of acetone. The mechanism of the reaction is probably as follows:

$$H^+ + CH_3COCH_3 = CH_3C^+(OH)CH_3 = CH_3C(OH)CH_2 + H^+$$

In addition to the acid-base reactions discussed in the preceding paragraph, many other catalytic reactions take place in the liquid state. Among these are the formation of ethyl ether from ethanol in the presence of sulfuric acid and the decomposition of hydrogen peroxide in the presence of iodide or bromide ions. The mechanism involving the formation of an intermediate compound is often well understood, although sometimes, as in the hydrogen peroxide decomposition, the exact nature of the intermediate compound has not been completely established.

16l. Heterogeneous Catalysis. As already stated, catalysis in which the catalyst is in a different physical state from the reacting materials is termed *heterogeneous catalysis.* The most important of such reactions are the gas phase reactions, which are catalyzed by metal or metal oxides in the form of a powder or a gauze or in a finely divided state on asbestos or a porous surface. Examples of such reactions are found in the contact process for the manufacture of sulfuric acid, wherein the oxidation of the sulfur dioxide is effected in the presence of a platinum catalyst, and in the oxidation of ammonia in the manufacture of nitric acid. Such reactions are of minor importance in biological work and are not discussed in detail. They are undoubtedly surface reactions, the reaction following the adsorption of the reactants on the surface of the catalyst.

An example of heterogeneous catalysis in solution is the decomposition of hydrogen peroxide in aqueous solution by various metals. Another example is the evolution of oxygen by potassium chlorate in the molten condition in the presence of manganese dioxide. Of great importance in biological and medical work is the action of *enzymes*. These substances are colloidal in nature; hence their action can be classed as heterogeneous. Enzymes are discussed in a subsequent paragraph.

16m. Promotors and Inhibitors. Many substances affect the efficiency of a catalyst. In some cases, as in that of arsenic compounds in the contact process for manufacturing sulfuric acid, the activity of the catalyst is completely destroyed. Substances having this effect are called *catalytic poisons*. Other substances merely decrease or retard catalytic activity; they are known as *inhibitors*. Some substances, known as *promotors*, when added to the system containing the catalyst increase the catalytic activity. The reasons for the effects of promotors and inhibitors are not well understood.

16n. Enzymes. As stated in 16l, enzyme action is a type of heterogeneous catalysis, since enzymes are colloidal in nature.

Enzymes are organic compounds produced by living cells. They are highly specific in catalyzing many reactions in and out of plant and animal bodies. Many have been isolated, and all of these have proved to be proteins.

In common with all catalysts, they do not influence the final condition of equilibrium but serve only to increase or decrease the time necessary for the establishment of the final equilibrium state. The mechanism of their operation is quite complex. Undoubtedly many intermediate compounds are formed, but exactly how the enzymes speed up reactions is not well understood. Their action is greatly affected by the environmental conditions. Being proteins, they are amphoteric, and it is not surprising to find that their activity is greatly affected by the pH of the solution. The concentration of other substances, especially electrolytes, often plays a profound part in enzyme activity. Their action is accelerated by increased temperature up to a certain point. After that the activity falls off, probably because of the destruction of the enzyme at the higher temperatures. The presence of inhibitors will decrease enzyme activity and can in certain cases completely destroy it. Such action is probably due to interaction of the inhibitor with the enzyme and results in the production of compounds without catalytic effect. Promotor action is very important in enzyme action. For example, if amylase, an enzyme found in pancreatic juice, is carefully purified, it is found to have no catalytic activity toward starch. But the addition of sodium chloride or potassium chloride restores its activity. There are other similar examples of promotor action. Such substances are termed *coenzymes*. In some cases two enzymes, each of which alone is noncatalytic for a given process, become quite active in the presence of each other.

Enzymes are necessary for the maintenance of all forms of higher life and probably of all forms of life. Their role in digestive processes, disease, and general body functions cannot be overemphasized. Not only are they important in living organisms, but also many industrial and everyday processes depend on their action. One of the most important is the fermentation industry. The use of yeast for breadmaking involves the action of enzymes for the production of carbon dioxide. The souring of milk is brought about by enzymes produced by certain bacteria. A number of catalysts found in plant and animal tissues are given in Table 16-1. The second column shows the reaction for which the enzyme has a specific catalytic effect.

Table 16-1. Enzymes and Reactions that they Catalyze

Enzyme	Reaction Catalyzed
Diastase	Conversion of starch to maltose
Invertase	Conversion of sucrose to dextrose and levulose
Lactase	Conversion of lactose to dextrose and galactose
Maltase	Conversion of maltose to dextrose
Pepsin	Changes of complex proteins to simpler proteins
Steapsin	Conversion of fats to glycerol and the corresponding fatty acid
Trypsin	Hydrolysis of proteins to amino acids
Zymase	Conversion of dextrose to ethanol and carbon dioxide

Of those listed in Table 16-1, diastase and maltase are found in sprouting grain. Invertase and zymase are found in yeast. Lactase, steapsin, pepsin, and trypsin are a few of the many enzymes found in the digestive tracts of the higher animals.

In conclusion note that although the enzymes listed in Table 16-1 are all effective in the breaking down of more complex molecules into simpler molecules, there are enzymes whose action is synthesis, or the formation of more complex molecules, from simpler substances.

REFERENCES

Bull, *Physical Biochemistry*, John Wiley and Sons, New York, 1951, Chapter 3.

Daniels and Alberty, *Physical Chemistry*, John Wiley and Sons, New York, 1961, Chapter 12.

Maron and Prutton, *Principles of Physical Chemistry*, The Macmillan Co., New York, 1958, Chapters 19 and 20.

Moore, *Physical Chemistry*, Prentice-Hall, Englewood Cliffs, New Jersey, 1962, Chapter 8.

Sheehan, *Physical Chemistry*, Allyn and Bacon, Boston, 1961, Chapter 10.

Daniels, Williams, Bender, Alberty, and Cornwell, *Experimental Physical Chemistry*, McGraw-Hill Book Co., New York, 1962, Chapter 7.

Crockford and Nowell, *Laboratory Manual of Physical Chemistry*, John Wiley and Sons, New York, 1956, Experiments 21, 22, and 23.

REVIEW QUESTIONS

1. Discuss some of the factors that affect the speed of a reaction.

2. What are some of the techniques used in the study of reaction kinetics?

3. What is meant by the *order* of a reaction? Distinguish between *zero-*, *first-*, *second-*, and *third-order reactions*. Give some examples of first- and second-order reactions.

4. Explain the differential expression for the velocity of a first-order reaction. Give two forms of the integral expression for a first-order reaction. Explain the significance of the terms in the various equations.

5. Give the fundamental expressions for the velocities of second-order reactions (*a*) when the reacting molecules are of different species and (*b*) when the reacting molecules are the same. What are the two forms of the integral equation for a second-order reaction when the two reacting molecules are the same?

6. What is meant by the *half-life period?* What relationship does the half-life period bear to the initial concentration in first- and second-order reactions? Explain how the half-life period can be used in the determination of the order of a reaction.

7. Discuss how the integral equations for first- and second-order reactions can be used in the plotting procedure for the determination of reaction order.

8. Discuss zero-order reactions. Give the equations for the speed of a zero-order reaction.

9. Why is the velocity constant sometimes referred to as the specific rate constant?

10. Discuss the various types of complex reactions discussed in the text. In what manner is the speed of the reaction affected in each case?

11. Discuss the effect of temperature change on reaction velocity.

12. What is meant by *activation energy* and the *activated state?* Discuss the significance of the differential and integral equations that give the relationship of the velocity constant to temperature.

13. What is *catalysis?* What is meant by the terms *homogeneous catalysis, heterogeneous catalysis, inhibitor, catalytic poison,* and *promoter.*

14. Discuss the general characteristics of catalytic processes. Discuss the effect of the concentration of the catalyst and the quantity of the catalyst on catalytic activity.

15. Discuss the probable mechanism of acid-base catalysis.

16. Discuss intermediate compound formation in catalytic processes.

17. Give several examples of catalytic processes, both heterogeneous and homogeneous, taking place in both the liquid and gaseous states.

18. In general, what are *enzymes?* Name several enzymes and give the reaction that each catalyzes. What is a coenzyme?

19. Why is the pH of a solution of major importance in enzyme action?

20. Discuss the effect of temperature change on enzyme activity.

PROBLEMS

I

1. In a study of the saponification of ethyl acetate in sodium hydroxide solution at 25°C, Walker [*Proc. Roy. Soc.* **A78,** 157 (1906)] found that the velocity constant had a value of 6.5 liters mole^{-1}min^{-1}. If the initial concentrations of the base and ester are 0.02M each, what will be the concentration of the ester at the end of 20 min? How many minutes will be required to reduce the initial concentration by 50 per cent?

2. Using the 20-, 60-, and 100-min data of Example 16-1, calculate the velocity constant for the decomposition of nitrogen pentoxide at 35°C. Using the average value of the constants obtained in this problem and Example 16-1, determine the fraction of the nitrogen pentoxide that would be decomposed in 175 min. Calculate the half-life period at this temperature.

3. From the value of the velocity constant for the saponification of ethyl acetate in sodium hydroxide solution at 25°C given in I-1, calculate the concentration of ethyl acetate when the original concentrations of the ester and the sodium hydroxide are 0.04M and the elapsed time is 20 min.

4. LaMer and Miller [*J. Am. Chem. Soc.* **57,** 2674 (1935)] found that the velocity constant for the decomposition of diacetone alcohol at 25°C, using 0.02M sodium hydroxide as the catalyst, has a value of 0.0455 min^{-1}. Calculate the half-life period of the alcohol in the given concentration of sodium hydroxide at this temperature. Starting with an initial concentration of 0.060 mole per liter, calculate the concentration of diacetone alcohol at the end of 20 min. What fraction will be decomposed at the end of 1 hr?

5. From the data of Example 16-3, calculate the concentration of methyl acetate at the end of 20 min at 25°C when equal volumes of 0.02M solutions of methyl acetate and sodium hydroxide are mixed at this temperature. Calculate the half-life period for these solutions. Calculate the half-life period if the two solutions are 0.04M each in methyl acetate and sodium hydroxide.

6. The specific rate constant for the reaction of 2,4-dinitrochlorobenzene with piperidine has been found by Bunnett and Crockford [*J. Chem. Ed.* **33,** 552 (1956)] to have the values of 1.11 at 25°C and 0.200 at 0°C. The constant is expressed in liters mole^{-1}min^{-1}. Calculate the energy of activation.

7. The values of the velocity constant for the decomposition of nitrogen pentoxide at 25° and 65°C are 3.46 × 10^{-5} and 4.87 × 10^{-3}, respectively, when the constant is expressed in seconds. Estimate the value of the velocity constant when the temperature is 40°C.

II

1. Eyring and Daniels [*J. Am. Chem. Soc.* **52,** 1472 (193)] have found that the velocity constant for the decomposition of nitrogen pentoxide in carbon tetrachloride is 0.469 × 10^{-4} at 25°C, the time being expressed in seconds. Calculate the half-life period at this temperature. What fraction of the initial concentration will remain at the end of (*a*) 40 min and (*b*) 80 min? With an initial concentration of 0.25 mole per liter, what will be the concentration of the pentoxide at the end of 35 min?

2. Calculate the half-life period and the velocity constant for the decomposition of hydrogen peroxide at 25°C in 0.02M KI from the fact that the fraction decomposed at the end of 25 min is 0.497.

3. By a plotting procedure show from the data of Example 16-2 that the decomposition of hydrogen peroxide in aqueous KI solution is a first-order reaction.

4. By a plotting procedure show from the data of Example 16-3 that the saponification of methyl acetate at 25°C is a second-order reaction.

5. Using the data of Example 16-3, calculate the concentration of methyl acetate, hydroxyl ion, and methanol at the end of 30 min when the starting concentrations of ester and sodium hydroxide are 0.04M.

6. Brown and Borkowski [*J. Am. Chem. Soc.* **74,** 1896 (1952)] have found that the values of the velocity constants for the hydrolysis of $(CH_2)_6CCH_3Cl$ in 80 per cent ethanol solution at 0° and 45°C are 1.06 × 10^{-5} and 2.92 × 10^{-3}, respectively, when the time is expressed in seconds. Calculate the energy of activation for the hydrolysis. What will be the value of the velocity constant at 30°C?

SEVENTEEN

Adsorption

The subject of adsorption at various types of interfaces is treated in this chapter. The factors determining the extent of adsorption and the theories explaining its mechanism are given. A number of applications are included.

THE PROCESS OF ADSORPTION

17a. Adsorption at Interfaces. It has long been known that certain forms of charcoal can take up relatively large quantities of many gases and can remove coloring matter from solutions of cane sugar and other organic substances. A similar property is exhibited by silica gel, made by drying a gelatinous precipitate of silicic acid. This substance is particularly effective in removing moisture from air, a property that has resulted in its extensive use in the storage of delicate instruments which might be harmed from contact with moist air. These processes are essentially a concentrating of a chemical substance at an interface between two phases—a property known as *adsorption*. The interface may be one between a solid and a liquid, a solid and a gas, a liquid and a liquid, or a gas and a liquid. The substance upon whose surface the adsorption takes place is called the *adsorbent*. In biological work the most important types of adsorption are those taking place at gas-solid and liquid-solid interfaces.

17b. Absorption of Gases by Solids. The best solid adsorbents are those substances of high porosity, such as finely divided platinum, wood charcoal, and silica gel. They present a large surface area upon which adsorption can take place. Appreciable adsorption, however, can take place on some smooth surfaces, such as those of platinum and glass. It will be recalled that it is an adsorbed film of liquid on a glass surface that causes the rise of water and many other substances in glass capillaries.

338

The process of the adsorption of gases by solids shows the following characteristics:

1. The adsorption is *selective*. Certain gases are adsorbed extensively, others only slightly, and some not at all, by a given adsorbent.

2. The adsorption is *very rapid*. An efficient gas mask is able to remove the harmful ingredients from the air in a fraction of a second. The speed of adsorption, however, depends on the degree of saturation of the adsorbent, being most rapid when only a small fraction of the adsorbent is saturated.

3. The extent of adsorption depends on the *temperature*. The higher the temperature above the critical temperature of a gas, the less it is adsorbed. Oxygen at room temperature is very poorly adsorbed by carbon, since its critical temperature is $-119°C$. On the other hand, chloropicrin, ammonia, and many other gases, well below their critical temperatures at 25°C, are extensively adsorbed. This effect makes the gas mask possible.

4. The extent of the adsorption depends on the *surface area of the adsorbent*. Hence, other factors being equal, the more porous the adsorbent, the greater its adsorbing power.

5. The extent of the adsorption depends on the *chemical nature of the adsorbent* as well as its history. Carbon prepared in various ways shows different degrees of adsorbing ability. Pretreatment and method of preparation determine the porosity of the product as well as its purity.

6. The extent of adsorption per unit weight of adsorbent depends upon the *partial pressure of the adsorbed gas*. The solid, however, will eventually become saturated, and, of course, once that condition has been reached, further increase in pressure will have no effect on the amount taken up. The quantitative relationship between the amount adsorbed and the partial pressure of the gas is discussed in 17d.

7. Adsorption in most cases is *reversible*. In the absence of chemical effects, increasing the pressure will increase the adsorption, and decreasing the pressure will result in a release of adsorbed gas. The same equilibrium will be established whether the final condition is reached by starting with a solid upon which no gas is adsorbed, or with a solid containing more gas than it could normally adsorb at the partial pressure of the experiment.

Table 17-1 gives the data for the adsorption of a number of gases by activated carbon at 15°C.

17c. Adsorption of Solutes by Solids. Charcoal is the most widely used adsorbent for removing substances from solution. It is employed in many manufacturing processes for removing undesirable coloring matter. In general, adsorption from solution shows the same characteristics as adsorption from gases. It is highly selective; either the solvent or the

Table 17-1. Adsorption of Various Gases by Activated Carbon at 15°C*

Gas	Volume (ml at standard conditions)
Chlorine	235
Ammonia	181
Hydrogen sulfide	99
Carbon dioxide	48
Carbon monoxide	9.3
Oxygen	8.2
Nitrogen	8.0
Hydrogen	4.7
Amount of adsorbent = 1 gram	
Pressure of gas = 1 atm	

* The data in this table are taken from McBain, *The Sorption of Gases by Solids*, George Routledge and Sons, Ltd., London, Table 22, page 102.

solute is adsorbed but seldom both. If more than one solute is present, one will probably be adsorbed more than the others. The extent to which a substance is adsorbed is determined largely by the manner in which it affects the interfacial tension of the solvent. Those substances that lower the interfacial tension most are those most strongly adsorbed. In a general way, the more complex the molecule, the more strongly it is adsorbed. Coloring matter is usually made up of molecules more complex than those of the solvent. The higher the temperature, other factors being equal, the less the adsorption. The temperature effect, however, is not as marked as for gaseous adsorption.

The amount of material adsorbed by a given weight of the adsorbent at a given temperature depends on the concentration of the solute, other factors being equal. Just as in the adsorption of gases, there is a definite saturation value for a given adsorbent under a given set of conditions, and further increase of concentration of solute can produce no further adsorption. The quantitative relationship between the amount of solute adsorbed by a given quantity of adsorbent and the concentration of the solute is given in the next section.

17d. The Effects of Partial Pressure and Concentration upon the Extent of Adsorption by Solids. As has been stated, the quantity of gas adsorbed by a given weight of an adsorbent up to the point of saturation is a function of the partial pressure of the gas. This is illustrated in Figure 17-1. In this figure the number of milliliters of ammonia adsorbed by 1 gram of coconut charcoal at 40°C is plotted as a function of the partial pressure of the gas. The curve rises sharply at the lower pressure and flattens out at about 200 mm of mercury. The logarithm of the volume adsorbed by 1 gram of the adsorbent plotted against the logarithm of the pressure of the gas is shown in Figure 17-2. Note that a straight line is obtained for the ascending portion of the concentration-pressure curve but that the points no longer fall on a straight line at the higher pressures where the curve begins to flatten. An equation, purely empirical and based on the straight line of Figure 17-2, has been developed for the relationship of quantity of material adsorbed as a function of pressure. It is known as the Freundlich adsorption equation and is usually expressed in the following form:

$$\frac{x}{m} = kp^b \qquad (17\text{-}1)$$

in which x is the number of grams of substance adsorbed by m grams of the adsorbent when the partial pressure of the adsorbed gas is p. In this expression k and b are empirical constants. On taking the logarithm of both sides, the expression assumes the form

$$\log \frac{x}{m} = \log k + b \log p \qquad (17\text{-}2)$$

In Figure 17-2 the data plotted on the ordinate were obtained by taking the logarithm of the volume occupied by the number of grams adsorbed by 1 gram of the adsorbent, rather than by taking the logarithm of the number of grams adsorbed per gram, as given by the left-hand term of Equation 17-2. Had the left-hand term been plotted against the logarithm of the pressure, the slope of the curve would have been the b constant of

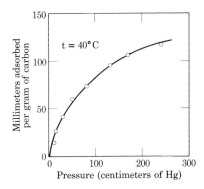

Figure 17-1. Adsorption of ammonia by carbon at 40°C. [Richardson, *J. Am. Chem. Soc.* **39**, 1828 (1917).]

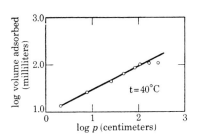

Figure 17-2. Adsorption of ammonia by charcoal at 40°C. [Richardson, *J. Am. Chem. Soc.* **39**, 1828 (1917).]

Equations 17-1 and 17-2, and the intercept on the y axis would have been at the point where the logarithm of the pressure becomes equal to zero.

A somewhat more complex equation based on theoretical considerations has been developed by Langmuir. It is known as the Langmuir adsorption equation and is usually written in the following form:

$$\frac{p}{y} = \frac{1}{a} + \frac{p}{b} \tag{17-3}$$

In this, y is the number of grams adsorbed by 1 gram of the adsorbent, p is the partial pressure of the gas, and a and b are constant. If p/y is plotted against p, a straight line should be obtained.

For solutes, the quantity adsorbed by a given mass of adsorbent is a function of the concentration of the solute up to the point at which saturation is reached. Equations similar to 17-1, 17-2, and 17-3 apply to solute adsorption in approximately the same way that 17-1, 17-2, and 17-3 apply to gaseous adsorption. In these modified equations the partial pressure of the gas is replaced by the concentration of the solute. The following equations are obtained:

$$\frac{x}{m} = kc^b \tag{17-4}$$

$$\log \frac{x}{m} = \log k + b \log c \tag{17-5}$$

$$\frac{c}{y} = \frac{1}{a} + \frac{c}{b} \tag{17-6}$$

The equations may be tested by applying them to the data obtained by Freundlich at 25°C for the adsorption of acetic acid on blood charcoal. These data are given in Table 17-2.

Table 17-2. The adsorption of Acetic Acid by Blood Charcoal at 25°C

Concentration (moles per liter)	Grams Adsorbed by 1 gram of Charcoal
0.0181	0.467
0.0309	0.624
0.0616	0.801
0.1259	1.11
0.2677	1.55
0.4711	2.04
0.8816	2.48
2.7850	3.76

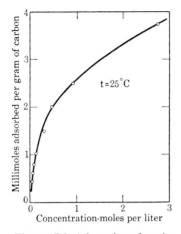

Figure 17-3. Adsorption of acetic acid by blood charcoal at 25°C. [Freundlich, *Z. physik. Chem.* 57, 386 (1906).]

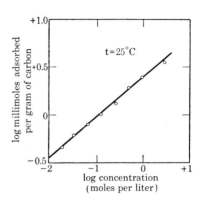

Figure 17-4. Adsorption of acetic acid by blood charcoal at 25°C. [Freundlich, *Z. physik. Chem.* 57, 385 (1906).]

Figures 17-3 and 17-4 show the plots for Equations 17-4 and 17-5. Close agreement with the empirical curves are obtained.

17e. Types of Adsorption. There are two main types of adsorption: *physical* and *chemical*. The latter is often referred to as *chemisorption*. In physical adsorption the adsorbed molecules are held to the surface of the adsorbent in the main by the same type of forces as those existing between gas molecules under high pressure. These are the van der Waals forces, for which the pressure correction term in the van der Waals equation is introduced. Physical adsorption is characterized by a comparatively low heat of adsorption, and for most gases this heat of adsorption is comparable in magnitude to the heat of liquefaction. In physical adsorption the adsorbed layer is often more than one molecule thick, often being multilayer in nature.

Chemisorption postulates actual reaction between the adsorbed molecules and the surface molecules or atoms of the adsorbent. Unlike physical adsorption, complete saturation of the surface would result in only a monomolecular layer. This condition of saturation has been reached in the flat portions of the curves in Figures 17-1 and 17-3. The heat of adsorption in chemisorption is very much higher than the heat involved with physical adsorption.

In many kinds of gaseous adsorption the molecule as a whole is adsorbed. In other cases such as the adsorption of hydrogen on platinum black, the process results in the breakdown of the molecule into atoms. Hydrogen and many other gases in this atomic condition are highly reactive, and the effect of a surface-type catalyst in certain gaseous reactions is probably due to this type of adsorption.

APPLICATIONS OF ADSORPTION

17f. General Applications. The application of adsorption to the removal of undesirable gases from gas mixtures is illustrated by the gas mask. Another application of gaseous adsorption occurs in the production of high vacua. At low temperatures carbon in a finely divided state will adsorb all gases. This makes it possible to lower the temperature of the charcoal sufficiently to produce a vacuum as low as 10^{-4} mm.

An interesting application of the adsorption of gases on the surface of a solid is encountered in the lubricating properties of graphite. In graphite the atoms of carbon are found in layers lying one over the other. The lubricating properties of graphite were formerly explained by saying that the layers would slide over each other readily because no attractive forces existed between the layers. It was found, however, that graphite lost its lubricating property at high altitudes. Subsequent research showed that at ordinary altitudes the pressures of the gases in the air were sufficient to produce an adsorbed layer of gases that eliminated the attractive forces between the layers. At high altitudes or in regions of low pressure, however, desorption took place. This results in the restoration of the attractive forces between the layer of carbon atoms in the graphite crystal. Hence the layers are no longer able to slide over each other and the lubricating property is lost. Graphite is a lubricant only when the surface of the planes of carbon atoms are covered with adsorbed gas.

Many drugs are selectively adsorbed. Their effectiveness in the body is probably due to the ability with which they are adsorbed by various body tissues. The body as a whole is made up of colloidal particles. As will be explained in the chapter on colloids, these particles have enormous surface areas and thus have great adsorptive powers.

Considerable trouble is often encountered in analytical chemistry because of the selective adsorption of certain ions by the precipitate. For example, in the precipitation of barium sulfate, if copper, cadmium, and other metal ions are present, they will be carried down to a considerable extent by the barium sulfate precipitate. Some anions are also adsorbed. This is true of the nitrate ion and therefore barium nitrate is not used as an analytical reagent for the precipitation of the sulfate ion.

Many colored materials, such as those found in sugar solutions, vinegar, and cottonseed oil, are removed with charcoal. Dye material that would otherwise be lost in the waste water may sometimes be recovered by adsorbing it with charcoal. The dye is subsequently dissolved out of the adsorbent with a suitable solvent and then recovered by evaporation of the solvent. The process of dyeing itself often is primarily one of adsorption on the fiber.

The removal of odors from gases is effected by adsorption on charcoal. Special applications are the removal of odors from refrigerators and in general air-conditioning procedures. Carbon dioxide, produced in fermentation, often has objectionable odors that make it unfit for carbonated beverages. These odors may be removed with charcoal.

In this chapter the discussion of adsorption has been limited almost entirely to adsorption at solid-liquid and solid-gas interfaces. Of almost equal importance to students in medicine and biology is adsorption at liquid-liquid interfaces. This type of adsorption plays a major role in *emulsion formation*. Emulsions, suspensions of droplets of one liquid in another, will be discussed in Chapter 18. The operation of liquid-liquid interfacial adsorption will be discussed in that section.

Adsorption at liquid-gas interfaces plays a major role in foam production and foam stabilization. *Foams* are systems in which globules of gas or vapor are enclosed by liquid films. Foams are quite important in the lathering of soap, the operation of fire extinguishers of the foam type, the preparation of foods such as meringues, and in producing the desired foaming of beer. Foams are objectionable in boiler operations and many laboratory procedures involving evaporation and distillation. Stable foams are produced by adding substances termed *foaming agents*. Egg white acts as such an agent in meringues. The froth or foam of carbon dioxide and water produced by foam-type fire extinguishers is stabilized with saponin or licorice extract. These agents are adsorbed in the gas-liquid interface, giving to the liquid surface the characteristics necessary to form a tough coherent film of liquid around the bubbles of gas.

17g. Chromatographic Analysis. The principle of selective adsorption, with the fact that the rate of adsorption varies with a given adsorbent for different materials, is used in *chromatographic analysis*. This is a process by which a mixture of substances is separated into its various components by passage through columns of a suitable adsorbent, a procedure that finds many applications at the present time. Because many of the early applications were with colored substances, the word *chromatographic* was used.

The mixture to be separated is dissolved in a suitable solvent and poured through the tube containing the adsorbent. The component most readily adsorbed is removed in the upper part of the tube. The next most readily adsorbed component is removed next, etc. As a result, the materials are partially separated and are found in various parts of the tube. There is, however, considerable overlapping of the zones in which each substance is principally located. Now pure solvent is poured through the tube. Each substance dissolves slightly as the solvent passes through the tube. It will subsequently be readsorbed lower down in the column, and with proper technique a complete separation of the original components can be effected.

An example of chromatographic analysis is the separation of the components found in the solution produced by extracting a green leaf with petroleum ether or another suitable solvent. By using adsorbing columns of powdered sugar, the carotenes, the two forms of chlorophyll, and other coloring material can be separated. Chromatographic analysis is also used in the separation of some of the vitamins.

After proper separation has been effected, the components can be recovered in their pure form by mechanically separating the column and extracting with the proper solvent. This process of desorption is called *elution*. If the components are sufficiently different in color, the determination of the regions of the adsorbing column in which each is found presents no difficulty. If they are colorless, however, ultraviolet photography or some other method of identification based on a physical property may have to be employed.

Research during World War II resulted in a very ingenious application of chromatographic analysis to the separation of the rare earth elements. Before this time, the separation of the rare earths was very difficult because of their similar chemical and physical properties. However, if an ammonium citrate solution of a definite pH containing mixtures of the rare earths is passed through a column containing the proper organic resins, selective adsorption takes place. With suitable techniques and with the subsequent use of ammonium citrate solution as an eluting agent, an excellent separation can be effected.

REFERENCES

Bull, *Physical Biochemistry*, John Wiley and Sons, New York, 1951, Chapter 10.
Daniels and Alberty, *Physical Chemistry*, John Wiley and Sons, New York, 1961, Chapter 21.
Maron and Prutton, *Principles of Physical Chemistry*, The Macmillan Co., New York, 1958, Chapter 7.
Moore, *Physical Chemistry*, Prentice-Hall, Englewood Cliffs, New Jersey, 1962, Chapter 18.

Daniels, Williams, Bender, Alberty, and Cornwell, *Experimental Physical Chemistry*, McGraw-Hill Book Co., New York, 1962, Chapter 14.

Crockford and Nowell, *Laboratory Manual of Physical Chemistry*, John Wiley and Sons, New York, 1956, Experiment 24.

REVIEW QUESTIONS

1. What is meant by the process of adsorption? Give some examples.

2. What are the characteristics of the process of adsorption of gases by solids? Discuss the factors determining the extent of this type of adsorption.

3. Describe and interpret the shape of the curve produced when the quantity of gas adsorbed by a given weight of adsorbent is plotted against the pressure of the gas.

4. Describe and interpret the shape of the curve produced when the quantity of solute adsorbed from solution by a given weight of adsorbent is plotted against the concentration.

5. What is the Freundlich adsorption equation? What is the Langmuir adsorption equation? What is the significance of each of the terms in these equations? Are these equations theoretically derived or are they empirical?

6. The plotting of what functions will give a straight line in (*a*) gaseous adsorption and (*b*) the adsorption of solutes if the Freundlich and Langmuir equations are used?

7. What are the two main types of adsorption? What is the mechanism of adsorption in each of these types?

8. Discuss some general applications of adsorption.

9. In general, what is chromatographic analysis? What is meant by elution?

EIGHTEEN

Colloidal Systems

This chapter gives a general discussion of colloidal systems, including the classification of colloids and the terms used in discussing colloidal state phenomena. Sols are considered from the standpoints of preparation, purification, and electrical properties. A simple explanation of the Donnan membrane equilibrium is given, and finally there is a discussion of emulsions and gels.

INTRODUCTION TO COLLOIDAL SYSTEMS

18a. Colloidal Systems. A colloidal system comprises two phases, one of which is the continuous dispersion medium and the other the dispersed phase. To have the properties of a colloidal system, the particles of the dispersed phase must have diameters above a certain limit and below another limit. Colloidal particles may be single molecules, termed *macromolecules*, or aggregations of many smaller particles. Among the substances that consist of macromolecules are various proteins and the high-polymer molecules consisting of chains of monomer units.

In the usual process of solution of a chemical compound, the result is a dispersion of the solute throughout the solvent in the form of ultimate particles, which are usually single molecules or ions. Even when the molecule is a bimolecular one such as that formed when benzoic acid dissolves in benzene, the size of the particle is extremely small, and consequently the number of particles per unit of volume is large. Such dissolved particles give specific properties to the solution, such as color and electrical conductivity, and show pronounced effects on the colligative properties of the solution. Such molecular and ionic dispersions produce a *homogeneous* system, since the presence of more than one phase cannot be detected by the physical methods now available.

On the other hand, it is often possible to produce a dispersion of one phase in another in such a manner that the resulting system consists of groups or clusters of molecules distributed throughout the solvent. The particle size in such a dispersion is very much greater than that in a true solution and the number of particles in a given volume is much smaller. In most cases the particles are still too small to be detected by ordinary microscopic means, although the presence of the particles is sometimes indicated by the cloudiness or color of the system. Such dispersions— called *colloidal dispersions*—have many properties quite different from those of true solutions and are therefore usually studied separately in physical chemistry. As stated earlier in this section, the macromolecules must be added to the colloidal aggregates in considering colloidal systems. Colloidal systems occur frequently, and their study is especially important to students of biology and medicine and in the study of polymer chemistry.

Colloidal systems are heterogeneous in that two phases are present. Although the particles do not settle out under the influence of gravity, as in the ordinary coarse-particle suspension, they can be separated by such physical means as centrifuging or by filtering through special filters. By definition, then, a *colloidal suspension is a heterogeneous dispersion of at least two immiscible phases.* The suspension is more or less permanent and possesses certain distinguishing properties, but there is no sharp line of distinction between colloidal suspensions and true solutions and between colloidal suspensions and coarse-grained suspensions. While most macromolecules have the properties of colloidal suspensions, they also possess some of the properties of true solutions.

18b. Terms Employed. In a discussion of colloidal systems the term *dispersed phase* refers to that substance dispersed through the *dispersion medium*. In other words, the dispersed phase is *discontinuous*, whereas the dispersion medium is *continuous*. In milk, for example, the fat globules are a dispersed phase and water is the dispersion medium. The dispersed phase is often called the *internal phase*, and the dispersion medium is called the *external phase*. The term *sol* is applied to the dispersion of a solid in a liquid, solid, or gaseous medium. The dispersion of a solid in a liquid is often termed a *colloidal solution*. If the dispersion medium is a gas, the resulting sol is termed a *solid aerosol*. If the dispersed phase is a liquid and the dispersion medium a gas, the resulting sol is termed a *liquid aerosol*. A dispersion of a liquid in a liquid is termed an *emulsion*. When the colloidal system becomes fairly rigid, it is referred to as a *gel*. Gelatin in water at low temperatures usually exists in the form of a gel. Other types of colloidal dispersions have special names and are listed in Table 18-1.

18c. Classification of Colloidal Systems. Colloidal systems can best be classified from the standpoint of the natures of the dispersion medium and

Table 18-1. Types of Colloidal Systems*

Dispersed Phase	Dispersion Medium	Name	Typical Examples
Solid	Liquid	Sol	Gold in water, arsenic trisulfide in water, sulfur in water
Liquid	Liquid	Emulsion	Water in benzene, milk, mayonnaise
Gas	Liquid	Foam	Froth on beer, meringue, whipped cream
Solid	Solid	Solid sol	Ruby glass, certain gems
Liquid	Solid	Solid emulsion	Milk quartz, opal
Gas	Solid	Solid foam	Pumice, lava
Solid	Gas	Solid aerosol	Smoke, volcanic dust, ammonium chloride fumes
Liquid	Gas	Liquid aerosol	Fog, mist

* Adapted from Weiser, *Colloid Chemistry*, 2nd Edition, John Wiley and Sons, 1949, Table 2, page 3.

the dispersed phase. There are eight *types* or *classes* based on this system of classification. These are given in Table 18-1. Typical examples of each class are included. A colloidal dispersion of a gas in a gas is an impossibility because all gases are mutually soluble in one another. Macromolecules have not been included in Table 18-1.

18d. General Characteristics. Certain general characteristics distinguish colloidal systems from true solutions and coarse suspensions. A brief discussion of these characteristics follows.

PARTICLE SIZE. In general, the particles of a coarse dispersion have a diameter greater than $0.5\ \mu$ ($1\ \mu = 1 \times 10^{-4}$ cm) and are visible under the microscope. Colloidal dispersions range in particle size from this value to a diameter of 1 millimicron ($1\ m\mu = 1 \times 10^{-7}$ cm). Particles below $1\ m\mu$ in diameter are considered to be molecular dispersions or true solutions.

FILTERABILITY. Ordinary filtration procedures will remove the particles from a coarse dispersion but will not remove colloidal particles. Colloidal particles can often, however, be removed by specially designed filters of extremely fine porosity, termed *ultrafilters*, which are usually prepared from very finely divided ceramic materials. This process of separation is termed *ultrafiltration* and is discussed in greater detail later in this chapter.

DIFFUSIBILITY. Ordinary suspensions and colloidal suspensions, unlike true solutes, have little power of diffusion. This is due to the huge size of the colloidal particles as compared to ordinary solute particles. The diffusibility of colloids is discussed in detail in 18f.

APPEARANCE. In appearance colloidal dispersions often seem as clear as true solutions. Again, they may be quite opaque, as iced tea sometimes appears after it has stood for some time. If, however, the apparently clear colloidal system is illuminated by a beam of light and observed at right angles to the path of the beam, even the clear colloidal solution will often take on a cloudy appearance. This phenomenon is known as the *Tyndall effect* and the observed cloudy path of the light through the colloidal solution is termed a *Tyndall beam*. Such a beam is illustrated in Figure 18-1. The Tyndall effect is discussed in detail in 18e.

SURFACE AREA. The total surface area of the particles in a colloidal system is enormous, compared with an equal mass of matter in the usual coarse-grained size. This can be demonstrated mathematically by taking a centimeter cube of material and dividing it into an increasing number of smaller cubes. The increase in surface area with decreasing particle size is shown in Table 18-2.

Table 18-2. Effect of Subdivision on Surface Area*

Number of Cubes	Length of Edge		Total Surface Area
1	1 cm	6 cm^2	0.93 sq in.
10^3	1.0 mm	60 cm^2	9.3 sq in.
10^6	0.1 mm	600 cm^2	93.0 sq in.
10^9	0.01 mm	6000 cm^2	6.5 sq ft
10^{12}	1.0 μ	6 m^2	64.6 sq ft
10^{15}	0.1 μ	60 m^2	645.8 sq ft
10^{18}	0.01 μ	600 m^2	717.6 sq yd (about $\frac{1}{7}$ acre)
10^{21}	1.0 mμ	6000 m^2	7176.0 sq yd (about $1\frac{1}{2}$ acre)

* Adapted from Weiser, *Colloid Chemistry*, 2nd Edition, John Wiley and Sons, 1949, Table 4, page 7.

The last three lines of Table 18-2 include particles of colloidal size. Of course, the data in this table were calculated on the assumption that

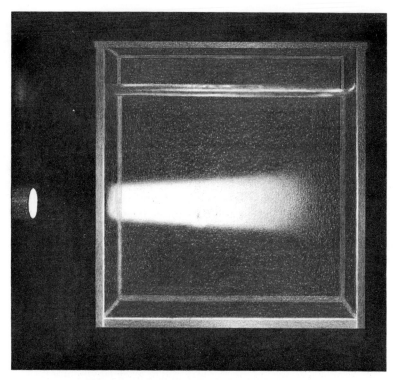

Figure 18-1. Tyndall cones in a hydrophobic sol.

each particle was a solid cube. If the colloidal particle is spongy, a much larger surface area results. Because of the great surface area, colloidal systems show extensive adsorption of foreign materials. If the adsorbed particles are ions, then the colloidal particle is likewise charged.

SURFACE CHARGE. Many of the properties characteristic of colloidal particles are due to surface charge. The means by which this charge is acquired and the electrical properties of colloidal particles are discussed in Part C.

18e. Optical Properties. In 18d it was stated that when a colloidal suspension is illuminated by a beam of light and observed at right angles to the beam, a cloudy appearance is often observed in the path of the light. This was represented in Figure 18-1. As stated, this phenomenon is known as the Tyndall effect and the beam is termed a Tyndall beam. The same effect is observed when a beam of sunlight shines through a narrow opening into a dark room. The presence of dust particles in the air is made apparent by the luminosity of the beam, and if no dust particles are present, no beam is observed. Likewise, a beam of light is not made luminous by the particles of a true solution. Whenever this type of beam is observed, colloidal particles are present. All but the smallest colloidal particles show this phenomenon.

Although the Tyndall beam appears simply as a luminous path of light when viewed by the naked eye, observation by an *ultramicroscope* shows that the beam consists of a series of discrete tiny bright spots. Each spot indicates the presence of a colloidal particle. Thus a colloidal particle too small to be seen by itself produces an effect that can be observed. Hence the number of the particles in a given volume can be counted and their movement observed. The ultramicroscope uses an intense horizontal beam of light, which is brought to a focus in the colloidal dispersion. The focus of the light is observed by a regular microscope whose optical axis is at right angles to the beam. The background of the field is dark, and the presence of the colloidal particles results in a series of bright spots of light against the dark background. Since the actual particles are not visible, their exact shape and size cannot be determined directly although in the case of large molecules some conclusions concerning their size and shape can be drawn. Their mass and size, however, can be estimated by counting the number of particles resulting from a given mass of the colloidal material dispersed in a given volume. It is possible to extend the limits of detection to extremely small particles by using a quartz lens, a shorter wavelength of light, and special photographic techniques.

The invention of the *electron microscope* has added greatly to the knowledge of the size and shape of very small particles. The operation of the electron microscope is based on the fact that a beam of electrons under a constant voltage has the properties of a beam of light. The electric and magnetic systems in the microscope focus the electron beam on a photographic plate. This focused beam is allowed to pass through the specimen being studied. Thus a picture of the subject is obtained. With such an instrument it is possible to obtain photographs under optimum conditions that show a 100,000-fold magnification. This instrument has made possible the actual photographing of a number of viruses and permits a detailed study of the shapes of bacteria. Also, the size and shape of many colloidal particles, such as paint pigments and abrasives, can be determined.

18f. Kinetic Behavior. Brownian Motion. In 1827 the botanist Robert Brown observed that pollen grains suspended in water show a ceaseless and haphazard motion. If a single particle is observed, it moves in a continuous series of short, straight paths, as illustrated in Figure 18-2. This type of motion is known as *Brownian motion*. It is observable in suspensions of certain gums, such as mastic, in water, and also when

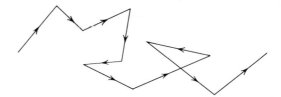

Figure 18-2. Successive movements of a particle in a colloidal suspension.

smoke is examined with a microscope under proper optical conditions. Brown concluded that the motion was not due to currents in the fluid or gas but was a property of the particles themselves.

It is now known that the motion is caused by collisions of the molecules of the liquid or gas with the suspended particles. It will be recalled from the study of the kinetic theory and the study of liquids that particles in the liquid and gaseous state are in constant motion travelling in straight lines until they collide with some other particle. At a given temperature the kinetic energy of a particle has a certain average value that is a function of its speed and mass. The bombardment of the colloidal particles by the molecules of the medium results in their acquiring the same kinetic energy as that of the bombarding molecules. Since the mass of a colloidal particle is large and the speed is small, compared to a molecule, the motion of the colloidal particle can be observed through a microscope. If the colloidal particle is in the larger size range, single collisions will have little effect, and because of its size it will on the average be bombarded equally from all sides. Changes in direction result when the number of bombardments on one side becomes momentarily larger than the bombardments from the other side.

Now, as the particles get increasingly smaller, the effect of single collisions becomes sufficient to cause the particle to change its direction. Therefore, with a sufficiently small particle, a rapid vibrational motion is superimposed on the linear motion. It is this vibrational effect, due to the single collisions, that is used in one of the procedures for determining the value of Avogadro's number.

Just as solute particles will diffuse in a liquid from a region of high concentration to one of lower concentration and gas molecules will distribute themselves evenly throughout the space in which the gas is confined, in the same manner colloidal particles will diffuse from a region of higher to a region of lower concentration. There is, however, one essential difference. The slower motion of the colloidal particles results in a much lower rate of diffusion. Furthermore, since the rate of diffusion is affected by the mass and shape of the colloidal particles, the process of diffusion can be employed to separate colloids and also to determine their size and shape.

The rate of diffusion can be determined by several methods. Direct chemical analysis of the suspension can be made at definite time intervals and at definite distances from the point of initial diffusion. The colloidal particles alter the index of refraction of the system, and the change in this property can be used to determine the rate of diffusion. Another method makes use of the change in the light-absorbing power with the movement of the colloidal particles. Movement can be detected with the ultramicroscope, or the particles can actually be photographed by the use of the electron microscope.

A mathematical equation relating the rate of diffusion of a colloid in terms of the radius of the diffusing particles, the temperature, the viscosity of the medium, and Avogadro's number has been developed by Einstein. With this expression the size of the particles can be determined from diffusion data. Conversely, if the rate of diffusion of particles of known radius can be determined, the expression can be used to determine Avogadro's number. This is one of the standard methods for this calculation.

18g. Osmotic Pressure of Colloids. Osmotic pressures, as well as freezing-point lowerings and boiling-point elevations produced by colloidal particles, are quite small. This is, of course, due to the large size of the particles. The number of particles produced by a given weight of colloid is much less than the number produced in a molecular solution containing the same weight of solute. Nevertheless, the effects exist, and, with proper care, osmotic-pressure measurements can be used to determine the average weight of the particles in a colloidal suspension. One of the major difficulties in such a measurement is encountered in trying to free the colloidal system from the electrolytes usually present. The smallest trace of electrolyte may have a greater effect on the osmotic pressure than the colloid itself. One method of overcoming this difficulty is to separate the colloidal suspension from pure water by a membrane impermeable to the colloid but permeable to the ions of the electrolyte or electrolytes present. After the ions have distributed themselves evenly throughout the two solutions, the osmotic pressure of each is measured. The osmotic pressure due to the colloidal particles is then the difference between the two measured pressures. This method has been used to measure the average molecular weight of egg albumen and hemoglobin. The value so obtained for hemoglobin was 67,000.

18h. Sedimentation of Colloidal Particles and the Ultracentrifuge. Because of their large mass colloidal particles tend to settle out in a gravitational field. This sedimentation is opposed by diffusion. If a colloidal dispersion is allowed to stand a sufficiently long time, a state of equilibrium results in which there is a greater concentration of the colloidal particles at the lower levels. Moreover, the larger particles will tend to be more concentrated in the lower levels than the lighter particles. Well-established formulas make possible the determination of particle size and mass from sedimentation data.

While gravitational effects are observable only with large particles, such effects can be greatly increased by the use of centrifugal force. For this purpose an instrument known as an *ultracentrifuge* is employed. With it centrifugal forces many thousand times the effect of gravity can be obtained. Speeds of 50,000 rpm are often used.

Optical methods are used to determine the rate of sedimentation, the movement of the colloidal particles being recorded on a photographic plate.

The principal use of the ultracentrifuge in the study of colloids is in the determination of their molecular weights. These molecular weights can be determined by one of two general methods. The speed of the centrifuge can be made large and the rate of sedimentation studied. Such a determination can usually be made in a few hours. The second method consists in rotating the centrifuge at a slower rate and determining the distribution of the particles in the centrifugal field. By the proper combination of data not only the mass of the average particle but also its size can be determined. The ultracentrifuge has been particularly effective in the study of the particle size and weight of proteins in both normal and pathological sera, toxins and antitoxins, and viruses. The procedures have also been applied to the study of the composition of complex ions in solutions of heavy metal salts.

SOLS.   THEIR PREPARATION AND PURIFICATION

18i. Classification of Sols. A sol is a dispersion of a solid in a solid, gas, or liquid. Of these, the last is by far the most important and the discussion that follows is limited to this classification. Sols are classified according to the liquid that comprises the dispersion medium. If the solid is dispersed in water, the system is termed a *hydrosol*. If alcohol is the dispersion medium, the sol is termed an *alcosol*. If the colloidal particles attract water and form a gelatinous mass, the hydrosol is called a *hydrophilic sol*. On the other hand, if the colloidal particles do not attract water to form a gelatinous mass, the hydrosol is called a *hydrophobic sol*. Examples of hydrophilic sols are the hydrous oxides and sols of starches and proteins. Hydrophobic sols are formed when many of the metals and salts, such as silver chloride and barium sulfate, are dispersed in water.

Sometimes the more general terms *lyophilic* (solvent-attracting) and *lyophobic* (solvent-repelling) are used instead of the less general terms hydrophilic and hydrophobic.

18j. Preparation. Hydrophobic sols are prepared by two general methods, *dispersion* and *condensation*. In the dispersion method large aggregates of matter are broken down into particles of colloidal size, whereas in the condensation method colloidal particles are built up from ions and molecules. A discussion of some of the special methods for each general type follows.

Dispersion Methods

MECHANICAL DISINTEGRATION. The mechanical disintegration of large aggregates to particles of colloidal size is carried out in a *colloid mill*. The effective parts consist of two rapidly rotating disks moving in opposite directions. These shear and pulverize the particles until they become of colloidal size. The colloid mill is used in the preparation of many commercial products as well as of colloidal systems in the laboratory. Paint pigments, for example, must have a small enough size to form a fairly stable suspension in linseed oil or other dispersing media.

ELECTROLYTIC DISINTEGRATION. This type of procedure is carried out in an electrolytic cell, the cathode of which is made of the metal to be dispersed. The electrolyte is a solution of sodium hydroxide, and a high-current density is employed. In such a cell sodium is discharged at the cathode and forms an alloy with the metal. The sodium in this alloy is immediately attacked by the water in the solution. In the ensuing disintegration of the alloy, the metal is dispersed in colloidal form in the electrolytic solution.

PEPTIZATION. The general term *peptization* is defined as any process that changes a material from a noncolloidal to a colloidal condition. The term, however, is usually restricted to processes in which a material is disintegrated to particles of colloidal size by the action of a solvent or some added substance termed a *peptizing agent*.

Peptization, in general, depends upon the adsorption of the dispersion medium by the dispersed phase. This is most likely to occur with substances that form lyophilic sols. Starch, dextrin, agar, and soap are peptized readily by water. They are all hydrophilic and adsorb water readily. Cellulose nitrate is lyophilic toward a number of organic solvents, hence is peptized by such solvents as amyl acetate and acetone. In these examples the solvent itself is the peptizing agent. Dried blood serum or

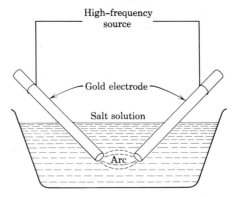

Figure 18-3. Production of colloidal gold by the arc process.

plasma, prepared by removing the corpuscles and certain other components from whole blood, is made ready for transfusion by peptization with water.

Substances such as silver chloride and many other salts and oxides are peptized by adsorbed ions. The general procedure in preparing sols by this method consists in precipitating them in a condition that is somewhat colloidal. The precipitate is then washed and treated with the proper electrolyte. A positively or negatively charged colloid results, depending upon which ion is preferentially adsorbed.

Condensation Methods

ARC PROCESS. In this process a high-frequency alternating current is passed between two metal electrodes in a suitable solvent. Figure 18-3 shows an arrangement for the production of a gold sol in water. The high heat of the arc vaporizes the metal, which then condenses in the solution in particles of colloidal size.

COLLOIDAL FORMATION BY REACTIONS IN SOLUTIONS. A number of reactions in solutions may be used to produce colloidal dispersions. The general method is described by considering some typical examples.

Hydrous oxide sols can often be prepared by allowing a salt of the metal involved to be hydrolyzed in aqueous solution, usually at a comparatively high temperature. For example, if a concentrated ferric chloride solution is added dropwise to boiling water, a colloidal suspension of ferric oxide is formed.

The *interaction of ions* under controlled conditions may sometimes be used to form a sol. A colloidal dispersion of silver chloride results when a dilute silver nitrate solution is added to a dilute solution of sodium chloride. Many sulfide sols, such as arsenious sulfide, can be prepared by passing hydrogen sulfide slowly into a suspension of the oxide.

Oxidation or *reduction* carried out under controlled conditions often produces sols. A gold sol may be prepared by reducing gold chloride with formaldehyde or hydroxylamine in an aqueous solution.

SOLVENT REPLACEMENT. A solvent is added to a solution containing a solute that is to be condensed to particles of colloidal size. The solute must not be soluble in the added solvent, but the two solvents must be completely miscible. Colloidal-sized particles of solute may form as the solute is "salted out." If ethanol is added to a solution of calcium acetate in water, a fairly hard jelly is produced. This jelly contains the added alcohol and will serve as a fuel. This procedure is used in the commercial production of "solid alcohol" or "canned heat."

18k. Purification. As shown later in this chapter, the presence of electrolytes in a colloidal suspension tends to precipitate the colloid. Hence to produce a stable sol, it is necessary to remove as many dissolved ions as possible. The purification of the sols from the ions present is effected by two main methods: ultrafiltration and dialysis.

In 18d a brief discussion of the general characteristics of colloidal suspensions is given. It is pointed out that although colloidal particles cannot be removed from the solution by ordinary means they can often be removed by *ultrafiltration. Ultrafiltration is the process of separating the colloidal particles from the solvent and solutes present by specially prepared filters, which are permeable to all substances present except the colloidal particles.* Many types of ultrafilters are in use. *Pasteur* filters made of fine unglazed porcelain can be used for the removal of bacteria. *Bechhold* filters, used extensively in biological work, are made by impregnating a cloth or paper framework with nitrocellulose. Pressure or suction is often applied to speed up the process of ultrafiltration. A biological example of ultrafiltration is the removal of water and other substances from the blood through the glomeruli in the kidneys.

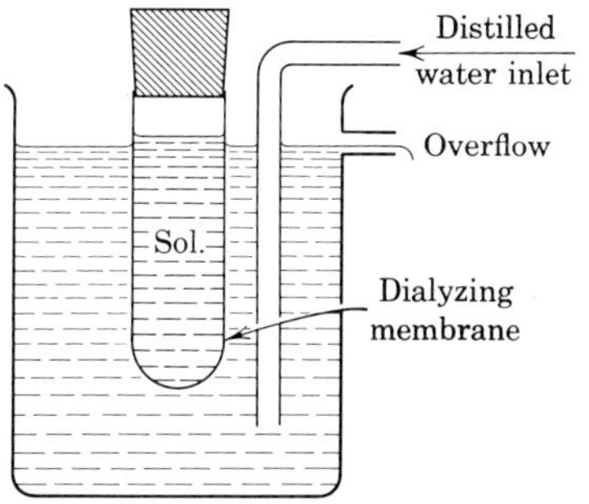

Figure 18-4. A simple dialyzing apparatus.

Dialysis is the process of removing a dissolved substance from a colloidal system by means of diffusion through a suitable membrane. The process is illustrated in Figure 18-4. The sac or membrane containing the colloidal

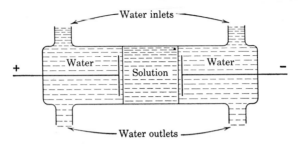

Figure 18-5. Electrodialysis apparatus.

system is made from one of the following: collodion, certain animal membranes, cellophane, nitrocellulose, or some similar substance. This membrane is permeable to the ions and other solute particles present in the solution but impermeable to the colloidal particles. Fresh water is continuously passed into the vessel in which the sac is suspended, for the rate of diffusion of the electrolyte through the membrane will depend on the difference in the ionic concentrations on the two sides of the membrane. The process can be hastened by the proper warming of the solution.

A modification of this procedure is known as *electrodialysis*. This is illustrated in Figure 18-5. Electrodes are so placed with relation to the membrane or membranes that the speeds of the ions are greatly increased by having them move under the influence of an electric field, the positive ions moving to the cathode and the negative ions to the anode.

SOLS: THEIR ELECTRICAL PROPERTIES

18l. Origin of the Surface Change. As stated earlier in this chapter, one of the distinguishing characteristics of colloidal particles is the presence of a charge on their surface. Certain colloidal particles, such as those of ferric oxide hydrosol, are positively charged, whereas others, such as those of an arsenious sulfide hydrosol, are negatively charged. Proteins and other similar types are amphoteric and may be either negatively or positively charged, depending on the pH of the solution and certain other factors.

There are two main methods by which the surface charge is acquired. In one of these the charge results from *direct ionization* of surface groups on the surface of the particles. This is true of proteins, which owe their charge to a great extent to ionization of the molecules in the surface of the colloidal particle. Congo red, as well as a number of other dyes, acquires a charge through the same type of process.

The second procedure is the acquiring of a charge through selective adsorption of ions from the solution in which the particles are suspended. For example, silver iodide sol adsorbs iodide ions rather than the positive ions with which the iodide ions are associated in the solution.

Figure 18-6 is a representation of a charged colloidal particle. In this case the charge is explained principally by the selective adsorption of positive ions. Around the particle there is an accumulation of negative ions because of the electrostatic attraction of the adsorbed layer of positive ions for the negative ions in the solution. Part of these negative ions, as indicated by the dotted line, tend to form a second layer that remains fixed to the colloidal particle. This layer, somewhat diffuse in nature, together with the positive layer, forms what is termed a *Helmholtz Double Layer*. Outside the dotted line all negative ions are freely movable and constitute an ion atmosphere analogous to that postulated by Debye and Hückel to exist around ions in solution.

Because of the surface charge a potential exists between the colloidal particle and the solution. That part of the potential existing between the fixed negative layer, indicated by the dotted line, and the solution as a whole is termed the *electrokinetic*, or *zeta* (ζ), *potential*. This potential plays a major part in the electrical properties of colloidal systems.

18m. Electrophoresis. Since colloidal particles are usually charged, they will move under the influence of an electric field just as ions do, the negatively charged colloidal particles moving toward the anode and the positively charged particles moving toward the cathode. This movement is termed *cataphoresis* or *electrophoresis*. The movement can be observed with the ultramicroscope or by the actual movement of a colloidal boundary. Thus we can determine the charge on the particular colloid, and,

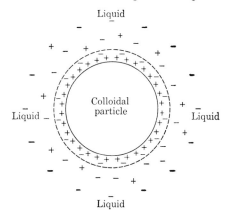

Figure 18-6.   Electrical double layer around a colloidal particle.

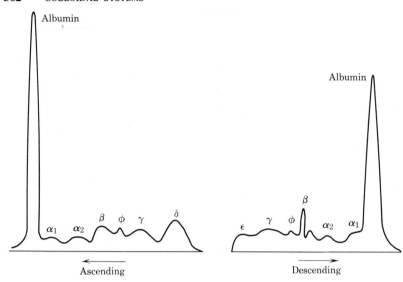

Schlieren patterns for human blood plasma

Figure 18-7.   Schlieren patterns for human blood plasma.

by observing the speed of the particles in an electric field of known strength, the mass of the individual particles can be calculated.

Electrophoresis often can be employed for the analysis of mixtures of proteins, nucleic acids, etc. In a properly designed apparatus and with the careful control of the concentrations of the ions in the solution, the various components of the mixtures, moving as they do with different speeds, will become separated in the electrophoretic tube. The refractive index of the solution at different points is measured and the refractive-index gradient is plotted against the distance in the cell. One such pattern is shown in Figure 18-7 for human blood plasma [R. A. Alberty, Introduction to Electrophoresis, *J. Chem. Educ.* **25**, 426, 619 (1948)]. The various proteins are represented by the peaks in the diagram. Thus we find albumen, α_1, α_2, β and γ globulins, and fibrinigen ϕ. The areas under the peaks are very nearly proportional to the concentrations of the proteins. Peaks are due to salt effects in the solution and not to another protein. The representation in Figure 18-7 is termed an *electrophoretic schlieren pattern*.

18n. Electro-Osmosis. If the colloidal particles are prevented from moving on the application of an electric field, the solvent moves in a direction opposite to that in which the colloidal particles would normally move. Such a flow of solvent is termed *electro-osmosis*.

If a liquid is forced through a capillary, for example, in the blood capillaries or the arteries, a potential develops between the ends of the capillary. This is termed a *streaming potential*. Since in living systems there is a constant ebb and flow of liquids, streaming potentials play an important part in many biological phenomena. The same phenomenon is observed when a liquid is forced through porous material. In a sense this is the reverse of electro-osmosis.

18o. The Precipitation of Colloids. The stability of colloidal systems is due in major part to the fact that particles of like charge repel each other. The particles of a particular colloid have the same charge, and the repulsive forces between these similarly charged particles prevent coagulation or flocculation. Any procedure that will destroy the surface charge produces coagulation.

One method of precipitating a colloid consists of adding a colloid of opposite charge. Precipitation results if positively charged ferric oxide sol is added to negatively charged arsenious sulfide. This is an example of *mutual precipitation of colloids.*

Although the presence of small amounts of electrolytes is necessary for the formation of the surface charge that stabilizes many colloidal systems, the presence of the same electrolytes in greater concentrations will cause the precipitation of the colloidal particles. As would be expected, negatively charged sols are precipitated by positive ions, and positively charged sols, by negative ions. Moreover, the greater the valence of the precipitating ion, the more effective its action. For example, divalent calcium ions and barium ions are many times more efficient than singly charged sodium or potassium ions in the precipitation of negatively charged arsenious sulfide. The triple-charged aluminum ion is far more efficient than the divalent positive ions. Similarly, positively charged proteins are precipitated more efficiently by divalent anions than by monovalent ions. Although the valency of the ion plays a major role in colloidal precipitation, there is a specific action on the part of the individual ions. Some monovalent ions are more effective than others. The arrangement of a given group of ions in the order of their precipitating power is termed a *Hofmeister series*. One such series for some of the monovalent anions is

$$C_2H_3O_2^- > Cl^- > NO_3^- > Br^- > I^- > CNS^-$$

18p. Protective Colloids. Lyophobic sols can often be stabilized by the addition of a lyophilic sol. The added colloid in such a case is termed a *protective colloid*. The protective action is supposed to be due to the fact that negatively charged hydrophilic or water-attracting colloids will often form a coating around the negative hydrophobic colloid. In like manner, positively charged hydrophilic colloids will often form a coating around positively charged hydrophobic colloids. The hydrophobic colloid then acts as a hydrophilic colloid and is less easily precipitated by the properly charged ions. This protecting ability is a characteristic property of many colloidal substances. The action of protective colloids plays an important part in many biological systems. It is used in a number of biological preparations and pharmaceutical products. Argyrol is a colloidal silver and silver oxide sol having pronounced antibacterial properties. The colloidal suspension is stabilized by certain protective colloids.

The fact that the protective ability of a colloid is a characteristic property has been adapted to the development of a method of identifying some colloids. This method sets up an arbitrary measure of the protective power known as the *gold number*. The gold number is defined as the *number of milligrams of the dry hydrophilic substance that will just prevent a color change from red to blue of 10 ml of a gold sol on the addition of 1 ml of 10 per cent sodium chloride solution*. The change in color of the gold sol indicates a partial flocculation. The gold numbers of a few hydrophilic sols are given in Table 18-3.

Table 18-3. Gold Numbers of Some Hydrophilic Sols*

Substance	Gold Number
Gelatin	0.005–0.01
Egg albumen	0.08–0.10
Gum arabic	0.10–0.15
Soluble starch	10–15

* Adapted from Weiser, *Colloid Chemistry*, 2nd Edition, John Wiley and Sons, 1949, Table 62, page 288.

The gold number of the spinal fluid can be used as a diagnositic test for meningitis; the gold number in a person suffering from this disease is greatly different from one not so afflicted.

18q. The Isoelectric Point. In 11k it is shown that proteins belong to that class of substances known as ampholytes. These substances in the undissociated state exist in the form of hybrid ions, which may undergo ionization to produce either anions or cations, depending on whether they interact with a proton or a hydroxyl ion. The following equations show how these two forms of ionization take place in a solution of glycine, a simple amino acid:

$$NH_3^+—CH_2COO^- + H_3O^+ \rightleftharpoons NH_3^+—CH_2—COOH + H_2O$$
$$NH_3^+—CH_2—COO^- + OH^- \rightleftharpoons NH_2—CH_2—COO^- + H_2O$$

The same types of reactions can take place in a protein. A positively charged ion produced by the proton interaction would migrate to the cathode in electrophoresis. On the other hand, the negatively charged ion produced by interaction with the hydroxyl ion would migrate to the anode. As seen in 11k, reactions of this type have characteristic ionization constants. The comparative magnitudes of these constants will determine whether the positive ion, the negative ion, or the hybrid ion will predominate in a solution of a given pH. There is one value of pH at which the protein will exist almost entirely in the form of the hybrid. At this point the positive and negative ions will have equal concentrations, and under these circumstances electrophoresis will not take place. At a pH above this value one of the ions will predominate, and the protein will migrate in an electric field. At a lower pH the other ion will predominate, and the protein will migrate in the opposite direction. *The pH at which the ampholyte does not migrate toward either pole is termed the isoelectric point of the substance.* This value is of major importance in the chemistry of proteins. The proteins are least stable at their isoelectric points; hence they are more easily coagulated at this pH. The isoelectric point for egg albumen is 4.8, that of hemoglobin 6.8, and that of lecithin 2.6.

18r. Donnan's Membrane Equilibrium. The *Donnan theory of membrane equilibrium* is concerned with the equilibria existing in systems that consist of a membrane separating two electrolytes, of which at least one contains an ion that cannot diffuse through the membrane. Although such equilibria can be quite complicated, a very simple case is used to illustrate the theory. Consider a membrane separating a solution of sodium chloride and Na^+R^-, in which R^- is an ion that cannot diffuse through the membrane. It is assumed that both electrolytes, Na^+Cl^- and Na^+R^-, are completely dissociated. The initial condition is represented diagrammatically in Figure 18-8(a). Since both the sodium ions and the chloride ions can penetrate the membrane, there will be a tendency for these two ions to diffuse through the membrane. The rate of diffusion is proportional to the activities of the ions. Hence the rate of diffusion from the left side to the right side is given by the expression

$$\text{Rate 1} \propto [Na^+]_1[Cl^-]_1 \quad \text{and} \quad \text{Rate 1} = k[Na^+]_1[Cl^-]_1$$

The rate of diffusion from the right side to the left side is given by the expression

$$\text{Rate 2} \propto [Na^+]_2[Cl^-]_2 \quad \text{and} \quad \text{Rate 2} = k[Na^+]_2[Cl^-]_2$$

These expressions are similar to those obtained for the forward and reverse rates of reversible reactions in Chapter 9. At equilibrium the rates of flow through the membranes from the two sides are equal. Therefore, at equilibrium Rate 1 equals Rate 2 and

$$[Na^+]_1[Cl^-]_1 = [Na^+]_2[Cl^-]_2 \qquad (18\text{-}1)$$

In words, the state of equilibrium is one in which the ionic product of the concentrations of the sodium and chloride ions is the same on the two sides of the membrane.

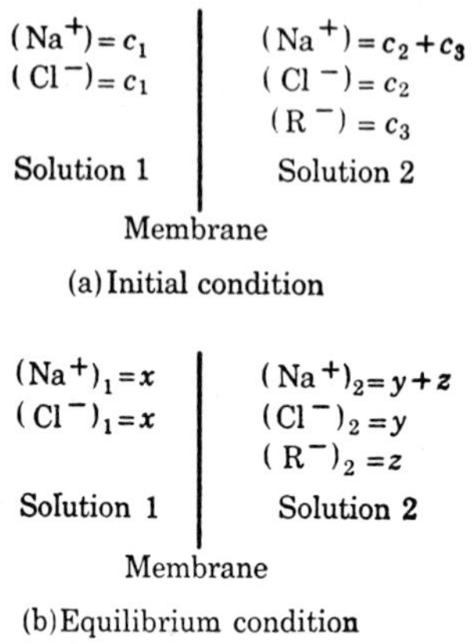

When equilibrium is established, let x equal the concentrations, or more exactly, the activities of the sodium and chloride ions in Solution 1.

$$x = [Na^+]_1 = [Cl^-]_1$$

In Solution 2 let

$$y = [Cl^-]_2 \quad \text{and} \quad z = [R^-]_2$$

Since the two solutions must be electrically neutral, the sum of the concentrations of the chloride ion and the R^- ion in Solution 2 will equal the concentration of the sodium ion

$$y + z = [Na^+]_2$$

(Figure panel:)

$(Na^+) = c_1$
$(Cl^-) = c_1$

Solution 1

$(Na^+) = c_2 + c_3$
$(Cl^-) = c_2$
$(R^-) = c_3$

Solution 2

Membrane

(a) Initial condition

$(Na^+)_1 = x$
$(Cl^-)_1 = x$

Solution 1

$(Na^+)_2 = y + z$
$(Cl^-)_2 = y$
$(R^-)_2 = z$

Solution 2

Membrane

(b) Equilibrium condition

Figure 18-8. Diagrammatic representation of a Donnan equilibrium.

Substituting in Equation 18-1, it follows that

$$x^2 = y(y + z) \qquad (18\text{-}2)$$

From this it is seen that x, the sodium-ion concentration in Solution 1, must be greater than y, the sodium-ion concentration in Solution 2. This gives rise to a potential difference across the membrane of a type similar to the potential difference in a concentration cell without liquid junction potential. The potential of such a cell is given by Equation 13-4.

$$E = \frac{RT}{nF} \ln \frac{a_1}{a_2}$$

Substituting from the above in this formula gives, for the potential across the membrane,

$$E = \frac{RT}{F} \ln \frac{x}{y} \qquad (18\text{-}3)$$

More complicated cases yield similar expressions when subjected to the same type of mathematical analysis. The greater the concentration of the nondiffusible ion, the greater the difference between the activities of the diffusible ions on the two sides of membrane, hence the greater the potential between the two solutions.

The Donnan theory of membrane equilibrium has played a vital role in the interpretation of many biological problems. Such an equilibrium will exist whenever a charged particle or ion is restrained in its movement in any way. The theory has been especially useful in interpreting the ionic exchange characteristic of red blood corpuscles during the respiratory cycle.

EMULSIONS

18s. Emulsions and Emulsification. An emulsion is a suspension of one immiscible liquid in another. The process of producing this dispersion is termed *emulsification*. If one liquid is water and the other an oil, emulsions of oil in water and water in oil are possible. Cod-liver oil is an example of an oil-in-water emulsion. Stiff greases are examples of emulsions of water in lubricating oils. In many emulsions the dispersed droplets are larger than those found in the upper limit of the colloidal particles of sols. An explanation as to why such large particles can exist in a suspended condition is discussed in the next paragraph.

18t. Emulsifying Agents. There are two general types of stable emulsions. In the first the droplets remain suspended because of their small size and their surface charge. The particles in such systems act like typical hydrophobic sols in electric fields and are acted on in a similar way by added electrolytes. Besides having particles of very small size, the concentration of the dispersed phase is small. In the second type of emulsion the particles are so large that the surface charge is insufficient to keep the dispersed phase in a suspended condition. To keep the particles from coalescing, it is necessary to add what is termed an *emulsifying agent*. This agent produces stabilization by forming, between the suspended droplets and the dispersing medium, an interfacial film of such characteristics that coagulation is prevented. Among the emulsifying agents are soap, gelatin, and many other hydrophilic sols. In the preparation of mayonnaise, egg albumen acts as the emulsifying agent for the oil and water. The digestion of fats in the intestines is aided by emulsification. A little of the fat forms a sodium soap with the alkaline solution of the intestine, and this soap emulsifies the fat, thus making it easier for the digestive enzymes to effect their metabolic functions.

In general, emulsifiers will cause the liquid for which they have a greater affinity to become the dispersion medium. Hydrophilic sols, such as the alkaline soaps and gelatin, produce oil-in-water suspensions. The cleansing power of soap in the removal of oils and greases depends upon this property of the soap emulsifier. The soap forms an adsorbed film that is effective in preventing the coagulation of the droplets of oil in the water. The result is an emulsion of the grease, which is easily washed away.

The exact role of the emulsifier is not thoroughly understood. Probably it varies from one emulsifying agent to another, but, in general, the explanation of the action lies in an alteration of the interfacial tensions of the dispersed phase and the dispersing medium. The most useful theory to explain this action is the Bancroft double interfacial tension theory. According to this theory, the emulsifying agent forms a film between the two phases with a minimum thickness of at least three molecules. At least one molecule of this film is of the emulsifier, one of the dispersed phase, and one of the dispersing medium. The film, of course, has two surfaces, one toward each phase. If the interfacial tensions between the agent and the two phases are different, bending will take place. If the interfacial tension between the emulsifier and the water, assuming an oil-water system, is less than that between the emulsifier and the oil, the film will tend to become convex on the water side and to produce an emulsion of oil in water. On the other hand, if the interfacial tension between the emulsifier and the oil is less than that between the emulsifier and the water, a water-in-oil emulsion will result. In the process of film formation those emulsifying agents that are chiefly adsorbed by the water phase produce oil-in-water emulsions. Water-in-oil emulsions result when the emulsifying agent is chiefly adsorbed by the oil phase. Emulsifying agents are usually peptized more by one phase than by the other. Adsorption then takes place more readily in that phase in which the greatest peptization is found. For example, the soluble soaps, gelatin, and many of the gums are peptized more readily by water than by oils, hence produce oil-in-water emulsions.

Emulsions may be "broken" or demulsified by destroying the interfacial film. One method of accomplishing this destruction is to add a substance that will react with the emulsifying agent. An acid or a calcium salt added to an oil-water dispersion emulsified by a soluble salt will break the emulsion by interaction with the soap to form the insoluble acid or the insoluble calcium soap. Emulsions can often be broken by adding an emulsifying agent whose action on the dispersed phase and dispersion medium is the opposite to that of the original emulsifying agent used to produce the stable emulsion.

18u. Preparation. The preparation of emulsions may be effected by one of the following general methods. The substance to be dispersed may be mixed with the emulsifying agent and thoroughly peptized by shaking or grinding. It is then shaken with water or the proper dispersing medium to produce the emulsion. Many pharmaceutical preparations are made in this way, various gums being used as the emulsifying agents. Conversely, the emulsifying agent may be mixed with the water or other dispersing medium and peptized. Then the oil or substance to be emulsified is added slowly with continuous shaking. In many cases emulsions are produced or stabilized by what are termed *homogenizers*. An example of the stabilization of an emulsion is the production of homogenized milk. In ordinary milk the fat globules are so large that they tend to separate from the remainder of the milk. By an homogenizer they may be broken down into particles so small that the cream does not separate. Homogenizers usually act by forcing the materials through capillary tubes under high pressure and allowing the issuing stream to impinge against a hard surface.

GELS

18v. General Characteristics. A gel is a semirigid sol in which the dispersion medium has been adsorbed by the sol particles. It is usually lyophilic. The result is a more or less continuous rigid structure, which sometimes may be spongy, but is usually considered as made up of many interlacing fibers. These may be extensively branched. The structure so produced varies from a soft jelly to harder types such as hair and horn. The general term *gel* is applied to both gelatinous precipitates and jellies. A gelatinous precipitate is produced when a highly insoluble substance undergoes a rapid precipitation. The result is a gelatinous mass with a supernatant liquid. A jelly differs from a gelatinous precipitate in that all the liquid is enclosed by the precipitated phase.

Gels may be classified as *elastic gels* and rigid or *nonelastic gels*. Typical examples of elastic gels are those produced from sols of gelatin, agar, starch, or pectin in water. Jams, jellies, and many kinds of puddings are also examples. One of the best known forms of nonelastic gels is silica gel. This was referred to in Chapter 17, and as stated in that chapter, its extensive use is due to its adsorbing power for moisture. Many of the metallic hydroxides and hydrated metal oxides are nonelastic gels. The term *nonelastic* refers to the condition of the gel in the dry state, all gels being elastic when moist. Some, like silica gel, become glassy on drying; others form a powder. The elastic gels are the most important to the biochemist. In the animal body many of the colloidal systems exist in the form of a gel. Many protoplasmic systems involve gels. The process of formation of a gel is termed *gelation*, and the clotting of blood is an example of this process. In the clotting of blood the fiberlike particles of the proteins form a fibrous meshwork enclosing serum and the corpuscles of the blood. Subsequently the contraction of the gel squeezes out the serum.

18w. Formation of Gels. Gel formation can be considered as an incomplete precipitation of a sol. In the course of gel formation the colloidal particles of the sol unite in threadlike aggregates, which interlock with one another to form a highly porous semisolid. In the process increased solvation of the colloidal particles may result. Most of the solvent, however, is probably held in the cavities of the semisolid structure. The threadlike aggregates may be molecular chains similar to those found in polymers. The aggregates in some cases are apparently crystalline.

In a very general way it can be said that the best conditions for gel formation are those intermediate between optimum conditions for sol stability and complete precipitation. Many gels can be produced by simply cooling a lyophilic sol. Agar and gelatin can be formed in this manner. Careful regulation of concentration is necessary, and there is a minimum concentration required for gel formation. The greater the state of subdivision of the sol, the smaller the value of this minimum concentration. The temperature of gelation is influenced by the pH of the solution and the presence of various ions; some gels are formed by the simple addition of an electrolyte to the sol. Sometimes the addition of the electrolyte produces a gel through double decomposition. For example, a silica gel is produced by the addition of hydrochloric acid in proper concentration to a solution of sodium silicate.

Reversible isothermal sol-gel transformation is found in certain sols, such as colloidal iron oxide and alumina. If these are allowed to stand undisturbed, gel formation takes place, and if the resulting gel is then shaken, a sol is reformed. Allowed to stand, it will revert to the gel condition. This reversible isothermal sol-gel transformation is known as *thixotropy*, a property possessed to a greater or lesser extent by many colloidal systems. Wet sand exhibits a type of thixotropy. It has the ability to resist compression and to hold a definite shape when stepped on, yet shaking tends to make it free-flowing. This property is used in the preparation of some drugs. The normal condition in the bottle is that of a gel. When the bottle is shaken, however, the drug becomes a liquid and in this condition can be poured from the bottle.

18x. Swelling of Gels. A characteristic property of many gels, particularly the protein gels, is their tendency to absorb water and other liquids and to swell. This process is sometimes termed *imbibition*. The extent of the swelling is determined by the individual nature of the gel, the temperature of the system, the pH of the solution, and the selective action of certain ions. Adsorption is accompanied by a very large increase in pressure, if the gel is confined, and, conversely, adsorption can take place against enormous pressures. For example, it has been found that dry starch can absorb water against an external pressure of 2500 atm. The extent of the swelling in proteins is at a minimum at the isoelectric point.

REFERENCES

Bull, *Physical Biochemistry*, John Wiley and Sons, New York, 1951, Chapters 4, 6, 9, 10, 11, 12, 15, and 16.

Daniels and Alberty, *Physical Chemistry*, John Wiley and Sons, New York, 1961, Chapter 20.

Maron and Prutton, *Principles of Physical Chemistry*, The Macmillan Co., New York, 1958, Chapter 8.

Moore, *Physical Chemistry*, Prentice-Hall, Englewood Cliffs, New Jersey, 1962, Chapter 18.

Sheehan, *Physical Chemistry*, Allyn and Bacon, Boston, 1961, Chapter 7.

Daniels, Williams, Bender, Alberty, and Cornwell, *Experimental Physical Chemistry*, McGraw-Hill Book Co., 1962, Chapter 13.

Crockford and Nowell, *Laboratory Manual of Physical Chemistry*, John Wiley and Sons, New York, 1956, Experiment 33.

Jirgensons and Straumanis, *A Short Textbook of Colloid Chemistry*, John Wiley and Sons, New York, 1954.

Weiser, *Colloid Chemistry*, John Wiley and Sons, New York, 1949.

REVIEW QUESTIONS

1. Discuss in detail the difference between colloidal systems and true solutions.

2. What is meant by each of the following terms: *dispersed phase, dispersion medium, internal phase, external phase, emulsion, sol, foam, aerosol, gel, discontinuous phase*, and *continuous phase?*

3. Prepare a table listing the types of colloidal systems. Show the dispersed phase and the dispersion medium. Name the type of system produced and give some examples of the various types of colloids.

4. Discuss particle size in colloidal systems.

5. Discuss filtrability in colloidal systems. What is ultrafiltration? What is an ultrafilter?

6. Discuss in general the appearance of colloidal systems. What is a Tyndall beam? What causes the appearance of the beam? What is the principle of the ultramicroscope? What is the principle of the electron microscope?

7. Discuss quantitatively the effect of subdivision on surface area. What general effect does subdivision have on the properties of colloidal systems?

8. Discuss the kinetic behavior of colloidal particles. Discuss Brownian movement.

9. Discuss the rate of diffusion of colloidal particles as compared with the rate of diffusion of molecularly dispersed solutes.

10. Discuss the osmotic pressure of colloids. How can osmotic pressure measurements be used to establish the molecular weight of colloids?

11. Discuss sedimentation in colloidal systems and the use of the ultracentrifuge.

12. Classify sols from the standpoint of the dispersion medium. Discuss the terms: *hydrosol, alcosol, hydrophilic sol, hydrophobic sol, lyophilic,* and *lyophobic.*

13. Discuss the dispersion methods for the preparation of sols. What is peptization? What is a peptizing agent?

14. Discuss the condensation methods for preparing sols. Discuss some chemical reactions that can be used in the preparation of sols. Discuss solvent replacement in the preparation of sols.

15. Discuss ultrafiltration and its use in the purification of sols. How is it carried out?

16. Discuss dialysis and electrodialysis. Describe an apparatus that can be used for dialysis.

17. How does the charge on a colloidal particle differ from the charge on the ions produced from the dissociation of molecules of electrolytes? What are the various methods whereby colloidal particles can become charged? What is meant by the zeta potential? Discuss the concept of the Helmholtz Double Layer.

18. What is cataphoresis? What properties of colloidal particles can be studied by observing their behavior in an electric field?

19. What is meant by *electro-osmosis?* What is meant by *streaming potential?*

20. Discuss the role of the surface charge in the stability and precipitation of colloids.

21. Discuss the mutual precipitation of colloids. Discuss the effect of various ions on the precipitation of colloids. On what characteristics of the ions does their efficiency as precipitating agents depend? What is a Hofmeister Series?

22. What is a protective colloid? Discuss the action of protective colloids. Define the term, gold number, and discuss its usefulness in the study of colloids.

23. Discuss the ionization of proteins. What are ampholytes? What is meant by the *isolectric point* of an ampholyte?

24. What conditions are necessary for the establishment of a Donnan equilibrium? In general, discuss the movement of the ions that takes place when a Donnan potential is established. Show by mathematical calculations why a Donnan equilibrium results in a difference in potential on the two sides of a membrane.

25. Discuss the preparation of emulsions. What is the role of the emulsifying agent?

26. Discuss the general characteristics of gels and their general method of preparation. Distinguish between elastic and nonelastic gels. What is thixotropy?

27. Discuss the swelling of gels and the factors that influence the extent of the swelling.

NINETEEN

Nuclear Chemistry

This chapter is concerned with nuclear chemistry. Among the subjects discussed are natural and artificial radioactivity; mass-energy relations in nuclear·interactions; rates of radioactive decay; transmutations by neutrons, protons, and deuterons; and atomic fission and fusion. A brief discussion of the uses of radioisotopes is included.

NATURAL RADIOACTIVITY

19a. The Structure of Atoms. It will be recalled that atoms consist of a very small but dense nucleus surrounded by a number of electrons equal to the *atomic number* of the element. In the nucleus are found the *protons* and *neutrons* and these two particles are called *nucleons*. The atomic number is the charge on the nucleus and the number of protons in the nucleus as well as the number of electrons as previously stated. The electrons are very far apart and are in energy groups called *orbitals*. Unlike the electrons, the nucleons are closely packed together. According to one theory, the nucleons are arranged in energy levels somewhat like the energy levels of the electrons. According to another theory, known as the liquid drop theory, the nucleons are held together in a formless cluster similar to the water molecules in a drop of water. While these two theories appear to be antagonistic, they converge when the atom is subjected to high excitation energy. Under such circumstances, the nucleons acquire the same energy values, thus producing the condition characteristic of the liquid drop theory.

The atoms of each element are characterized by always having the same number of protons in the nucleus. This was stated above in defining the atomic number. The number of neutrons may vary, however. Atomic species of the same element all with the same atomic number but having different numbers of neutrons are called *isotopes*. For example, the oxygen found in the air consists of three isotopes each with eight protons in the nucleus but with eight, nine, or ten neutrons. These different species may also be called *nuclides*, a nuclide being an atom characterized by a given number of neutrons and protons. The total number of neutrons and protons is termed the *mass number* of the particular species. It is also the nearest whole number to the *isotopic weight*. The isotopic weight of a nuclide is its comparative mass referred to an arbitrarily selected standard. This standard is the most abundant isotope of carbon with an assigned value of 12.0000.

Although the isotopes of a given element have essentially the same chemical properties, they have slightly different physical properties. The lower atomic-weight nuclide of a given isotopic pair will give compounds that in the gaseous state will have slightly greater velocities at a given temperature. Hence the lighter species will diffuse more rapidly through a small hole. This is the basis of the separation of isotopes by the gaseous diffusion methods. The ions of the lighter isotope will move more rapidly in the process of electrolysis. Deuterium was first separated from the ordinary isotope of hydrogen by electrolytic methods based on the difference in the ionic velocities. There are, however, often fundamental, even sensational, differences in the manner in which nuclei of some isotopes undergo nuclear transformations into new elements. A consideration of nuclear transformation of radioactive nuclei comprises a major part of the remainder of this chapter.

Just as atoms are represented by certain letters, or pairs of letters, for example, S, O, Cu, and Al, we may write the symbols for various nuclides by adding a subscript to designate the atomic number and a superscript to designate the mass number. For example, the three isotopes of oxygen found in nature may be represented in this way:

$$^{16}_{8}O \qquad ^{17}_{8}O \qquad ^{18}_{8}O$$

The nuclide with eight neutrons is by far the most abundant isotope found in air, constituting 99.76 per cent of the atoms. In the same manner, the three naturally occurring isotopes of uranium are represented as follows:

$$^{234}_{92}U \qquad ^{235}_{92}U \qquad ^{238}_{92}U$$

19b. Radioactivity in Nature. The work of Becquerel in 1895 marked the beginning of the study of natural radioactivity. He discovered that uranium salts emit radiations, which have great penetrating power and which cause changes in a photographic plate even after passing through a screen of black paper. Later Marie and Pierre Curie were able to isolate the element radium from pitchblende. Radium is highly radioactive either in its elemental state or in the form of salts. The great contribution of the Curies was the skill used in isolating a few milligrams of radium from tons of pitchblende. The work of these and a number of other investigators established the fact that several of the heavier elements emit rays that can be detected and studied. It was also found that the atoms giving off these radiations undergo nuclear change with the resulting formation of new elements. Moreover, the rate of evolution is constant and spontaneous and cannot be altered by changes in the environment, such as an increase in temperature. The spontaneous emission of radiation by an element is called *radioactivity*.

19c. The Nature of Radioactive Rays. Experimentation has established the fact that three types of rays are given off in natural radioactive change: the *alpha particle*, the *beta particle*, and the *gamma ray*. The α particle is a doubly charged helium ion. In other words, it is a particle made up of two neutrons and two protons in the exact combination in which they are found in the helium isotope of mass number 4. The α particle is able to ionize gases, but its velocity, as compared with the β and γ radiations, is low, and its penetrating power under similar circumstances is about one hundredth that of the β particle. Since an α particle has a mass number of 4 and a charge of 2^+, its loss from the nucleus of an atom reduces the mass number by 4 and the nuclear charge by 2.

The β particle, or β ray, has a negative charge of 1 and a mass $1/1840$ that of the proton. It proves to be an electron. Since it comes from the nucleus, it is probably formed in the conversion of a neutron to a proton. The loss of a β ray by a radioactive atom produces no significant change in the nuclear mass but does change the charge by one unit. This causes an increase of one in the atomic number. The penetrating power of the β ray is fairly large, and it is able to ionize gases. Its velocity depends on the source, but on the whole it is very great and often approaches the velocity of light.

The γ rays have no charge, as is shown by the fact that they are totally unaffected by electric and magnetic fields. They prove to be light waves of very short wavelength. They affect photographic plates, ionize gases, and have a penetrating power from ten to one hundred times that of the β ray. Gamma rays probably accompany most radioactive changes. Their evolution changes neither the mass nor the charge of the emitting element and therefore does not affect the position of the element in the periodic table.

19d. The Radioactive Disintegration Theory. The theory of radioactive disintegration was first proposed by two English scientists, Rutherford and Soddy, in 1903. Their conclusions were based on a large mass of experimental information accumulated during the preceding decade, particularly by French and British chemists and physicists. Their theory differentiated between the radioactive nuclides and the stable or non-radioactive nuclides. Most of these radioactive nuclides have atomic numbers above 82 and mass numbers above 206. They number about forty. They undergo *spontaneous* disintegration with the emission of α or β particles, as discussed in 19c. As already stated, the evolution of the α particle results in a decrease of 2 in the atomic number and a decrease of 4 in the mass number. The evolution of the β particle results in an increase of 1 in the atomic number and no change in the mass number. For example, a radium atom of atomic number 88 and mass number 226 will, on the evolution of an α particle, become an atom of radon, with all the properties of an inert gas and an atomic number of 86 and a mass number of 222. The α particle becomes an atom of helium, after proper neutralization of its charge. The radon in turn, on the evolution of an α particle, becomes radium A with a mass number of 218 and an atomic number of 84. Actinium, with an atomic number 89 and a mass number 227 emits a β particle and becomes radioactinium, with an atomic number of 90 but with the same original mass number of 227.

Since, on disintegration, radioactive elements produce new elements, their products have different chemical and physical properties. It is therefore possible to separate these new elements rather easily and to study their individual properties. Such studies have resulted in the conclusion that all natural radioactive changes among the heavier elements belong in one of three radioactive disintegration series, termed the *uranium series*, the *actinium series*, and the *thorium series*. The parent elements are uranium I, protactinium, and thorium. Successive changes take place in each series with the evolution of α or β particles. In all three series the *end product* is an element of atomic number 82 with the chemical properties of lead but with mass numbers of 206, 207, and 208. These end products are, therefore, isotopes of lead. A study of the series shows the existence of many isotopes. For example, the element with atomic number 84 has isotopic forms with mass numbers of 210, 211, 212, 214, 215, 216, and 218. The uranium series is shown in Table 19-1.

A distinguishing characteristic of the radioactive disintegration of an element is the *half-life period*. *This half-life period is the time necessary for the conversion of half of a given mass of a radioactive element into its next disintegration product.* If a given sample of uranium I is studied, it is found that half of this sample will be converted to uranium X_1 in 4.5×10^9 years. The remaining half will continue to disintegrate, and at the end of the same number of years only half of it will remain. Half of the remaining quarter of the original sample will be converted at the end of the next

Table 19-1. The Uranium Disintegration Series

Radioelement	Element	Mass Number	Atomic Number	Particle Emitted	Half-life Period
Uranium I	Uranium	238	92	Alpha	4.5×10^9 yr
↓					
Uranium X_1	Thorium	234	90	Beta	24.5 days
↓					
Uranium X_2	Protactinium	234	91	Beta	1.14 min
↓					
Uranium II	Uranium	234	92	Alpha	2.7×10^5 yr
↓					
Ionium	Thorium	230	90	Alpha	8.3×10^4 yr
↓					
Radium	Radium	226	88	Alpha	1590 yr
↓					
Radon	Radon	222	86	Alpha	3.82 days
↓					
Radium A	Polonium	218	84	Alpha	3.05 min
↓					
Radium B	Lead	214	82	Beta	26.8 min
↓					
Radium C	Bismuth	214	83	Alpha or beta	19.7 min
Radium C′	Polonium	214	84	Alpha	1.5×10^{-4} sec
Radium C″	Thallium	210	81	Beta	1.32 min
Radium D	Lead	210	82	Beta	22 yr
↓					
Radium E	Bismuth	210	83	Beta	5.0 days
↓					
Radium F	Polonium	210	84	Alpha	140 days
↓					
Radium G	Lead	206	82	...	End Product

4.5×10^9 yr, and the process will continue in this manner. The time in this case is extremely large, but many radioactive elements have short half-life periods. The half-life period of thorium A, for example, is 0.16 sec.

19e. Rate of Radioactive Decay. The best method for identifying and determining the amount of a radioactive element is to measure its rate of disintegration. The process of radioactive disintegration of a radioactive element is a *first-order reaction*, since only a single species is involved (Chapter 16). This means that the rate of disintegration decreases in an exponential or logarithmic manner. Therefore, the number of atoms that will disintegrate in a unit of time is proportional to the total number of atoms of that species present at that particular time. Since disintegration is taking place continuously, the number of atoms present, and hence the rate of disintegration, is constantly changing. To express this mathematically, the methods of calculus must be used. If dN represents the number of atoms of a given species that disintegrate in a small interval of time, dt, then dN/dt represents the rate of disintegration. Since the rate of disintegration is proportional to the number of atoms, N, of the species present at any one time, it follows that

$$\frac{dN}{dt} = -\lambda N \tag{19-1}$$

where λ is a proportionality constant, called the *radioactive constant*. The negative sign shows that the number of atoms present *decreases* with time.

The numerical value of the radioactive constant is specific for a given radioactive nuclide, the greater the radioactivity the larger the value of λ. On rearranging Equation 19-1 and integrating, we obtain

$$\ln N_t = -\lambda t + \ln N_0$$

wherein N_0 is the number of atoms present at any starting time and N_t is the number remaining after the time interval t.

Changing to Briggsian logarithms gives

$$\log N_t = -0.4343\lambda t + \log N_0 \tag{19-2}$$

and

$$\log \frac{N_t}{N_0} = -0.4343\lambda t \tag{19-3}$$

Equation 19-2 shows that if we could measure N_t as a function of time, the plot of $\log N_t$ versus t would give a straight line and the slope of this line would be -0.4343λ. While it would be difficult to obtain the absolute value of N_t, it can be shown that the intensity of radiation, I_t, is proportional to N_t. The proportionality constant for this relationship would also hold for the initial intensity, I_0, which would give us a measure of N_0. To determine the intensity, we use an accurate counting device, such as a Geiger-Müller counter or a scintillation counter. Substituting I_t and I_0 for N_t and N_0, equation 19-2 becomes

$$\log I_t = -0.4343\lambda t + \log I_0$$

By plotting $\log I_t$ versus t, a straight line will result, as illustrated in Figure 19-1. The slope of the line in this plot is -0.0526 with the time in

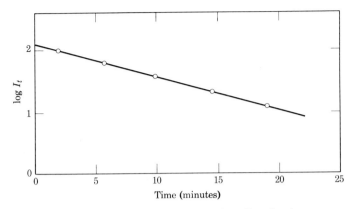

Figure 19-1. Log I_t versus time curve in radioactive decay.

minutes. Hence λ can be obtained by dividing this slope by -0.4343. This gives a value for λ of 0.121 reciprocal minutes.

The half-life period, $t_{1/2}$, defined earlier in this chapter, may be readily evaluated from Equation 19-3 because at the half-life point $N_t/N_0 = \frac{1}{2}$. Substituting in Equation 19-3, the following relations are obtained:

$$\log \tfrac{1}{2} = -0.4343\lambda t_{1/2} \tag{19-4}$$

or

$$\log 2 = 0.4343\lambda t_{1/2} \tag{19-5}$$

Since in the example shown in Figure 19-1, λ was found to be 0.121 reciprocal minutes, $t_{1/2}$, as evaluated from Equation 19-5, is calculated to be 5.73 min.

For elements of very long or extremely short half lives methods other than the one described must be used to evaluate λ because the change in number of counts at reasonable time intervals is too small or too large for proper evaluation.

19f. Radioactive Equilibrium. In 19e it was presumed that a single species of radioactive element was present. If the parent element is present along with a radioactive daughter element, a state of equilibrium will eventually be obtained when the daughter element disintegrates as fast as it is formed from its parent. According to Equation 19-1, the rate of disintegration of a parent element is equal to $\lambda_1 N_1$, in which the subscript 1 represents the parent element. Similarly, $\lambda_2 N_2$ represents the rate of disintegration of the daughter. At the equilibrium condition the rate of formation of the daughter from its parent exactly equals the rate of disintegration of the daughter, or

$$\lambda_1 N_1 = \lambda_2 N_2 \tag{19-6}$$

in which N_1 and N_2 are the numbers of atoms of parent and daughter at equilibrium.

If the daughter element is itself a parent of another daughter, represented by the subscript 3, and so on, for a large series of parent-daughters, as shown in the uranium series in Table 19-1, the general condition for equilibrium is given by

$$\lambda_1 N_1 = \lambda_2 N_2 = \lambda_3 N_3 = \lambda_4 N_4 = \cdots \tag{19-7}$$

Thus, for any two members of a series, regardless of whether they are parent-daughter or whether they are several generations apart,

$$\lambda_a N_a = \lambda_b N_b \tag{19-8}$$

$$\frac{N_a}{N_b} = \frac{\lambda_b}{\lambda_a} = \text{constant} \tag{19-9}$$

in which N_a and N_b represent the number of atoms of element a and b, respectively, in a given series.

Equation 19-9 has some interesting and useful facets. For example, radium is always found in naturally occurring uranium ores in the ratio of 1 part Ra to about 2.8 million parts U, as demanded by the relative values of their decay constants. The reason for this may be seen from Example 19-1.

Example 19-1. (a) Calculate the disintegration constants for uranium I and radium from the half-life periods of each in Table 19-1. (b) Calculate the relative proportion of uranium and radium in an equilibrium amount of the two.

(a) From Table 19-1, $t_{1/2}$ for $U_1 = 4.5 \times 10^9$ yr and $t_{1/2}$ for Ra $= 1590$ yr. Therefore, from Equation 19-5

$$\lambda \text{ for } U_1 = \frac{\log 2}{4.5 \times 10^9 \times 0.4343} = \frac{0.3010}{4.5 \times 10^9 \times 0.4343}$$

$$= 1.54 \times 10^{-10} \text{ yr}^{-1}$$

and

$$\lambda \text{ for Ra} = \frac{\log 2}{1590 \times 0.4343} = \frac{0.3010}{1590 \times 0.4343}$$

$$= 4.36 \times 10^{-4} \text{ yr}^{-1}$$

(b) *Solution from disintegration constants:* From Equation 19-9,

$$\frac{N_{U_1}}{N_{Ra}} = \frac{4.36 \times 10^{-4}}{1.54 \times 10^{-10}} = 2.83 \times 10^6$$

Solution from half-life periods: Since the numerical value of the disintegration constant is proportional to the half life, the half-life periods may be used in Equation 19-9. Therefore,

$$\frac{N_{U_1}}{N_{Ra}} = \frac{4.5 \times 10^9}{1590} = 2.83 \times 10^6$$

ARTIFICIAL RADIOACTIVITY

19g. Atomic Disintegration. In 1919 Rutherford noted that protons are produced when α particles of high velocity are passed through nitrogen gas. Subsequent studies resulted in the conclusion that interaction between α particles and nitrogen atoms produced atoms of oxygen and hydrogen. This reaction can be represented by the equation

$$^{14}_{7}N + ^{4}_{2}He \rightarrow ^{17}_{8}O + ^{1}_{1}H$$

The α particle is represented by the symbol $^{4}_{2}He$. *The subscript 2 gives the nuclear charge or atomic number, and the superscript 4 gives the mass number,* which is the nearest whole number to the atomic weight. As the α particle reacts with a nitrogen atom of mass number 14, an oxygen atom of mass number 17 and a proton are formed. In this particular reaction the number of reacting atoms is small compared to the total number present in a particular system, being of the order of 20 reactions for every million α particles sent into the system.

Since the discovery by Rutherford, many other examples of *artificial transmutation* of elements have been discovered and studied. In this work Irene Curie and her husband F. Joliet of France and E. O. Lawrence and Glenn Seaborg of the University of California have made notable contributions. From the many studies carried on, it has been found that in addition to α particles three other particles are particularly useful in producing artificial transmutation. These are the neutron, $^{1}_{0}n$; the proton, $^{1}_{1}H$; and the deuteron $^{2}_{1}H$. The deuteron is an atom of the hydrogen isotope of mass number 2, deuterium, stripped of its electron, just as the proton is an atom of ordinary hydrogen stripped of its electron. Another very important particle from the standpoint of the utilization of atomic energy is the triton, $^{3}_{1}H$, which is an atom of the hydrogen isotope tritium stripped of its electron.

Since neutrons do not carry a charge, they are not repelled by the positively charged nucleus in the manner protons and deuterons are repelled. Hence they are very effective in producing disintegration. A beam of neutrons can be obtained in a number of ways, but the usual source is a beryllium salt in the presence of a naturally radioactive substance that emits α particles. The production can be represented by the equation

$$_2^4\text{He} + {}_4^9\text{Be} = {}_6^{12}\text{C} + {}_0^1\text{n}$$

The speed of the neutrons may be altered by passing the beam through a *moderator*, which may be paraffin wax, graphite, or a compound of hydrogen or deuterium. The moderator slows down or even captures the neutron.

Nuclear reactions differ from ordinary reactions not only because entirely new elements are formed but also because enormous quantities of energy are involved. This will be elaborated on in the next section.

19h. The Mass-Energy Relationship. From detailed calculations Einstein has shown that *the mass of a body is a measure of its energy content*, and that when the energy of a body is changed by an amount ΔE, the mass of the body changes by $\Delta E/c^2$. Thus,

$$\Delta E = \Delta mc^2 \qquad (19\text{-}10)$$

where c is the velocity of light.

If c is expressed in centimeters per second, and m in grams, E is in ergs. Equation 19-10 then becomes

$$\Delta E \text{ (ergs)} = \Delta m \times (2.998 \times 10^{10})^2$$
$$= \Delta m \times 8.99 \times 10^{20} \qquad (19\text{-}11)$$

In chemical reactions energy is usually expressed in defined calories; 1 defined cal is equivalent to 4.184×10^7 ergs. Therefore, Equation 19-11 becomes

$$\Delta E \text{ (cal)} = m \times 2.15 \times 10^{13} \qquad (19\text{-}12)$$

If the mass unit in the Einstein equation is converted into *atomic mass units* (a.m.u.), $(1/6.02) \times 10^{-23}$ gram, and the energy units, into *million electron volts* (1 Mev $= 1.6 \times 10^{-6}$ erg), the equation becomes

$$\Delta E \text{ (Mev)} = m \text{ (a.m.u.)} \times 931 \qquad (19\text{-}13)$$

In an ordinary chemical reaction, even one of such comparatively high energy as the combustion of methane, a gram of methane produces only about 10^4 cal. Calculations from this show that the mass loss equivalent to this number of calories is extremely small. Thus, from Equation 19-12,

$$1 \times 10^4 = m \times 2.15 \times 10^{13}$$
$$m = 4.65 \times 10^{-10} \text{ gram}$$

This mass loss per gram of fuel is far less than 1 part in a billion, an amount that could not be detected with our best weighing devices. Thus, ordinary chemical reactions obey the law of conservation of mass within experimental means.

In 1932 Cockcroft and Walton, working in Rutherford's laboratory, used fast-moving protons obtained from the ionization of hydrogen in a discharge tube to bombard lithium atoms. Alpha particles are produced by this bombardment, and 17.2 Mev of energy are produced for *each lithium atom* reacting. The reaction may be written

$$_3^7\text{Li} + {}_1^1\text{H} \rightarrow {}_2^4\text{He} + {}_2^4\text{He} + 17.2 \text{ Mev}$$

Using Equation 19-13 and substituting the energy involved,

$$17.2 \text{ Mev} = m \text{ (a.m.u.)} \times 931$$

$$m = 0.0185 \text{ a.m.u.}$$

Thus each transformation involves a mass loss of 0.0185 atomic mass units. The isotopic weights of ^{7}Li, ^{1}H, and ^{4}He are now known with great accuracy, so that mass changes may be determined. Thus,

Particles Reacting	Particles Produced
^{7}Li = 7.0182	^{4}He = 4.0039
^{1}H = 1.0081	^{4}He = 4.0039
8.0263	8.0078

Difference = 8.0263 − 8.0078 = 0.0185 a.m.u. Since experimental values and calculated values agree, this constitutes experimental proof of the Einstein equation. Note that in the above calculations we have used the readily available isotopic weights as given in the physical atomic weight scale. Of course the answer is the same regardless of the scale used.

19i Proton Transmutations. Charged particles such as protons and deuterons may be accelerated to high velocities and correspondingly high energies in such devices as the cyclotron. With a proton as the bombarding particle, many reactions with the lighter elements have been observed in which the proton is captured and gamma rays are simultaneously emitted. Such an interaction is called a *proton capture–gamma emission type* and is written (p, γ). The new element formed has both an atomic number and an atomic mass *one* larger than the element being bombarded. Two examples of the (p, γ) type are

$$_{13}^{27}\text{Al} + {}_1^1\text{H} \rightarrow {}_{14}^{28}\text{Si} + \gamma$$

$$_9^{19}\text{F} + {}_1^1\text{H} \rightarrow {}_{10}^{20}\text{Ne} + \gamma$$

If the proton is sufficiently accelerated, many interactions of the *proton capture–neutron emission* type have been observed. Such a reaction type may be abbreviated (p, n). A specific example is

$$_{11}^{23}\text{Na} + {}_1^1\text{H} \rightarrow {}_{12}^{23}\text{Mg} + {}_0^1\text{n}$$

$^{23}\text{Na}(\text{p, n})^{23}\text{Mg}$ is the adopted short hand notation for this reaction.

It should also be noted that reactions in which more than one particle is ejected for each proton captured, (p, 2n) and (p, np), have been observed along with the relatively rare (p, α) and (p, d) types.

19j. Deuteron Transmutations. Interactions of the *deuteron capture-proton emission type* (d, p), are quite common. Thus,

$$_{48}^{114}\text{Cd} + {}_1^2\text{H} \rightarrow {}_{48}^{115}\text{Cd} + {}_1^1\text{H} \quad \text{or} \quad {}^{114}\text{Cd}(\text{d, p})^{115}\text{Cd}$$

$$_{83}^{209}\text{Bi} + {}_1^2\text{H} \rightarrow {}_{83}^{210}\text{Bi} + {}_1^1\text{H} \quad \text{or} \quad {}^{209}\text{Bi}(\text{d, p})^{210}\text{Bi}$$

Bismuth 210, produced by the reaction shown above, is identical with naturally occurring radium E (see Table 19-1). It emits beta particles and has a half life of 5 days.

A reaction of particular interest because of its possible use in fusion bombs is shown by the equation

$$_1^2\text{H} + {}_1^2\text{H} \rightarrow {}_1^3\text{H} + {}_1^1\text{H} \quad \text{or} \quad {}^2\text{H}(\text{d, p})^3\text{H}$$

in which tritium, an isotope of hydrogen of mass number equal to three, is produced.

Many reactions of the (d, n) type, as well as reactions of the (d, 2n) and (d, α) types, are known.

19k. Neutron Transmutations. By far the most common type of neutron transmutation is that in which the neutron is captured by the nucleus of the target element and the excess energy of the new nucleus is emitted as gamma radiation (n, γ). Neutrons of low energy are easily captured by most nuclear species. The product is nearly always isotopic with the target element, but its mass number is one unit higher. Thus

$$_{29}^{63}\text{Cu} + {}_0^1\text{n} \rightarrow {}_{29}^{64}\text{Cu} \quad \text{or} \quad {}^{63}\text{Cu}(\text{n, }\gamma)^{64}\text{Cu}$$

is a typical reaction.

Fast neutrons give rise to many types of reactions, among them the (n, p) which is most common and the (n, α) which is less common. As already mentioned, the large variety of interactions possible with the neutrons results from the fact that the nucleus of the target element does not repel the uncharged neutron.

Nuclear reactions have been discovered in which the bombarding particle is an accelerated ion larger than an α particle.

Most of the nuclides produced are radioactive, each with its own characteristic half life. Some uses of the isotopes are mentioned later in this chapter.

NUCLEAR FISSION

19l. Types of Nuclear Fission. In the atomic disintegrations found in natural radioactivity and in the transmutations discussed so far, the products differ but little in atomic weight and atomic number from the parent atom or target element. In 1939, however, a different type of disintegration was discovered. Here, a complete rupture of the nucleus occurs, and two fragment elements of roughly equal weight are formed. The first and best known example of fission occurs when a uranium atom of mass 235 interacts with a slow neutron. Here the fission results in two fragments whose atomic numbers lie between those of bromine and lanthanum. The interaction may be represented as

$$^{235}_{92}U + ^1_0n \rightarrow 2 \text{ fission fragments} + 2 \text{ or more neutrons}$$

Subsequently, it has been found that particles other than slow neutrons could be used to induce fission and that other elements of large atomic number could be used as the target. ^{235}U may be split by either thermal neutrons of about 0.03 electron volt or by fast neutrons with energies exceeding 1 Mev. ^{238}U undergoes fission only with high energy neutrons (exceeding 1 Mev). Two other nuclei, which do not occur in nature, are fissionable by neutrons of all energies. These are uranium 233 and plutonium 239. The latter is discussed in 19o.

The variety of possible fission reactions may be seen by noting that both thorium and protactinium are fissionable on bombardment with fast neutrons. Nine Mev deuterons produce fission in both thorium and uranium, and 32 Mev α particles, 7 Mev protons, and 6.3 Mev gamma rays are also effective.

Until 1947 fission had not been discovered in any element of atomic number less than 90. The successful fission of bismuth, lead, thallium, mercury, gold, platinum, and tantalum, however, has now been accomplished at the University of California Radiation Laboratory by high energy (100 Mev or greater) α particles, deuterons, or neutrons.

19m. Energy of Fission. The remarkable thing about fission reactions is the extraordinary amount of energy involved in the transformation. Before the discovery of fission in 1939 the largest known nuclear reaction energy was 22.4 Mev. The fission of ^{235}U, however, is nearly ten times greater, or about 200 Mev. This means that there is a greater than ordinary loss of mass and a correspondingly larger liberation of energy. For ^{235}U the isotopic weight is 235.118. As an atom of this isotopic weight captures a neutron, a mass of 1.009 is added, making a total of 236.127 atomic mass units for the mass of the particle undergoing fission. As explained in 19l, the atom undergoing fission may split in many ways. The products obtained in greatest yields, however, have mass numbers of 95 and 139. These add to 234, but several neutrons, assumed to be two for this calculation, are liberated. The isotopic weights of ^{95}Mo and ^{139}La, both stable nuclei, are 94.936 and 138.950, respectively. These, along with 2 × 1.009 for the masses of the two neutrons, add up to a total of 235.904. Thus, the excess mass that is converted into energy is

$$236.127 - 235.904 = 0.223 \text{ a.m.u.}$$

Multiplying this mass loss by 931 (see Equation 19-13) gives

$$0.223 \times 931 = 208 \text{ Mev per atom undergoing fission}$$

If the amount of energy released per pound of disintegrated uranium is calculated, it becomes equal to the amazing total of 11,400,000 kw-hr. Energy of the same order of magnitude is obtained from other fission reactions.

19n. The Fission Bomb. In 19l it was pointed out that ^{235}U undergoes fission by interaction with either slow (thermal) neutrons or fast neutrons. It was also pointed out that every disintegration results in the evolution of at least two neutrons. These neutrons can escape, or under conditions whereby a large enough mass of ^{235}U is present, they can interact with other uranium atoms, each of which in turn evolves at least two more neutrons capable of reacting with other ^{235}U atoms. Thus, from one initial interaction of a stray neutron, it is possible to set up a *chain reaction* in a properly sized mass of this uranium isotope. Once started, the reaction not only produces the particles necessary for further reaction but produces them in an ever-increasing number. The speed of the reaction becomes enormous in an unbelievably short time. The atomic bomb is constructed so that conditions are ideal for such a self-propagating chain reaction. Such an explosion releases a tremendous quantity of energy in the form of heat and light. The temperature of an A-bomb explosion is thought to be about 10,000,000°C; the result is an enormous heat and shock wave. Some of the energy of the explosion is released immediately as γ radiation. Radioactive isotopes are also formed that continue to give off their deadly radioactive rays for a long period of time.

19o. The Transuranic Elements. In 19n it was pointed out that neutron interaction may produce a number of types of transmutation. On bombardment of ^{238}U with neutrons of the proper speed, an isotope of mass number 239 can be obtained. This has a half-life period of 23 minutes and spontaneously emits an electron changing into an element of atomic number 93 with a mass number of 239. It is called *neptunium*. Thus neptunium becomes the first of the *transuranic elements*, a group of elements of atomic number greater than those occurring in nature. The half-life of neptunium is 2.3 days. It changes spontaneously into plutonium, another transuranic element with an atomic number of 94 and a mass number of 239. These changes may be represented as

$$^{238}_{92}U + ^{1}_{0}n \rightarrow ^{239}_{92}U \rightarrow ^{0}_{-1}e + ^{239}_{93}Np$$

$$^{239}_{93}Np \rightarrow ^{239}_{94}Pu + ^{0}_{-1}e$$

This isotope of plutonium is interesting because of its half-life of 24,000 years. This makes it possible to store it in quantity over a period of years without any substantial loss. It also undergoes a self-propagating chain-reaction fission similar to that of ^{235}U. Thus this nuclide of plutonium can be used for bomb production. It can be produced in quantity in breeder reactors more efficiently than ^{235}U can be isolated from its natural isotope mixture with ^{238}U.

At the present time transuranic elements have been prepared up to and including element 103. These include americium, curium, berklium, californium, einsteinium, fermium, mendelevium, nobelium, and lawrencium of atomic numbers 95, 96, 97, 98, 99, 100, 101, 102, and 103. Transformations leading to the production of elements through atomic number 100 may be represented as shown in the following series of steps. In considering these reactions, keep in mind that the many neutron captures by the nuclei are not easily accomplished. Only in a high neutron flux situation can the reactions be carried out even on a minute scale, each successive step becoming less probable until the final product is obtained only in micro amounts.

$$^{239}_{94}Pu + 2^{1}_{0}n \rightarrow ^{241}_{94}Pu \xrightarrow[\text{decay}]{\beta} ^{241}_{95}Am + ^{1}_{0}n \rightarrow ^{242}_{95}Am$$

$$^{242}_{95}Am \xrightarrow[\text{decay}]{\beta} ^{242}_{96}Cm + 7^{1}_{0}n \rightarrow ^{249}_{96}Cm \xrightarrow[\text{decay}]{\beta} ^{249}_{97}Bk$$

$$^{249}_{97}Bk + ^{1}_{0}n \rightarrow ^{250}_{97}Bk \xrightarrow[\text{decay}]{\beta} ^{250}_{98}Cf + 3^{1}_{0}n \rightarrow ^{253}_{98}Cf$$

$$^{253}_{98}Cf \xrightarrow[\text{decay}]{\beta} ^{253}_{99}Ei + ^{1}_{0}n \rightarrow ^{254}_{99}Ei \xrightarrow[\text{decay}]{\beta} ^{254}_{100}Fm$$

These are included only to show the variety of nuclear transformations involved when neutrons alone are used. Note the various beta decay processes that are spontaneous transformations with characteristic half-life periods. In addition to the use of neutrons for the production of transuranic elements, techniques have been worked out for the utilization in bombardment procedures of helium ions, oxygen ions, and the hexavalent ion of nitrogen.

19p. Atomic Fusion. As early as 1929 Atkinson and Houtermans, in Germany, considered it possible that the energy of the stars results from nuclear fusion reactions occurring at the high temperatures of the stars. Only at such temperatures, they reasoned, would two nuclei have enough kinetic energy to permit them to overcome the electrostatic repulsion barrier that operates to keep them apart. Calculations showed that for nuclei of the isotopes of hydrogen the energy required to make the nuclear reaction occur at an appreciable rate is about 0.1 Mev. Temperatures of about 1000 million °C are required to give the particles an *average* kinetic energy of 0.1 Mev. At star temperatures of 10 to 30 million°, however, energy distributions would be such that enough particles might acquire sufficient energy to make them react.

Since 1938 two sets of nuclear fusion reactions have been accepted to account for star energies. The first is known as the *carbon cycle*, in which carbon acts as an intermediary in facilitating the combination of four protons to form a helium nucleus. The second is called the *proton-proton chain*, which may be written in its stepwise course:

$$\,^1_1H + \,^1_1H \rightarrow \,^2_1D + \,^0_1e + \text{energy}$$

$$\,^2_1D + \,^1_1H \rightarrow \,^3_2He + \text{energy}$$

$$\,^3_2He + \,^3_2He \rightarrow \,^4_2He + 2\,^1_1H + \text{energy}$$

The explosion of the hydrogen bomb was the first thermonuclear fusion explosion to be brought about on the earth. It is to be hoped that, ultimately, such nuclear reactions may be carried out in a controlled manner for the production of energy for peaceful uses. The light nuclei that appear to offer prospects for success involve the hydrogen isotopes, deuterium, and tritium, in these reactions

$$\,^2_1D + \,^2_1D \rightarrow \,^3_2He + \,^1_0n + 3.2 \text{ Mev}$$

$$\,^2_1D + \,^2_1D \rightarrow \,^3_1T + \,^1_1H + 4.0 \text{ Mev}$$

$$\,^3_1T + \,^2_1D \rightarrow \,^4_2He + \,^1_0n + 17.6 \text{ Mev}$$

If these reactions can be made to occur at a reasonable rate, the deuterium present to the extent of about 0.015 atomic per cent in natural waters would constitute an inexhaustible source of energy.

USES OF RADIOISOTOPES

19q. Nuclear Reactors as a Source of Power. Extensive work is being centered around the construction of plants using atomic fission reactions as a source of industrial power. Such plants must contain enough fissionable material to sustain a self-propagating chain reaction but must be designed so that only the proper number of neutrons liberated in the fission reaction shall be allowed to induce other atoms to undergo fission. In other words, the fission reaction must be controlled so that the chain reaction cannot get out of hand. A number of materials absorb neutrons, and when these moderators (water, heavy water, graphite, beryllium) are used properly in a *nuclear reactor*, fission is allowed to proceed at a controlled rate.

The original reactors (called atomic piles) contained fissionable uranium and ordinary uranium, which is converted into plutonium through neutron bombardment. This material was arranged in the proper geometric shape and interspaced with cadmium or graphite rods as moderators, which could be put into place or moved as necessary to control the neutron flux in the reactor. Many types of reactors have now been tried and successful installations have been developed for ship propulsion. The most dramatic development in this area is the operation of the power plants on nuclear-powered submarines. Successful industrial installations have been developed but as yet the operating costs are too high for their successful competition with other sources of power in the United States. Also, the original installation of a reactor for power purposes costs far more than the plant supplying the same amount of power from fossil fuels.

19r. Isotopes as Tracers. The use of both radioactive and nonradioactive isotopes as tracers has become so extensive that only a few broad generalizations can be made here. Isotopes of most of the elements are available through the large variety of nuclear reactions that have now been discovered. It should be emphasized again that the chemical properties of the isotopes of a given element are essentially identical. A radioisotope, however, is easily detected with a counting device, and a nonradioactive isotope is detected by a mass spectrometer. Thus the isotope acts as a "label" to permit the fate of a compound containing a given element to be traced through a series of chemical changes. By such a *tracer element* the fate of a compound may be followed as it is assimilated, used, and eliminated in a living organism without necessarily interrupting the life process.

A simple experiment might be developed to find out how long it takes for alcohol to be assimilated and to begin elimination as carbon dioxide in the breath of the human organism. The subject drinks ordinary alcohol enriched with a tracer amount of alcohol containing ^{14}C atoms in place of one of the ordinary carbon atoms. The breath is then checked at proper intervals until radiocarbon is detected.

Another example involves the use of radiophosphorus in fertilizer to study the rate at which phosphorus compounds are absorbed by plants; or photosynthesis can be studied by allowing plants to absorb CO_2 enriched with a suitable amount of ^{14}C atoms. The great progress made in recent years in the study of the processes involved in photosynthesis has been due to a great extent to the use of this radioactive carbon. By means of this isotope along with the use of the isotopes of hydrogen and oxygen it has been possible to trace in detail many of the steps in the formation of complex organic substances from the water and carbon dioxide taken in by the plant body.

The main advantage in using radioisotopes is the ease with which they are detected either by the ionizing effect of their radiations in Geiger-Müller tubes or other counting devices or by photographing the emitted radiations. The spontaneous decay of the radioelement means that the tracer is steadily decreasing, so that for short half-lived elements the duration of the experiment may be limited. A radioelement is usually effective for no more than eight or ten half lives. The possible harmful effects of the radiations, both on the experimenter and the organism on which the radioelement is used, must be considered. Provided recognized precautions are taken, all danger can be eliminated.

19s. Tracer Elements for Biological Studies. It was mentioned in 19r that exchange studies, such as those on the intaking of phosphorus by plants from fertilizers and soils and those on intermediate products in biological syntheses, may be undertaken with radioelements. The number of studies already made because of this research tool is extremely large. Something like 30 elements are known to play a part in the life processes, among them, carbon, phosphorus, sulfur, chlorine, potassium, calcium, manganese, cobalt, iron, zinc, and iodine. Radioisotopes are available for all of these, but no radioisotopes of nitrogen and oxygen with reasonably long half lives have yet been discovered. Most tracer work with these elements involves the stable nuclides, ^{15}N and ^{18}O, both readily available. With these nuclides, more difficult techniques are involved because the mass spectrometer must be used to detect the products.

19t. Radioisotopes in Medicine. There are many examples of the use of radioisotopes, both for diagnostic and therapeutic purposes. Only a few cases are given here. Radiosodium is used to diagnose restricted circulation of blood. The proper quantity of sodium chloride in which some of the sodium is labeled with ^{24}Na is injected into the patient's arm.

A counter is then placed in contact with one of the feet. If circulation is normal, radioactivity is detected shortly in the foot and reaches a maximum value in less than half an hour. If the circulation is impaired, radioactivity will increase slowly. By moving the counter to different parts of the body, the position of the impairment can often be located.

Radioiodine, like ordinary iodine, is rapidly taken up by the thyroid gland. Here it may be used for diagnostic purposes in the functioning of the thyroid or for therapeutic purposes, for the gamma radiations cause a partial destruction of thyroid activity in hyperthyroidism.

Gamma radiations from radium have long been used in the treatment of cancer. Now radiocobalt may be used with the same results, and the cost of this isotope is small compared to the cost of radium. ^{60}Co is a gamma emitter with a half-life of 5.3 years; it is easily prepared by the neutron bombardment of ordinary ^{59}Co.

19u. Measurement of Radiation. Since overexposure to X-rays or to radiations from radioactive elements is harmful to living organisms, all work with radioactive materials must be accompanied by proper safety precautions. Alpha particles, with their very small penetrating power in air, offer little trouble unless their emitters happen to be ingested. Gamma rays, X-rays, and neutrons have high penetrating power and may cause cell destruction deep within the body. Beta particles have intermediate penetrating power but can cause serious skin burns.

The exact mechanisms associated with cell destruction by the various particles are not well understood; but whatever the mechanisms, the over-all effects of radiation on the body cells are well known. Unless there has been extreme exposure, which may cause death in less than two weeks, there is a delay between the time of exposure and evidence of the worst effects on the body tissues. This delay may extend over a period of months or even years.

The unit of radioactive decay is the *curie*. Originally the term referred to the quantity of radon in equilibrium with 1 gram of radium. Later it came to be used as a unit of disintegration rate for any radioactive substance, being defined as that quantity that gives the same number of disintegrations per second as 1 gram of pure radium. By agreement the curie is now defined as the quantity of any radioactive nuclide in which the number of disintegrations per second is 3.700×10^{10}. Two smaller units, the *millicurie*, which is one thousandth part of a curie, and the *microcurie* (10^{-6} curie) are in common use. These units are encountered frequently in decay and tracer work, particularly in noting the amount of pure radioisotope present with a quantity of its stable element. The *specific activity* of a given substance is expressed as the number of curies per gram of the element present, the weight to include both active and stable isotopes. On this basis, the specific activity of pure radium is 1 curie, which goes back to the original manner in which the curie was defined.

Since various radiations show different effects on living cells, there has been considerable difficulty in developing units to express radiation exposure in quantitative terms. The *roentgen* was originally intended to apply to X-ray and gamma radiations and is defined as the quantity of rays necessary to produce, as a result of ionization, one electrostatic unit of electricity in 1 cubic centimeter of dry air under standard conditions. This is equivalent to 86 ergs per gram of air. In this sense it is a unit of energy dissipation. In actual cases involving man it has been found that the absorption of 1 roentgen of X-rays by soft tissue involves the absorption of 97 ergs.

Because the absorption of the same number of ergs of different ionizing radiations may not have the same biological effects, other units have been developed in an effort to express equal biological damage. One of these is the *roentgen equivalent physical*, abbreviated *rep*, which is defined as the amount of radiation required to produce the same harmful effect upon tissue as a roentgen of gamma rays. This, as seen in the prior paragraph, has a value of 97 ergs.

Because the absorption of different quantities of different ionizing radiations which provide the same amount of energy may not have the same biological effect in a human body, another unit, the *roentgen equivalent man*, abbreviated *rem*, has been introduced. It is defined as the quantity of radiation that produces the same biological damage in man as that resulting from the absorption of 1 rep of X-rays or gamma radiations.

REFERENCES

Bull, *Physical Biochemistry*, John Wiley and Sons, New York, 1951, Chapter 1.

Daniels and Alberty, *Physical Chemistry*, John Wiley and Sons, New York, 1961, Chapter 24.

Maron and Prutton, *Principles of Physical Chemistry*, The Macmillan Co., New York, 1958, Chapter 21.

Moore, *Physical Chemistry*, Prentice-Hall, Englewood Cliffs, New Jersey, 1962, Chapters 11 and 20.

Sheehan, *Physical Chemistry*, Allyn and Bacon, Boston, 1961, Chapter 10.

Daniels, Williams, Bender, Alberty, and Cornwell, *Experimental Physical Chemistry*, McGraw-Hill Book Company, 1962, Chapters 16 and 23.

Glasstone, *Sourcebook on Atomic Energy*, D. Van Nostrand Co., New York, 1958.

Friedlander, Kennedy, and Miller, *Nuclear and Radiochemistry*, John Wiley and Sons, New York, 1964.

REVIEW QUESTIONS

1. What determines the atomic weight and the atomic number of an element? What is the present standard upon which the atomic weights are based? What are meant by the terms *isotopic weight* and *mass number?*

2. Compare the chemical and physical properties of the isotopes of a given element.

3. What is natural radioactivity as distinguished from artificial radioactivity? Name and give the properties of the three types of rays given off in natural radioactive processes.

4. What is a radioactive disintegration series? What determines the changes in mass and the changes in position in the periodic table in a radioactive disintegration series? What is meant by the half-life period of a radioactive element?

5. If spontaneous radioactive decay is considered to be a chemical reaction, what is the order of the process and why?

6. Give the differential equation for the rate of disintegration of a radioactive element. Give the integral equation that relates the concentration or quantity of a radioactive element to the time and the initial quantity or concentration.

7. What function of the concentration or quantity of a radioactive element, when plotted against time, gives a straight line? How is the slope of this line used to determine the numerical value of the disintegration constant? How is this disintegration constant related to the half-life period?

8. Explain what is meant by radioactive equilibrium. What mathematical expression relates the quantities of the various radioactive elements to their disintegration constants in a sample containing the members of a radioactive disintegration series? How may this expression be used in the determination of the relative quantities of the radioactive elements present?

9. What procedure is used to show the mass numbers and atomic numbers of isotopes?

10. What are the names and symbols of the particles discussed in this chapter that are used to bring about nuclear transformation?

11. Give the Einstein equation that shows the mathematical relation between mass and energy. Show that this equation is dimensionally correct.

12. What is an atomic mass unit? In what units is the energy usually expressed in connection with mass-energy calculations? What relationship exists among these units?

13. Calculate the energy equivalent to (*a*) 1 gram of matter and (*b*) 1 atomic mass unit.

14. Discuss the type of equation used to show nuclear transformations. What shorthand notations are used in representing these equations?

15. Complete the following nuclear equations:

(*a*) $^{114}_{48}\text{Cd} + ^{2}_{1}\text{H} \rightarrow ^{115}_{48}\text{Cd} +$

(*b*) $^{32}_{16}\text{S} + ^{1}_{0}\text{n} \rightarrow ^{32}_{15}\text{P} +$

(*c*) $^{239}_{92}\text{U} \rightarrow ^{239}_{93}\text{Np} +$

(*d*) $^{6}_{3}\text{Li} + ^{1}_{0}\text{n} \rightarrow ^{3}_{1}\text{H} +$

(*e*) $^{59}_{27}\text{Co} + ^{3}_{1}\text{H} \rightarrow ^{61}_{27}\text{Co} +$

(*f*) $^{23}_{11}\text{Na} + ^{1}_{1}\text{H} \rightarrow ^{23}_{12}\text{Mg} +$

(*g*) $^{14}_{7}\text{N} + ^{4}_{2}\text{He} \rightarrow ^{1}_{1}\text{H} +$

(*h*) $^{24}_{12}\text{Mg} + ^{4}_{2}\text{He} \rightarrow ^{27}_{14}\text{Si} +$

(*i*) $^{40}_{18}\text{Ar} + ^{1}_{1}\text{H} \rightarrow ^{40}_{19}\text{K} +$

16. Write a nuclear equation for each of the following:
(*a*) Cadmium-115 emits a beta particle
(*b*) Bromine-75 emits a positron
(*c*) Astatine-212 emits a helium-4 nucleus
(*d*) Calcium-45 emits a beta particle

17. Give some examples of transmutation brought about by protons. List the usual types of particles formed in proton-induced reactions.

18. Give some examples of transmutations brought about by deuterons.

19. What property possessed by the neutron makes it unique as a bombarding particle? Give some examples of reactions brought about by neutrons.

20. Complete the following nuclear equations:

(*a*) $^{63}_{29}Cu + ? \rightarrow ^{66}_{31}Ga + ^{1}_{0}n$

(*b*) $^{7}_{3}Li + ^{4}_{2}He \rightarrow ? + ^{1}_{0}n$

21. Write nuclear equations for the following transmutations:

(*a*) $^{39}_{19}K$ (p,α)   (*d*) $^{23}_{11}Na$ (d,α)

(*b*) $^{58}_{26}Fe$ (d, p)   (*e*) $^{255}_{101}Md(\alpha, 2n)$

(*c*) $^{3}_{1}H$ (d, n)   (*f*) $^{23}_{11}Na$ (d, p)

22. What is meant by nuclear fission? How is nuclear fission brought about? In what way do fission reactions differ from most nuclear reactions? Discuss the evolution of energy in fission reaction.

23. What are the transuranic elements? Name those produced to date. Discuss the decay processes involved in the production of the transuranic elements.

24. What is meant by atomic fusion? What is the general nature of fusion reactions. Give the equations involved in the proton-proton chain reaction.

25. Explain why fusion processes are sometimes referred to as thermonuclear reactions.

26. Give a brief discussion of the following: (*a*) nuclear reactors as a source of power, (*b*) isotopes as tracers, (*c*) tracer elements in biological studies, and (*d*) radioisotopes in medicine.

PROBLEMS

Note: See Table 19-1 when additional data are needed.

I

1. Calculate the decay constants of uranium II and uranium X_2 from their half-life periods. How long would it take for 25 per cent of an original sample of each to be decomposed?

2. Calculate the weight of radium E in equilibrium with one gram of radium D.

3. Calculate the weight of uranium II in equilibrium with 2 grams of uranium X_2.

4. How many grams of radium would be required to give the same radioactivity as 1.06×10^{-5} grams of ionium?

5. Given the following nuclear reaction:

$$^7_3Li + ^1_1H \rightarrow 2^4_2He$$

The isotopic weights are as follows:

$$^7_3Li = 7.0182 \qquad ^1_1H = 1.0081 \qquad ^4_2He = 4.0039$$

Calculate the energy liberated by the formation of (a) one atom of helium and (b) one mole of helium. Express your answers in Mev and calories.

6. A radioactive isotope of a certain element gives off gamma rays with an intensity of 3.4 Mev per atom. What is the mass loss when an Avogadro number of atoms of the element undergo transformation? How many calories are produced?

7. Radiocarbon (^{14}C with a half-life period of 5720 years) is produced in the upper atmosphere in small quantities by cosmic rays. Growing plants incorporate this isotope in their structure from the $^{14}CO_2$ of the atmosphere. When the plant dies, the process stops and the radioactive carbon decays in the plant tissues with the above half-life period. If a sample of new wood gives 16.0 counts per minute and a sample of wood of equal weight from an ancient campsite gives 9.0 counts per minute, how old is the wood?

8. A sample of wood from an ancient structure proves to be 5.4×10^3 years old. A sample of new wood of the same weight gives a count of 18.0 per minute. How many counts per minute are given off from the sample of wood from the ancient structure?

9. A sample of a radioactive element was measured in a counting chamber, and the following results were obtained:

Time in hr	0	5	10	15	20
Counts per min	15,000	3750	937	234	58

By the use of a plotting procedure, calculate the disintegration constant and the half-life period. Check your answer by calculating this constant from the proper integral equation.

II

1. Calculate the decay constants of radium D and radium F from their half-life periods. How long would it take for 40 per cent of an original sample of each to be decomposed?

2. Calculate the weight of radium D in equilibrium with 0.03 gram of radium E?

3. How many grams of radium would be required to give the same amount of radioactivity as 3 mg of radium A?

4. Given the following nuclear reaction:

$$2^1_1H + 2^1_0n \rightarrow ^4_2He$$

The isotopic weights are as follows:

$$^1_1H = 1.0081 \qquad ^1_0n = 1.0090 \qquad ^4_2He = 4.0039$$

(*a*) Calculate the number of calories of energy liberated by the formation of 5 grams of helium. (*b*) Calculate the energy (expressed in Mev) liberated by the formation of 0.5 mole of helium.

5. A certain radioactive isotope gives off gamma rays with an energy of 2.2 Mev per atom. How much loss in mass and how many calories of heat are produced when 1 gram-atomic weight of the element undergoes transformation?

6. A sample of a certain radioactive element was measured in a counting chamber and the following results were obtained:

Time in yr	0	4	8	12	16	20
Counts per min	17,800	8900	4550	2275	1137	569

Plot the log of the intensity (counts per minute) versus time. Calculate the decay constant and the half-life period (*a*) from the slope of the curve and (*b*) from the proper integral equation.

ANSWERS TO PROBLEMS

The answers given below are for the first set of problems at the end of each chapter.

Chapter 2. Gases

1. 488 ml, 0.698 gram, 1.31×10^{22}
2. 4.15 grams
3. Increase of 573°
4. 155.0 liters, 5.17×10^{-4} mole
5. 0.107 atm, same pressure
6. 78.1, 1.97×10^{21}
7. N_2: mf = 0.1053, P = 0.0442 atm
   O_2: mf = 0.0526, P = 0.0221 atm
   H_2: mf = 0.8421, P = 0.3536 atm
   total pressure = 0.420 atm
   remove 2.375 grams of H_2
   introduce 4.750 grams of H_2
8. 12.3 liters, 0.500 grams, mf: H_2 = 3.333, O_2 = 0.667
9. 2.00 grams, 0.651 liter
10. 204 ml
11. 5.15×10^4 cm per sec, 4.93×10^4 cm per sec
12. $-93.3°C$
13. 0.707, 0.707
14. 100.6°C
15. 0.354
16. 16.0
17. 28.3 min
18. 12.65 atm, 12.79 atm
19. (a) 0.436 liter
    (b) 1.23 atm
    (c) 2.27×10^{19} molecules
    (d) 30.03
    (e) 8.6°C
20. (a) 405.6 liters
    (b) 183.3 mm
    (c) O_2, mf = 0.127
         N_2, mf = 0.191
         He, mf = 0.509
         H_2O, mf = 0.174
    (d) 129.7 grams, 129.7 grams
    (e) 4.82×10^{18} molecules

Chapter 3. Liquids

1. 7,530 cal (calculated from the $10° - 60°$ data pair)
2. 10.6 cm, 1.65×10^{-2} cm
3. 23.7 dynes per cm
4. 1.118
5. 1.202 grams per cm^3
6. 33.9 dynes per cm
7. 1.11
8. 6.34×10^{-3} poise, 0.629
9. 233 sec

Chapter 4. Basic Thermodynamics

1. 1076 cal, 1494 cal
2. 1786 cal
3. 37.9°C
4. 24.7°C
5. 4638 joules, 32.2 min
6. 9430 cal, 8530 cal
7. 39,875 cal
8. 4054 cal
9. (*a*) 3470 cal, 2474 cal
   (*b*) 3478 cal, 2482 cal
10. 9.92 liter-atm, 1.00×10^{10} ergs, 240.2 cal, 1005 joules
11. 103.5 cal

Chapter 5. Thermochemistry

1. -173.7 Kcal, -173.3 Kcal
2. -54.63 Kcal
3. -114.4 Kcal
4. -184.61 Kcal
5. -29.763 Kcal
6. -37.31 Kcal
7. -22.28 Kcal
8. -11.52 Kcal

Chapter 6. Solutions I: Nonelectrolytes

1. Solute	Molality	Molarity	Mole Fraction Solute
(*a*) Sodium hydroxide	2.778	2.773	0.0476
(*b*) Sulfuric acid	3.400	3.004	0.0577
(*c*) Sodium carbonate	1.535	1.513	0.0269

2. $M = 1.136$, $m = 1.167$, mf $= 0.0206$
3. 1.47×10^{-3} moles per liter, 2.94 mg per liter
4. 3.18×10^{-2} gram, 0.149 gram
5. 9.425 liters (200 mm Hg), 2.480 liters (760 mm Hg)
6. N_2: 6.17×10^{-2} gm, 49.4 ml, 0.541
   O_2: 5.97×10^{-2} gm, 41.8 ml, 0.459
7. 184.1 mm Hg
8. 8.22 gm
9. 1.15 mm, 4.48°C, 80.71°C
10. Benzene: 43.85 mm Hg
    Toluene: 23.08 mm Hg
    Total pressure: 66.93 mm Hg
11. Toluene: 0.635, Benzene: 0.365
12. (a) -0.422°C, 100.116°C
    (b) 4.28°C, 80.81°C
13. 147.7
14. -0.258°C, 549 grams
15. 150.5 grams
16. 3.25×10^3 grams
17.

	Boiling point	Freezing point	Vapor pressure
20°	80.35°	5.00°	74.14 mm
40°	—	—	179.73 mm
60°	—	—	385.67 mm

vapor pressure at normal boiling point: 754.3 mm

Chapter 7. Solutions II: Osmotic Pressure

1. 6.80 atm, 7.36 atm, 7.93 atm, 8.27 atm
2. 0.0535, 1076 mm
3. -0.0604°C, 100.017°C, 17.51 mm
4. 1.96×10^{19}, same
5. 7.02 liters, 6.34 liters
6. 2.077×10^{20}
7. 3.29 atm, 7.15 grams
8. -0.559°C
9. 9.70 atm
10. 10.29 grams

Chapter 8. Solutions III: Solutions of Electrolytes

1. 0.050, 0.080, 0.768, 0.854
2.

	Ion	Activity coefficient	Activity
(a)	Li$^+$	0.770	0.0385
	Cl$^-$	0.770	0.0385
(b)	K$^+$	0.718	0.0144
	NO$_3^-$	0.718	0.0431
	Ca^{2+}	0.266	0.0054

(c)	Al^{3+}	9.7×10^{-5}	1.24×10^{-5}
	NO_3^-	0.358	0.137
(d)	K^+	0.338	0.0825
	SO_4^{2-}	0.0132	0.00322
	Mg^{2+}	0.0132	0.00161

3.	Concentration of salt	Ion activities NaCl	Ion activities KCl	Osmotic pressure NaCl	KCl
	0.01	0.0093	0.0090	—	
	0.05	0.0411	0.0408	2.02 atm	2.00 atm
	0.10	0.0778	0.0770	3.81 atm	3.77 atm
	0.50	0.340	0.325	—	
	1.00	0.656	0.607	—	
	1.50	0.988	0.875	—	

4. 1.904 grams, 1.060 grams
5. $Na^+ = 0.0645$, $SO_4^{-2} = 0.00692$, $Cl^- = 0.0129$
6. 0.1021

Chapter 9.   Chemical Equilibrium

1.	Acid	Alcohol	Ester	Water
(a)	1.330	1.330	2.670	2.670
(b)	1.562	0.562	1.438	2.438
(c)	0.667	0.667	1.333	1.333
(d)	0.420	2.420	1.580	2.580

2. Ester: 18.58 grams, Water: 3.80 grams, Alcohol: 1,790 grams, Acid: 17.35 grams
3. Ester: 17.47 grams, Water: 10.52 grams, Alcohol: 16.11 grams, Acid: 4.92 grams
4. 1.12×10^{-5}
5. NO_2: 2.37×10^{-3} mole per liter
   N_2O_4: 0.499 mole per liter
6. NO_2: 1.83×10^{-3} mole per liter
   N_2O_4: 0.2994 mole per liter
7. 1.65×10^{-4}, 1.28×10^{-2}
8. $P_{H_2} = 30.2$ atm, $mf(H_2) = 0.801$, $mf(N_2) = 0.093$, $mf(NH_3) = 0.106$
9. Total moles = 6.84, total weight = 41.20 gm
   Moles of each gas present: $NH_3 = 0.725$, $N_2 = 0.636$, $H_2 = 5.49$

10.	moles	mole fraction
Ester	0.660	0.1057
Acid	0.340	0.0545
Hydrocarbon	5.24	0.8397

11.	partial pressure	concentration (moles per liter)
PCl_3	1.26 atm	0.0293
PCl_5	0.886 atm	0.0206
Cl_2	1.26 atm	0.0293

12. 141 grams

Chapter 10. Entropy and Free Energy

1. (a) 6.68 E.U., (b) −39.08 E.U., (c) −2.63 E.U., (d) 1.09 E.U.
2. 1.613 E.U.
3. 1.613 E.U.
4. −3.280 E.U.
5. (a) 0.932 E.U., (b) 1.311 E.U.
6. −75.56 E.U.
7.

	$\Delta S°$	$\Delta H°$	$\Delta G°$
(a)	−148.2 E.U.	−745.638 Kcal	−701.46 Kcal
(b)	−2.77 E.U.	−60.724 Kcal	−52.448 Kcal
(c)	−7.87 E.U.	−15.649 Kcal	−13.304 Kcal
(d)	−19.24 E.U.	13.357 Kcal	19.090 Kcal
(e)	−0.35 E.U.	15.896 Kcal	16.000 Kcal

8. (a) 3.8×10^{513} (b) 2.5×10^{38}
   (c) 5.52×10^{9} (d) 1.06×10^{14}
   (e) 1.94×10^{-12}
9. 1.26×10^{-12}
10. (a) 3088 cal   (b) −5108 cal
    (c) −71,497 cal   (d) −9564 cal
    (e) −72,604 cal   (f) −6267 cal

Chapter 11. Ionic Equilibrium and Buffer Action

1. (a) 2.54   (b) 12.50
2.

	$[OH^-]$	pH	pOH
(a)	1.63×10^{-3}	11.21	2.79
(b)	1.59×10^{-3}	11.20	2.80

3.

	$[H^+]$	$[OH^-]$
(a)	5.37×10^{-11}	1.86×10^{-4}
(b)	5.37×10^{-6}	1.86×10^{-9}

4.

	$[H^+]$	α
(a)	2.13×10^{-3}	8.20×10^{-3}
(b)	6.60×10^{-6}	1.10×10^{-4}
(c)	5.92×10^{-3}	2.37×10^{-2}
(d)	3.49×10^{-3}	4.36×10^{-2}

5.

	α	[HA]	Grams
(a)	1.69×10^{-2}	0.533	89.1
(b)	4.00×10^{-2}	0.110	11.13

6.

	$[H^+]$	pH	α
(a)	1.17×10^{-5}	4.93	7.31×10^{-5}
(b)	7×10^{-3}		

7. 1.75×10^{-5}, 4.76

8.

	H^+	OH^-	$C_2H_3O_2{}^-$	Ca^{++}
Concentration	5.83×10^{-6}	1.72×10^{-9}	0.420	0.210
Number of moles	8.74×10^{-6}	2.58×10^{-9}	0.630	0.315

9. $[H^+] = 1.85 \times 10^{-4}$, pH $= 3.73$, $[CO_3{}^{2-}] = 5.6 \times 10^{-11}$
10. 4.74, 1.35×10^{-3}
11. 1.15 grams
12. 1.47×10^{-11}
13. 0.588 gram per liter
14. Yes—both cases
15. 0.160 mg
16. 6.3×10^{-5} mole per liter
17. $[S^{-2}] = 1.64 \times 10^{-21}$, 1.30
18. (a) 2.27×10^{-11}, (b) 3.17×10^{-5}, (c) 1.40×10^{-5}
19.

	(a)	(b)
$[H^+]$	3.25×10^{-7}	5.25×10^{-6}
$[OH^-]$	3.09×10^{-6}	1.90×10^{-9}
$[Bz^-]$	0.06	—
$[K^+]$	0.06	—
$[NH_4{}^+]$	—	0.05
$[Cl^-]$	—	0.05
h	5.15×10^{-5}	1.05×10^{-4}

20. $[H^+] = 7.45 \times 10^{-6}$, $[OH^-] = 1.34 \times 10^{-9}$, $[Na^+] = 0.10$, $[Cl^-] = 0.20$
21. (a) 5.63×10^{-3} (b) 5.63×10^{-3}
22. 3.16×10^{-9} mole per liter, 8.50
23. four-fold
24. (a) 9.1×10^{-10} (b) 6.60×10^{-6}
25.

	(a)	(b)
$[H^+]$	3.68×10^{-5}	2.02×10^{-10}
$[Na^+]$	0.0667	—
$[NH_4{}^+]$	—	0.0139
$[C_2H_3O_2{}^-]$	0.0667	—
$[OH^-]$	2.72×10^{-10}	4.95×10^{-5}
$[Cl^-]$	—	0.0139

26.

	pH	pOH	$[H^+]$	$[OH^-]$
(a)	4.68	9.32	2.10×10^{-5}	4.76×10^{-10}
(b)	4.20	9.80	6.30×10^{-5}	1.59×10^{-10}
(c)	9.38	4.62	4.17×10^{-10}	2.40×10^{-5}

27. 7.3×10^{-10}
28. 3.3×10^{-9}
29. 11.66, 3.85×10^{-2}
30. 8.31
31. $[H^+] = 1.75 \times 10^{-5}$, pOH $= 9.24$, $\alpha = 3.5 \times 10^{-5}$
32. 0.316
33. (a) 0.813 (b) 1.63 (c) 0.407 (acid/salt)
34. 26.35 grams

35. pH	Milliliters of sodium acetate solution
5.6	724
5.4	457
5.2	288
5.0	182
4.8	115
4.6	72.4
4.4	45.7
4.2	28.8
4.0	18.2
3.8	11.5
3.6	7.24

36. pH	Milliliters of disodium phosphate solution
5.8	5.88
6.0	9.25
6.2	14.65
6.4	23.3
6.6	36.9
6.8	58.4
7.0	92.5
7.2	146.5
7.4	233.0
7.6	368.0
7.8	584.0

Chapter 12. Conductivity

1. (*a*) 1.08×10^5 coulombs, 1.119 Faradays   (*b*) 1.08×10^6 joules
   (*c*) 12.53 liters of H_2, 6.27 liters of O_2
2. Gold: 14.7 grams, silver: 24.0 grams, copper: 7.12 grams
3. (*a*) 0.0926 amp   (*b*) 68.8 ml   (*c*) 1.56×10^{21} (*d*) 230 hr
4. (*a*) 0.0668 amp   (*b*) 0.2004 amp   (*c*) 0.1336 amp   (*d*) 0.1336 amp
   (*e*) 0.0668 amp
5. (*a*) 1.47×10^{-4} mho   (*b*) 1.067×10^{-2} mho   (*c*) 1.63×10^{-4} mho
   (*d*) 2.35×10^{-5} mho
6. Plotting procedure
7.

Concentration	Degree of dissociation
0.0005	0.173
0.001	0.125
0.01	0.0416
0.10	0.0133

8. Potassium chloride: 1.330×10^{-4} mho, 7.52×10^3 ohm
   Acetic acid: 4.45×10^{-5} mho, 2.25×10^4 ohm
9. Plotting procedure

10. H+   0.434 cm, 0.347 cm
    OH$^-$ 0.246 cm, 0.197 cm
    $C_2H_3O_2{}^-$ 0.0504 cm, 0.0403 cm
    Ba^{2+} 0.0804 cm, 0.0643 cm
11. 0.3591
12. 4.205×10^{-4} mho/cm, 420.5 mho $\times$ cm^2/equivalent
13. 3.148×10^{-4} mho, 3.177×10^3 ohm
14. 123.8 mho $\times$ cm^2/equivalent

Chapter 13. Electromotive Force

1. (a) 0.00357 volt
   (b) 0.0643 volt
   (c) 0.0640 volt
   (d) 0.2176 volt
2. (a) 0.8475 volt
   (b) −0.7474 volt
   (c) −0.4595 volt
   (d) −0.3246 volt
3.

	Negative electrode	~ Positive electrode	Cell potential
(a)	0.822 volt	−0.2571 volt	1.0793 volts
(b)	0.1395 volt	−0.7559 volt	0.8954 volt

4. (a) 1.230 volts   (b) 1.229 volts   (c) 2.372 volts
5. (a) 0.1184 volt   (b) 0.1184 volt   (c) 0.1184 volt
6. 106/1, $4.70 \times 10^{-4} m$
7. 1.38×10^{-38}
8. 0.2072 volt, −0.7638 volt, 0.971 volt
9. 0.388 volt
10. 0.1056m
11. $1 \times 10^{-2} m$
12. 0.0114 volt
13. 0.0102 volt
14. $1.91 \times 10^{-4} m$
15. $\Delta G° = -5129.4$ cal, $\Delta S° = -16.1$ E.U., $\Delta H° = -9939$ cal
16. $\Delta G° = -72.040$ cal, $\Delta S° = -50.32$ E.U., $\Delta H° = -87,305$ cal
   $K = 5.5 \times 10^{52}$, $dE/dT = -0.0011$ volt per degree
17. 1.553 volts
18. $\Delta G° = -52,401$ cal, $\Delta S° = -27.68$ E.U., $\Delta H° = -60,650$ cal

Chapter 14. The Determination of Hydrogen-ion Concentration

1.

	H	pH
(a)	7.10×10^{-7}	6.15
(b)	8.63×10^{-7}	6.06
(c)	2.79×10^{-7}	6.55

2. 10.52
3. (a) 0.0596 volt, (b) 0.0602 volt

4. pH = 7.52, (b) pOH = 6.48, $[OH^-]$ = 3.31 × 10^{-7}
5. 9.25 × 10^{-6}
6. 0.897 volt (740 mm), 0.897 (760 mm)
7. (a) 5.68, (b) 5.61, (c) 5.68
8. 6.54
9. −0.102 volt
10. 5.78
11. 3.75
12. (a) 4.85, (b) 9.08, (c) 8.08
13. 7.91
14. (a) 3.80, (b) 4.28, (c) 6.75, (d) 8.88, (e) 11.69
15. (a) 0.471 volt   (b) 0.499 volt   (c) 0.646 volt   (d) 0.772 volt
    (e) 0.938 volt

Chapter 15.   Oxidation-Reduction Potentials

1. (a) −0.316 volt   (b) −1.624 volts   (c) −1.148 volts   (d) −0.224 volt
    (e) 1.321 volts
2. (a) 0.110 volt   (b) 1.378 volts   (c) 0.902 volt   (d) 0.022 volt
    (e) 1.075 volts
3. ratio: 0.0585, 2.56m
4. 0.715 volt
5. 0.781 volt (concentration tripled), 0.991 volt (concentration increased
    100-fold)
6. −0.045 volt
7. 0.096 volt
8. Oxidized form: 63.1%, reduced form: 36.9%
9. 0.238 volt

Chapter 16.   Reaction Kinetics.   Catalysis

1. 0.0056M, 7.70 min
2. 8.01 × 10^{-3}, 0.754 decomposed, 86.5 min
3. 6.46 × 10^{-3}M
4. Half-life period: 15.2 min, 0.0241M (20 min), fraction: 0.935
5. 3.03 × 10^{-3}M, 8.70 min (0.02M solutions), 4.35 (0.04M solutions)
6. 11,080 cal
7. 2.1 × 10^{-4}

Chapter 19.   Nuclear Chemistry

1.	Decay constant	Time
Uranium II	2.57 × 10^{-6} yr^{-1}	1.12 × 10^5 yr
Uranium X$_2$	6.08 × 10^{-1} min^{-1}	0.473 min

2. 6.23 × 10^{-4} gram
3. 2.50 × 10^{11} grams

4. 2.00×10^{-7} gram

5.

	mev	cal
(a)	8.61	3.29×10^{-13}
(b)	5.18×10^{24}	1.98×10^{11}

6. 3.65×10^{-3} gram, 7.84×10^{10} cal
7. 4750 yr
8. 9.36
9. 0.276 (slope), 0.280 (integral equation)

Index

Natural Numbers	0	1	2	3	4	5	6	7	8	9	PROPORTIONAL PARTS								
											1	2	3	4	5	6	7	8	9
10	0000	0043	0086	0128	0170	0212	0253	0294	0334	0374	4	8	12	17	21	25	29	33	37
11	0414	0453	0492	0531	0569	0607	0645	0682	0719	0755	4	8	11	15	19	23	26	30	34
12	0792	0828	0864	0899	0934	0969	1004	1038	1072	1106	3	7	10	14	17	21	24	28	31
13	1139	1173	1206	1239	1271	1303	1335	1367	1399	1430	3	6	10	13	16	19	23	26	29
14	1461	1492	1523	1553	1584	1614	1644	1673	1703	1732	3	6	9	12	15	18	21	24	27
15	1761	1790	1818	1847	1875	1903	1931	1959	1987	2014	3	6	8	11	14	17	20	22	25
16	2041	2068	2095	2122	2148	2175	2201	2227	2253	2279	3	5	8	11	13	16	18	21	24
17	2304	2330	2355	2380	2405	2430	2455	2480	2504	2529	2	5	7	10	12	15	17	20	22
18	2553	2577	2601	2625	2648	2672	2695	2718	2742	2765	2	5	7	9	12	14	16	19	21
19	2788	2810	2833	2856	2878	2900	2923	2945	2967	2989	2	4	7	9	11	13	16	18	20
20	3010	3032	3054	3075	3096	3118	3139	3160	3181	3201	2	4	6	8	11	13	15	17	19
21	3222	3243	3263	3284	3304	3324	3345	3365	3385	3404	2	4	6	8	10	12	14	16	18
22	3424	3444	3464	3483	3502	3522	3541	3560	3579	3598	2	4	6	8	10	12	14	15	17
23	3617	3636	3655	3674	3692	3711	3729	3747	3766	3784	2	4	6	7	9	11	13	15	17
24	3802	3820	3838	3856	3874	3892	3909	3927	3945	3962	2	4	5	7	9	11	12	14	16
25	3979	3997	4014	4031	4048	4065	4082	4099	4116	4133	2	3	5	7	9	10	12	14	15
26	4150	4166	4183	4200	4216	4232	4249	4265	4281	4298	2	3	5	7	8	10	11	13	15
27	4314	4330	4346	4362	4378	4393	4409	4425	4440	4456	2	3	5	6	8	9	11	13	14
28	4472	4487	4502	4518	4533	4548	4564	4579	4594	4609	2	3	5	6	8	9	11	12	14
29	4624	4639	4654	4669	4683	4698	4713	4728	4742	4757	1	3	4	6	7	9	10	12	13
30	4771	4786	4800	4814	4829	4843	4857	4871	4886	4900	1	3	4	6	7	9	10	11	13
31	4914	4928	4942	4955	4969	4983	4997	5011	5024	5038	1	3	4	6	7	8	10	11	12
32	5051	5065	5079	5092	5105	5119	5132	5145	5159	5172	1	3	4	5	7	8	9	11	12
33	5185	5198	5211	5224	5237	5250	5263	5276	5289	5302	1	3	4	5	6	8	9	10	12
34	5315	5328	5340	5353	5366	5378	5391	5403	5416	5428	1	3	4	5	6	8	9	10	11
35	5441	5453	5465	5478	5490	5502	5514	5527	5539	5551	1	2	4	5	6	7	9	10	11
36	5563	5575	5587	5599	5611	5623	5635	5647	5658	5670	1	2	4	5	6	7	8	10	11
37	5682	5694	5705	5717	5729	5740	5752	5763	5775	5786	1	2	3	5	6	7	8	9	10
38	5798	5809	5821	5832	5843	5855	5866	5877	5888	5899	1	2	3	5	6	7	8	9	10
39	5911	5922	5933	5944	5955	5966	5977	5988	5999	6010	1	2	3	4	5	7	8	9	10
40	6021	6031	6042	6053	6064	6075	6085	6096	6107	6117	1	2	3	4	5	6	8	9	10
41	6128	6138	6149	6160	6170	6180	6191	6201	6212	6222	1	2	3	4	5	6	7	8	9
42	6232	6243	6253	6263	6274	6284	6294	6304	6314	6325	1	2	3	4	5	6	7	8	9
43	6335	6345	6355	6365	6375	6385	6395	6405	6415	6425	1	2	3	4	5	6	7	8	9
44	6435	6444	6454	6464	6474	6484	6493	6503	6513	6522	1	2	3	4	5	6	7	8	9
45	6532	6542	6551	6561	6571	6580	6590	6599	6609	6618	1	2	3	4	5	6	7	8	9
46	6628	6637	6646	6656	6665	6675	6684	6693	6702	6712	1	2	3	4	5	6	7	7	8
47	6721	6730	6739	6749	6758	6767	6776	6785	6794	6803	1	2	3	4	5	5	6	7	8
48	6812	6821	6830	6839	6848	6857	6866	6875	6884	6893	1	2	3	4	4	5	6	7	8
49	6902	6911	6920	6928	6937	6946	6955	6964	6972	6981	1	2	3	4	4	5	6	7	8
50	6990	6998	7007	7016	7024	7033	7042	7050	7059	7067	1	2	3	3	4	5	6	7	8
51	7076	7084	7093	7101	7110	7118	7126	7135	7143	7152	1	2	3	3	4	5	6	7	8
52	7160	7168	7177	7185	7193	7202	7210	7218	7226	7235	1	2	2	3	4	5	6	7	7
53	7243	7251	7259	7267	7275	7284	7292	7300	7308	7316	1	2	2	3	4	5	6	6	7
54	7324	7332	7340	7348	7356	7364	7372	7380	7388	7396	1	2	2	3	4	5	6	6	7